PREFACE TO THE FOURTH EDITION

DURING the fifteen years which have elapsed since the appearance of the first edition of this book, recognition of the educational value of qualitative organic chemical analysis has widely extended, with the result that methods of the type advocated for such work have received increasing attention in publications appearing in the scientific journals during this period. At the same time the normal progress of organic chemistry has disclosed a variety of new reactions and compounds ; so that it has been considered advisable to subject the portion of the text dealing with the qualitative aspect of organic analysis to a thorough revision.

The reference tables have also been almost entirely rewritten, in order to take advantage of the new data appearing in the recent literature and to present in fuller detail the information therein summarised, a certain amount of which has had to be experimentally determined by the author.

As a result of all this development, the goal referred to by Professor Collie in the Introduction is sensibly nearer, though still a long way off. Progress in this direction must continue to remain chiefly a by-product of organic chemical research. It may however fairly be claimed that for the commoner types of organic compounds, such as the fatty acids or the simple primary aromatic amines, analytical identification is now far more firmly on a systematic basis than it was in 1911.

The author has great pleasure in expressing his gratitude for valuable criticism and suggestions from Dr. O. L. Brady and Mr. F. P. Dunn.

H. T. CLARKE.

ROCHESTER, NEW YORK

CONTENTS

CHAP.   PAGE

I PRELIMINARY INVESTIGATION   I

Purity, 1. General and Physical Characteristics, 7. Examination for Elements, 9. Approximate Constitution, 13. Tabular Summary of Preliminary Tests, 16.

II EXAMINATION FOR RADICLES.   26

Carbon, Hydrogen, Nitrogen detected, 28. Carbon, Hydrogen, Sulphur detected, 54. Carbon, Hydrogen, Halogen detected, 62. Carbon, Hydrogen, Nitrogen, Sulphur in conjunction, 68. Carbon and Hydrogen alone detected, 71

III SEPARATION OF MIXTURES OF ORGANIC COMPOUNDS 98

IV CLASSIFIED TABLES OF COMMON ORGANIC COMPOUNDS 103

Hydrocarbons, 104. Aliphatic Ethers, 110. Phenolic Ethers, 111. Alcohols, 113. Phenols, 120. Aldehydes and Acetals, 126. Ketones, 130. Quinones, 133. Saturated Carboxylic Acids, 136. Unsaturated Acids, 142. Aliphatic Hydroxy Acids, 145. Phenolic Hydroxy Acids, 147. Alkyl and Acyl-Hydroxy Acids, 148. Ketonic Acids, 149. Acid Anhydrides, 150. Alkyl Esters of Simple Carboxylic Acids, 150. Aryl Esters of Carboxylic Acids, 155. Esters of Aliphatic Hydroxy Acids, 156. Esters of Aromatic Hydroxy Acids, 157. Esters of Ketonic Acids, 159. Lactones, 160. Carbohydrates, 161. Glucosides, 165. Aliphatic Chlorohydrocarbons, 167. Aliphatic Bromohydrocarbons, 170. Aliphatic Iodohydrocarbons, 171. Aromatic Chlorohydrocarbons, 173. Aromatic Bromohydrocarbons, 174. Aromatic Iodohydrocarbons, 176. Aliphatic α-Halogen-Substituted Ethers, 177. Other Aliphatic Halogen-Substituted Ethers, 178. Aromatic Halogen-Substituted Ethers, 178. Halogen-Substituted

Alcohols, 179. Halogen-Substituted Phenols, 181.
Halogen-Substituted Aldehydes, 182. Halogen-Sub-
stituted Ketones, 184. Carboxylic Acid Halides, 185.
Alkyl Chloroformates, 185. Aliphatic Halogen-Sub-
stituted Carboxylic Acids, 186. Aromatic Halogen-
Substituted Carboxylic Acids, 188. Halogen-Sub-
stituted Carboxylic Esters, 189. Aliphatic Primary
Amines, 191. Aliphatic Secondary Amines, 194. Ali-
phatic Tertiary Amines, 195. Aromatic Primary
Amines, 196. Aromatic Secondary Amines, 201. Aro-
matic Tertiary Amines, 203. Heterocyclic Bases, 205.
Aminophenols, 207. Aldehyde-Ammonias, 209. Simple
Amides and Imides, 210. Substituted Amides and
Imides, 216. Esters Amides, 222. Amino Acids, Esters,
and Amides, 223. Purines, 228. Aldoximes, 229.
Ketoximes, 229. Simple Nitriles, 231. Substituted
Nitriles, 232. isoCyanates, 234. Hydrazine Derivatives,
234. Hydrazones, 236. Aliphatic Nitro-Hydrocarbons,
237. Aromatic Nitro-Hydrocarbons, 238. Nitro
Ethers, 241. Nitro Alcohols, 243. Nitrophenols, 244.
Nitro Aldehydes, 245. Nitro Carboxylic Acids, 247.
Nitroso Compounds, 249. Azo Compounds, 251. Azoxy
Compounds, 253. Nitro Amino Compounds, 253. Nitro
Carboxylic Amides, 255. Alkyl Nitrates and Nitrites,
257. Halogen-Substituted Amines, 257. Halogen-
Substituted Amides, 259. Halogen-Substituted Nitro-
Hydrocarbons, 259. Mercaptans, 262. Sulphides and
Disulphides, 264. Sulphoxides and Sulphones, 265.
Simple Sulphonic Acids, 266. Substituted Sulphonic
Acids, 268. Sulphonic Esters, 270. Alkyl Sulphates,
271. Alkylsulphuric Acids, 272. Sulphinic Acids, 272.
Thiocarboxylic Acids, 273. Sulphochlorides, 273. Sul-
phonamides, 274. Substituted Sulphonamides, 275.
Thioamides, 275. Sulphur-containing Amino Acid, 276.
Aminosulphonic Acids, 277. Nitrosulphonic Acids, 277.
Thiocyanates, 278. isoThiocyanates, 278. Phenolic
Phosphates, 279. Alkaloids, 279. Dyes, 285.

V   QUANTITATIVE DETERMINATION OF CONSTITUENT
       ELEMENTS   290

    Carbon and Hydrogen, 290. Nitrogen, 297. Halogens,
       306. Sulphur, 311. Phosphorus, 312.

VI QUANTITATIVE DETERMINATION OF RADICLES.   .   314

    Decomposition of Metallic Derivatives, 314. Hydrolysis
       of Esters and Amides, 317. Estimation of Primary and
       Secondary Amines, 319. Methoxyl or Ethoxyl Groups,
       320. Estimation of Unsaturation, 324. Fehling's
       Solution, 327. Pavy's Solution, 330.

CONTENTS

CHAP.   PAGE

VII DETERMINATION OF SOME PHYSICAL PROPERTIES . 333

   Molecular Weight, 333. Vapour-density, 338. Density of
      Liquids, 344. Optical Rotation, 347.

   INDEX OF SUBSTANCES 352

   GENERAL INDEX 360

INTRODUCTION

ORGANIC analysis, qualitative and quantitative, has of recent years acquired increasing importance in the training of the chemist. And this with reason, for the examination of unknown organic compounds has, perhaps, an even greater educational value than has that of inorganic substances. The examination of inorganic ions too often tends to degenerate into a series of arbitrary tests,—memorised, and applied without much consideration of their theoretical bearing. In organic analysis conditions are too varying to permit of this ; no hard and fast rules can be laid down, and each observed reaction and characteristic must be brought into line if the definite constitution of the substance under examination is to be ascertained.

At the present time hardly any books exist which deal with the systematic testing of organic substances. There are many that describe the preparation of organic substances, give quantitative methods, and deal with special analysis of distinct classes of compounds. But the book that would enable the chemist to find out qualitatively the nature of the multitudinous carbon derivatives met with in ordinary work in an organic laboratory,—that book is wanted.

Every year sees the domain of organic chemistry growing in a manner hardly to be paralleled in any other science : as a result, the number of new substances being discovered makes it increasingly difficult to write a practical book that will deal with even the more common of them. Another difficulty is that the methods employed must necessarily be quite different from those in use for testing inorganic substances, for by far the majority of organic compounds contain the same elements. Groups, not elements, are the chief things to be looked for, melting and boiling points have to be determined, and other physical data also give valuable information to the chemist as to the nature of the compound under examination.

It is by no means easy to arrange a general plan for testing organic compounds so that one can say for certain what the particular compound may be. But as organic chemistry is an eminently practical science, there ought to be good practical books dealing with the subject,—books where the descriptions are concise, where the treatment of the subject is systematic and not merely an enumeration of special tests for special compounds, and where the student has to use his head as well as the information supplied by the text-book. Mr. Clarke has in this book recognised these requirements.

The most important novelty, however, in the book is to be found in the Chapter 'Tables of Compounds.' In this chapter Mr. Clarke has collected together the data that are wanted by the ordinary student after he has determined as far as possible the nature of the organic compound he is analysing : i.e. the nature of the radicles present, the elements present, its melting and boiling point, and possibly its molecular weight. Under ordinary conditions, after these data have been obtained, a lengthy hunt through a dictionary or manual of organic chemistry must be made to try to find what particular substance agrees with the facts discovered. In the 'Tables of Organic Compounds' a complete list is given of all the more important compounds likely to be met with, together with their properties, and thus much valuable time is gained through the possibility of making a direct comparison of the properties under investigation.

Mr. Clarke's book covers a very considerable amount of ground, and gives practically all that an average student should need. It will be of great assistance to anyone testing organic substances, and will help to put qualitative organic chemistry on as systematic a basis as qualitative inorganic chemistry has been for many years.

J. NORMAN COLLIE.

University College, London,
    June, 1911.

ORGANIC ANALYSIS

CHAPTER I

PRELIMINARY INVESTIGATION

Purity

IN undertaking the analysis of an organic substance the first consideration is that of purity, for without the certainty of this, all experimental examination is likely to lead to unreliable results.

When the substance is a liquid, the initial procedure is to heat a small quantity in a test-tube, in order to ascertain whether it will boil without decomposition.[1] If this is found to be the case, the entire quantity is submitted to fractional distillation, the liquid being boiled in a suitable distilling flask provided with a long, water-jacketed side-arm (Fig. 1). The temperature of the evolved vapour is continually observed, and the receiver is changed as soon as the temperature remains constant. A pure liquid should pass over within a range of not more than two degrees. When no constant boiling-point is observable (a sure indication of the presence of more than one compound) the liquid must be systematically fractionated, preferably with the use of a distilling column, care being taken to carry out the distillation as slowly as possible at all times. By such treatment the liquid will tend to

---

[1] The boiling-point of a pure liquid can be estimated with a fair degree of accuracy merely by holding a thermometer in the vapour of the liquid boiling in the test-tube. The reading is generally a few degrees too low.

accumulate in two or more fractions, the boiling ranges of
which include the boiling-points of the pure components
under atmospheric pressure.

For temperatures materially above 100° C. a stem-correc-
tion must be applied unless the entire thread of the thermometer is surrounded by the vapour. A formula for this
purpose has been worked out, but as this involves a knowledge
of the average temperature of the exposed portion of the
thread (a value difficult to ascertain, depending upon the

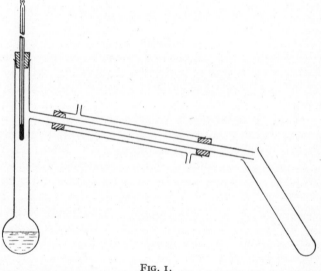

Fig. 1.

thermal conductivities of the mercury thread and the glass
wall of the thermometer), it is advisable to calibrate the
thermometer by direct comparison with short-stem standard
instruments.

When the liquid appears to be in any degree decomposed
at its boiling-point, fractionation must be carried out under
reduced pressure. A small trial sample should as before be

heated in a test-tube, but under the ' vacuum ' afforded by a filter-pump. Conditions being suitable, the entire quantity may be fractionated as before, except that the receiver now consists of a small distilling-flask attached to the filter-pump by means of pressure-tubing, a manometer being placed between the receiver and the pump. In order to obviate ' bumping ' it is advisable to lead into the liquid a fine capillary tube admitting a very slow current of air, or to place in the liquid a few pieces of porous earthenware. All stoppers should be of indiarubber, and it is well to replace the usual form of distilling flask by one having a double neck, as recommended by Claisen (Fig. 2).

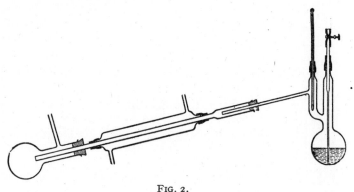

FIG. 2.

In the case of solids, a little of the original substance is finely powdered, pressed out upon a porous plate or upon several thicknesses of hardened filter-paper, dried thoroughly in air at about 40° or in a desiccator, and submitted to melting-point determination. A small quantity of the sample is forced into the open end of a thin-walled glass capillary tube 6–8 cm. long and sealed at one end ; it is then shaken down to the closed end by repeatedly dropping the capillary tube on to a hard surface through a vertical glass tube 6–8 mm. in diameter and 40–60 cm. long. The fine tube is then attached (either by moistening it with the liquid of the bath or by the use of a small indiarubber band) to a calibrated thermometer so that the enclosed sample is as near as possible to the middle of the thermometer bulb. The thermometer is now suspended in a bath of concentrated sulphuric acid or of medicinal mineral oil, with the bulb a few millimetres below the surface. A wide test-tube forms a suitable vessel for the bath, which should consist of the acid for temperatures below about 150°

and of the oil for higher temperatures.   The bath (Fig. 3) is heated steadily by a small flame, with continual stirring, and the temperature at which the sample melts is noted. A stem correction (see p. 2) must be applied for temperatures above 100°. It is advisable to repeat the determination, heating the bath rapidly to within some ten degrees of the melting-point and thereafter in such a way that the temperature rises about two degrees per minute.   In this way the range over which the substance melts, that is to say the temperature interval through which softening begins and finally a clear melt is formed, can be accurately observed.

For solids of low melting-point it is often more convenient to record the setting-point : a sample of the substance, sufficient in quantity to cover the bulb of the thermometer, is melted

FIG. 3.

in a test-tube and then slowly cooled, stirring continually with the thermometer. The temperature at which crystals first appear and that at which the substance becomes too solid to stir constitute the setting range. For a relatively pure compound this range extends over only one or two degrees, since the latent heat of solidification checks the fall in temperature ; a wide setting range, like a wide melting range in the capillary tube method, indicates the presence of impurity.

An apparatus has been developed by Johnston and Lynn [1] for the estimation on the foregoing principle of the setting-point of any organic substance that melts without decomposition. The sample is melted in a narrow test-tube, and a thermometer is immersed in the liquid. When cold, the solidified sample, with test-tube and thermometer attached, is placed within an electrical heating coil which in turn is surrounded by a vacuum jacket (Fig. 4). The coil must be placed in shunt with a variable resistance, which should be capable of giving 250 ohms for a d.c. supply at 110 volts. To determine the melting range, an electric current is supplied to the coil, such that the equilibrium temperature (previously determined by calibration of the instrument) lies 30–40° above the melting-point of the substance. Temperature readings are taken every minute and plotted against time. At the melting temperature the readings become nearly constant over the time interval during which the sample (if it is nearly pure) melts. With impure samples the normal heating curve of the apparatus, for the selected setting of the resistance, undergoes a marked extension, but this is not horizontal.

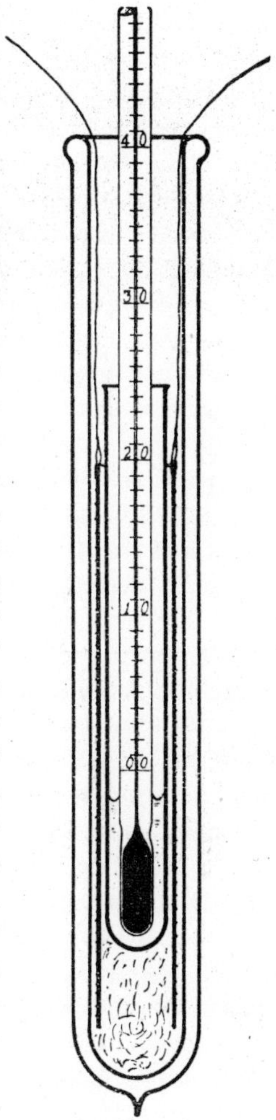

An even sharper break in continuity is obtained on plotting the cooling curve. To determine this, the sample is heated

Fig. 4.

[1] *Private communication.*

electrically to a point well above its melting temperature; the resistance is set so that the equilibrium point lies about 40° below the solidification temperature, and readings are made on the thermometer every minute. The temperature falls along the normal curve until the sample is slightly cooler than its setting point; it then rises sharply (as crystallisation sets in) to the solidification temperature and remains almost constant during the change of state. When less than 1 per cent. of impurity is present, this portion of the cooling curve slopes over less than one degree.

The melting-point as determined by the above apparatus coincides with the setting point; it is as a rule slightly lower (though more accurate) than the melting point indicated by the capillary tube method. The use of the apparatus is, as above stated, applicable to the determination of melting point and purity of only those compounds that melt without the least decomposition.

If the melting point as determined in the capillary tube is not sharp (i.e. the range extends over appreciably more than one degree), or if the extension in the cooling curve deviates considerably from the horizontal, the original sample must be recrystallised from some suitable solvent. Solvents may be tried in the following order: alcohol, water, ligroin, acetone, benzene, acetic acid, chloroform, ether. The recrystallisation is effected by maintaining a certain quantity of the solvent at its boiling-point in a conical flask—under reflux if the solvent is highly volatile—and gradually adding small quantities of the original substance until no more is taken up into solution. A small volume of the solvent is then added, the hot solution rapidly filtered through a fluted filter-paper on a funnel without a stem, and the filtrate allowed to cool, the vessel being occasionally scratched on the inside with a glass rod, to induce crystallisation. When cold, the solid which has separated is filtered off by suction, pressed upon a porous plate, dried in a vacuum desiccator, and the melting-point determined. This process must be repeated until the melting-point is sharp and shows no change on further recrystallisation ; it may then be regarded as pure. If, however, the melting-point after one recrystallisation is identical with that of the original substance, no further purification is necessary.

Should the substance appear to contain tarry or coloured impurities, it is advisable to add some decolorising carbon to the hot solution before filtering.

It is well to ascertain whether a solid can be distilled or sublimed. Not only is the boiling-point of a substance solid at ordinary temperatures a valuable additional characteristic to be taken into consideration, but solids can often be obtained in a higher state of purity by distillation or sublimation than by crystallisation. The precaution should of course be taken of heating a small quantity, in order to make sure that it can be distilled without decomposition. When this is possible, a distilling flask with a wide side-tube should be employed, without a condenser, and any distillate solidifying at the outset melted by gently warming the tube. This distillation of solids may often advantageously be carried out under reduced pressure ; in such a case a distilling flask with a wide (10–15 mm.) side-arm should be employed, in order to avoid stoppage by solidified distillate.

General and Physical Characteristics

It is of great importance to investigate the solubility of the substance in various solvents, for information as to the chemical nature of the compound can frequently be obtained from consideration of this characteristic property.

Thus, in general, salts are more or less soluble in water, but insoluble in ether ; acids are often soluble in hot water, and sparingly so in cold water, while being as a rule soluble in alcohol or ether ; hydrocarbons are all insoluble in water, but soluble in ether, and so on. As a general rule, compounds are dissolved by liquids containing similar groups of atoms.

The boiling- and melting-points should always be kept in

mind, so as to exclude erroneous conclusions which might otherwise be deduced from considerations of other properties and reactions.

Whether the substance is soluble in water or not, its reaction towards litmus paper should be examined, since this at once affords a clue for the allotment of the compound into one of three great classes. It frequently happens that substances, such as certain acids, though but sparingly soluble in water, are sufficiently so to have an appreciable effect upon litmus paper.

The odour of a substance may sometimes give an indication of the class to which it belongs, though this is not to be relied upon with too great assurance, as the sense of smell varies greatly with individuals ; moreover, substances of different constitution may have similar odours.

Similarly the colour of the substance affords an indication of the class to which the compound is likely or unlikely to belong, but at present so little is known about the relations of colour and constitution that no definite rules can be enunciated. Moreover, the removal of the last traces of coloured impurities from colourless substances is occasionally a matter of extreme difficulty, and unrecognised failure in this respect may lead to faulty conclusions.

It is always advantageous, in the case of a liquid, to know its density, as definite generalisations can be drawn from this property, which also aids in the final identification of liquids. The details for procedure will be found on pages 344–346.

Much information is afforded in doubtful cases by a knowledge of the approximate molecular weight, based upon cryoscopic or ebullioscopic determinations. The methods are described on pages 333 and 337. Rapid quantitative determinations, such as the titration of known weights of organic acids with standard alkali, the volumetric estimation of ionisable halogen in salts, or the quantitative saponification of esters, are of great value, and should be carried out whenever possible.

Many compounds occurring in nature, such as sugars,

glucosides, alkaloids, terpenes and allied bodies, hydroxy- and amino-acids, exist in optically active forms. When the presence of such a substance is suspected, it is well to determine the rotatory power according to the method given on page 347.

Examination for Constituent Elements

A small quantity of the substance should at first be heated upon a nickel spatula until completely ignited, in order to ascertain the presence of any non-volatile residue. Should a residue be found which appears to consist of a heavy metal or its oxide, it will be necessary to ignite another small portion in a porcelain crucible. Substances leaving a residue consisting of an alkali carbonate or an oxide of a metal of the calcium group may preferably be heated on a piece of platinum foil. All such residues must be subjected to a complete qualitative analysis. The nature of the flame formed, as well as the odour of the vapours evolved, should be observed and recorded.

The next operation is to fuse a portion of the substance in a small glass tube with metallic sodium, heating completely to dull redness after action has ceased. The hot tube should then be dropped into a test-tube half filled with pure water, caution being necessary in this operation, as the sodium present may cause an explosion unless the tube is entirely red-hot at the time of immersion in the water.

The contents of the test-tube should thereupon be poured into a thoroughly clean mortar, finely ground, and the mixture filtered. To a portion of the filtrate two drops of a freshly prepared solution of ferrous sulphate are added. Since the mixture is alkaline, on account of the decomposition of some of the water by the excess of sodium, a precipitate of ferrous hydroxide will appear. The mixture must then be boiled for about one minute, cooled, and a drop of ferric chloride added. If nitrogen was present in the original substance, it will have been converted by the action of the sodium and carbon into sodium cyanide, and by boiling the alkaline cyanide solution with ferrous hydroxide, sodium ferrocyanide will have been produced. Now if on addition of an excess of hydrochloric acid a blue coloration or precipitate of ferric ferrocyanide is formed, it may be taken as proof that both carbon and nitrogen are present in the substance :—

$$FeSO_4 + 2NaCN = Fe(CN)_2 + Na_2SO_4$$
$$Fe(CN)_2 + 4NaCN = Na_4Fe(CN)_6$$
$$3Na_4Fe(CN)_6 + 4FeCl_3 = Fe_4[Fe(CN)_6]_3 + 12NaCl.$$

Should the substance be very volatile, it may be found difficult to make the sodium react sufficiently with it. In such a case it is advisable to support the tube, which should be of hard glass, in a piece of asbestos board so that it hangs in a vertical position by the flange around the open end. The sodium is then to be heated by itself, and the substance dropped in small portions upon it, thus giving it a better opportunity to react. The sodium may with advantage be replaced by potassium.

In the absence of carbon of course no cyanide is produced, although nitrogen may be present. In carrying out this test, only a faint greenish-blue coloration may occasionally be produced, which forms a blue precipitate on prolonged standing. In such a case it is advisable to repeat the test with great care, employing larger quantities. The presence of sulphur occasionally tends to obscure the cyanide test, owing to the reduction of ferric iron to the ferrous condition by the hydrogen sulphide liberated on the addition of acid. In such cases black ferrous sulphide is precipitated on the addition of the ferrous sulphate solution, and it will be well to make sure that enough of this reagent has been added, and to filter the solution after boiling, before adding the ferric chloride and hydrochloric acid.

To another portion of the filtrate a drop of sodium plumbite solution is added. A black precipitate or dark coloration indicates the presence of a sulphide in the solution. Since all organic sulphur compounds yield sodium sulphide by the reducing action of sodium at high temperatures, this extremely sensitive test may be taken as proof of the presence of sulphur in the substance.

Should no sulphur or nitrogen be detected, a third portion of the filtrate should be rendered acid with nitric acid, and silver nitrate added. A precipitate of silver halide indicates the presence of halogen in the substance. When sulphur or nitrogen are present, this portion of the filtrate must, before adding the silver nitrate, be boiled with excess of dilute nitric acid for about five minutes in order to remove the hydrogen sulphide or cyanide from the solution. The silver halides may be identified or separated by the standard methods. The presence of halogen may be confirmed by heating a copper wire in an oxidising flame until the green colour is no longer perceptible. A minute portion of the substance is now placed on the wire, which is again held in the flame ; should halogen be present in the substance, the flame will again be coloured green, owing to the formation of volatile copper halide. This test is extremely sensitive, and care must be taken not to contaminate the wire with laboratory dust or the fingers after its initial heating.

Phosphorus may be detected by either of the following methods :—(1) A small quantity of the substance is heated with a mixture of concentrated sulphuric and nitric acids until a clear solution is obtained. On diluting with water, and filtering if necessary, the solution is boiled with an excess of ammonium nitrate, cooled, and ammonium molybdate solution added to the mixture. On gentle warming a yellow precipitate of ammonium phosphomolybdate indicates the presence of phosphorus. (2) Small portions of the substance are carefully added to a fused mixture of equal parts of potassium carbonate and potassium nitrate in a nickel crucible, and the mixture heated until effervescence ceases. The cooled melt is dissolved in excess of dilute nitric acid, and ammonium molybdate added to the warm solution as described under the first method. The second method, being the more rapid, should always be employed unless the substance is very volatile.

The presence of carbon and hydrogen may be proved in the following manner. A portion of the substance is intimately mixed with about four times its weight of *absolutely dry* powdered copper oxide, and introduced into a long hard glass test-tube. Above this is placed a layer of pure copper oxide, and a delivery-tube attached to the mouth of the tube by means of a cork. The mixture is then heated so that the

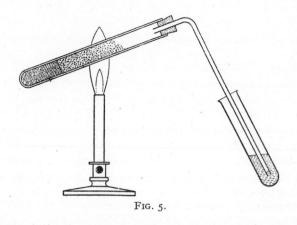

FIG. 5.

upper layer receives the greater part of the heat, the delivery-tube being introduced into a test-tube containing baryta water. The presence of carbon will then be indicated by a precipitate of barium carbonate from the baryta solution, while the formation of drops of moisture condensing on the cooler parts of the hard glass tube will show the presence of hydrogen in the compound (Fig 5).

The presence of oxygen in an organic compound is not as a rule susceptible of direct proof by ordinary methods. Advantage may, however, be taken in many instances of the property possessed by oxygen-containing substances of forming brown solutions of iodine, in contrast to the violet solutions formed by hydrocarbons and their halogen derivatives. The procedure for this test is described on page 72.

Approximate Constitution

If the substance is soluble in water, ionised radicles must be at once tested for in the solution. When halogens, sulphur or phosphorus have been detected in the substance, the usual routine tests for inorganic acid radicles should be applied, in order to determine whether these elements exist wholly or in part as ionisable radicles. When nitrogen has been shown to be present, the solution must be examined for a nitrate or a nitrite. The metals in water-soluble metallic salts will generally exist in the ionised condition. It is also well to test for the presence of the commoner organic acids, which may possibly be present in the form of salts of organic bases. The tests for such acids are given in detail in the appended tables.

In all cases where the presence of ionised acid radicles has been shown, a cold solution of caustic soda must be added, in order to liberate the free base. This may then be filtered off, distilled out, or extracted with ether when a solid is not precipitated, and examined independently. The presence of a salt of ammonia or of a volatile amine, such as methylamine, will be indicated by the evolution of ammoniacal odours in the cold. Similarly, the acid should be liberated by the action of dilute sulphuric acid from substances ascertained to be salts of organic acids, and prepared in a pure state for examination.

It should be borne in mind when testing for ionised halogen that acid halides, on treatment with water, yield a mixture of the corresponding acid and halogen hydracid, and in such a case it will of course be futile to attempt to isolate any base. In many instances, however, an acid halide will be detected by the action of a drop of water on a small quantity of the substance, fumes of the hydracid being thereby liberated.

$$CH_3 \cdot CO \cdot Cl + H_2O = CH_3 \cdot CO \cdot OH + HCl.$$

In addition, most α-chloro ethers evolve hydrochloric acid on treatment with water.

The nature of the vapours evolved on strongly heating the substance, as well as the character of the flame formed on ignition, constitute fairly definite indications of the general class to which it belongs. Thus the odour of phenols, aromatic nitro-compounds and aldehydes, and amines, as well as the decomposition-products of carbohydrates and certain hydroxy-acids, are all more or less characteristic ; while the rule that unsaturated substances and saturated compounds containing more than four or five atoms in the molecule burn with a smoky flame is generally applicable.

The action of hot and cold concentrated sulphuric acid should be tried. Although it is difficult to draw up a complete table of inferences, it should be observed whether the substance dissolves and whether change of colour, charring, or effervescence is produced. The nature of any gases evolved should also be examined.

The effect of heating in a tube with soda-lime and with zinc dust should also be observed, any well-defined distillate or sublimate being isolated and examined.

Unsaturated linkages may be detected by the action of bromine water and of neutral permanganate solution. Unsaturated compounds decolorise these reagents, while in general saturated compounds do not. These reactions, however, do not afford a very certain test, as most polyhydroxylic compounds, many aldehydes, certain acids and esters, most phenols and ketones, and several other types of compound are thus attacked.

Unsaturated compounds in which an ethenoid linkage is conjugated with an aromatic nucleus may absorb bromine but slowly. Hence this test must not be considered to have failed until, after gentle warming, the mixture has stood for at least five minutes without appreciable diminution in the intensity of the colour of the bromine. Thus cinnamic acid scarcely decolorises bromine water until the solution is warmed. Phenolic and certain other classes of compounds yield in general precipitates of bromo-derivatives when treated with bromine water. Such precipitates should be collected and purified for examination.

A solution of bromine in carbon tetrachloride, chloroform, or glacial acetic acid is similarly decolorised by substances containing unsaturated linkages. In all cases such bromine addition products should be isolated for examination. Hydrobromic acid is evolved on warming most aromatic compounds with bromine in carbon tetrachloride, owing to the facility with which the majority of substituted benzene derivatives are brominated. Bromine, in non-aqueous as in aqueous solution, is absorbed by many phenolic, ketonic and by certain other types of compound. In carbon tetrachloride or chloroform, however, evolution of hydrobromic acid will take place on warming, owing to its slight solubility in these non-hydroxylic solvents. Amines also absorb bromine with formation of addition or substitution products, liberation of hydrobromic acid being, however, not necessarily a concomitant.

Unsaturated substances in general are also attacked by either fuming sulphuric acid or fuming nitric acid, in the latter case decomposition often taking place with violence.

Many compounds containing a triple linkage form insoluble metallic derivatives when treated with an ammoniacal solution of silver nitrate or cuprous chloride, from which precipitate the free acetylenic compound can be regenerated by warming with very dilute mineral acid. Acetylenic copper and silver compounds are not formed by disubstituted acetylenes of the general formula $R \cdot C \vdots C \cdot R$, owing to the absence of a replaceable hydrogen atom.

A rough tabular summary showing the effects produced by the foregoing tests on different classes of compound is given on the following pages. By its aid, some indication of the type of compound to be especially tested for, by the specific methods later enumerated, will be obtained.

CARBON and HYDROGEN detected

I. **Treat with cold and hot water, and test solution or mixture with litmus.**

    A. Soluble in the cold :

        (i) Strongly acid : Simple aliphatic carboxylic acids of low mol. wt. ; most aliphatic hydroxy-acids ; most polyhydroxylic phenolic acids ; a few simple esters of very low mol. wt.

        (ii) Faintly acid : Some simple phenols ; most polyhydroxylic phenols.

        (iii) Neutral : Alcohols of low mol. wt. ; most polyhydroxylic alcohols ; aldehydes and ketones of low mol. wt. ; sugars ; most glucosides.

    B. Sparingly soluble in the cold, more soluble on warming :

        (i) Strongly acid : Simple carboxylic acids of fairly high mol. wt. (including some aromatic acids) ; many aromatic hydroxy-acids and their acyl derivatives.

        (ii) Faintly acid : Most monohydroxylic phenols.

        (iii) Neutral : A few carbohydrates and glucosides ; simple quinones.

    C. Insoluble :

        (i) Strongly acid : Some acids of very high mol. wt. ; acid anhydrides (slowly decomposed on warming with water).

        (ii) Faintly acid : Some phenols of high mol. wt. ; keto-enolic esters.

        (iii) Neutral : Hydrocarbons ; simple ethers ; alcohols, aldehydes, ketones, and quinones of very high mol. wt. ; almost all esters ; a few fatty acids of very high mol. wt.

II. **Treat with $NaHCO_3$ solution all substances that show an acid reaction.**

    A. CO_2 evolved : All carboxylic acids.

    B. No CO_2 evolved : Phenols ; keto-enolic esters, &c.

III. Treat with cold and hot concentrated NaOH solution.
    A. Substances which are insoluble or sparingly soluble in cold water :
        (i) Soluble in the cold : All carboxylic acids ; all phenols ; keto-enolic esters and similar compounds.
        (ii) Gradually dissolve on warming : A few esters and lactones ; acid anhydrides.
        (iii) Insoluble: Hydrocarbons; ethers; alcohols and ketones of very high mol. wt. ; many esters (in general only very slowly decomposed).
    B. The following classes of compounds undergo pronounced decomposition on warming with aqueous alkali : Most acid anhydrides ; a few esters and lactones ; aldehydes ; sugars ; glucosides.

IV. Treat with concentrated H_2SO_4.
    A. Cold.
        (i) Soluble :
            (a) without decomposition : Some aromatic hydrocarbons ; almost all ethers ; most alcohols ; most phenols ; some ketones ; simple carboxylic acids ; most aromatic hydroxy acids ; a few esters.
            (b) with decomposition : Almost all unsaturated compounds ; some aromatic hydrocarbons ; most aliphatic hydroxy-acids ; most esters ; sugars (brownish colours) ; some glucosides (red or other pronounced colours).
        (ii) Insoluble : Saturated hydrocarbons ; some aromatic hydrocarbons.
    B. Hot.
        (i) Gases evolved :
            (a) with charring : Aldehydes ; ketones ; acetals ; carbohydrates ; glucosides.
            (b) without charring : Simple alcohols of low mol. wt. (evolve gaseous unsaturated hydrocarbons) ; formic and oxalic acids and their derivatives (yield CO).

(ii) Pungent vapours evolved, without charring :
Simple phenols ; certain simple carboxylic acids ; many esters.

(iii) No gases evolved, with charring : Most
polyhydroxylic phenols ; many aromatic
hydroxy-acids and certain of their derivatives.

(iv) Soluble unchanged : Some carboxylic acids ;
some aromatic ketones of high mol. wt.

V. Dissolve in water or alcohol and treat with one drop of FeCl₃ solution.

A. Reddish coloration or precipitate : Almost all
simple carboxylic acids.

B. Intense yellow coloration : Aliphatic α-hydroxy-
acids.

C. Green, blue, or violet colorations : Most phenols
and phenolic compounds (some in alcoholic
solution only) ; keto-enolic esters and similar
compounds.

VI. Treat with a solution of KMnO₄ in dilute H₂SO₄.
Decolorisation by :

(a) Almost all unsaturated compounds.

(b) Certain easily oxidisable substances such as
formic acid and malonic acid and their esters ;
many aldehydes ; simple quinones ; some aliphatic hydroxy-acids ; many polyhydric alcohols
and phenols ; certain sugars.

VII. Treat with bromine water in the cold or warm.

A. Decolorisation without formation of much acid :
Almost all unsaturated compounds.

B. Decolorisation with formation of much acid :
Many aldehydes and ketones ; other compounds
readily brominated, such as phenols and their
derivatives.

VIII. Treat with a solution of bromine in CCl₄, CHCl₃, or CS₂.

A. Instant decolorisation in the cold, without evolution of HBr : Almost all unsaturated compounds.

B. Decolorisation with evolution of HBr on warming ;
Substances which are readily brominated, such

as many aldehydes and ketones ; most phenols and phenolic compounds ; certain unstable hydrocarbons (such as terpenes).

C. Rapid decolorisation only on warming, without evolution of HBr : Unsaturated compounds in which the unsaturated linkages are either conjugated with aromatic and similar residues or largely surrounded by substituents (e.g. (i) Cinnamic acid ; (ii) Tetrasubstituted ethylenes).

IX. Ignite with dry soda-lime.

A. Hydrogen or hydrocarbons evolved : Simple aliphatic and aromatic carboxylic acids.

B. Phenols evolved : Aromatic hydroxy-acids.

C. Odour of ' burnt sugar ' : Most aliphatic hydroxy-acids ; sugars ; glucosides.

X. Ignite with zinc dust.

Hydrocarbons are produced from many phenols, quinones, and aromatic ketones of high mol. wt. This treatment may also result in the disruption of some carboxylic acids, with formation of hydrocarbons and other compounds.

CARBON, HYDROGEN, and NITROGEN detected

I. Treat with cold and hot water, and test solution or mixture with litmus.

A. Soluble in the cold :

(i) Acid or faintly acid : A few aromatic amino-acids ; some aliphatic simple amides of low mol. wt. ; a few simple urethanes ; a few oximes of low mol. wt. ; some nitro-phenols ; nitrates of weak organic bases.

(ii) Neutral : Aliphatic amino carboxylic acids ; a few aliphatic substituted amides ; some purines ; a few aromatic nitroamines ; salts of organic acids with nitrogenous bases or ammonia ; nitrates of strong organic bases.

(iii) Alkaline or faintly alkaline : Aliphatic primary, secondary, and tertiary amines of fairly low mol. wt. ; guanidine and its alkyl derivatives ; some aromatic diamines.

B. Sparingly soluble in the cold, more so on warming :

     (i) Acid or faintly acid : Some simple amides ; some nitrophenols ; some nitro carboxylic-acids ; formanilide.

     (ii) Neutral : Some aliphatic and aromatic substituted amides ; a few purines ; some aromatic nitroamines.

     (iii) Alkaline or faintly alkaline : Some aromatic diamines and aminophenols.

C. Insoluble :

     (i) Acid or faintly acid : A few purines ; alkyl nitrates and nitrites.

     (ii) Neutral : Some aromatic amines of high mol. wt. ; simple and substituted amides of very high mol. wt. ; most alkaloids ; simple nitriles ; *iso*cyanides ; most oximes ; hydrazones ; most substituted urethanes ; nitro hydrocarbons ; nitro ethers ; nitroso, azoxy, azo, and hydrazo compounds.

     (iii) Alkaline or faintly alkaline : Most simple aromatic amines ; most substituted hydrazines ; a few alkaloids.

II. **Treat substances insoluble or sparingly soluble in cold water with dilute acid and with dilute alkali.**

    A. Soluble in dilute acid : All primary amines ; all aliphatic and most aromatic secondary and tertiary amines ; many substituted hydrazines ; some simple and substituted amides ; some oximes ; some purines ; most alkaloids.

    B. Soluble in dilute alkali : Many simple amides and imides ; a few primary substituted amides ; amino carboxylic acids ; nitro carboxylic acids ; oximes ; nitrophenols ; some purines.

III. **Treat with cold and hot concentrated alkali.**

    A. Ammonia or ammoniacal vapours evolved in the cold : Ammonium salts of organic acids ; salts of simple aliphatic amines.

    B. Ammonia or ammoniacal vapours evolved only on heating : Simple amides and imides ; urea and mono-substituted ureas ; urethanes ; nitriles (slowly) ; acyl derivatives of simple aliphatic primary and secondary amines ; some aromatic nitroamines; most polynitro aromatic compounds; guanidine and its alkyl derivatives.

C. Separation of an insoluble compound in the cold: Salts of insoluble bases.

D. Separation of an insoluble compound on heating: Acyl derivatives of insoluble primary and secondary amines; many substituted urethanes of high mol. wt.

IV. Boil with Sn and concentrated HCl, then add alkali in excess.

A. Ammonia or ammoniacal vapours produced: Simple amides and imides; acyl derivatives of amines of low mol. wt.; nitriles; *iso*cyanates of aliphatic radicles of low mol. wt.; *iso*cyanides; aliphatic oximes; ammonium salts.

B. Liquid or solid bases produced: Nitro, nitroso, azoxy, azo, and hydrazo compounds; acyl derivatives of amines of high mol. wt.; nitriles, *iso*cyanates, and *iso*cyanides of high mol. wt.; hydrazones.

V. Heat with soda-lime.

A. Ammonia or ammoniacal vapours produced: Simple amides and imides; nitriles; many alkaloids; purines; many substituted hydrazines; many amino carboxylic acids of low mol. wt.; simple urethanes; many aromatic nitroamines.

B. Liquid or solid bases produced: Acyl derivatives of primary and secondary amines; amino carboxylic acids of high mol. wt.; many hydrazine derivatives; substituted urethanes of high mol. wt.

CARBON, HYDROGEN, and SULPHUR detected

I. Treat with cold and hot water, and test solution or mixture with litmus.

A. Soluble in the cold:
  (i) Acid: Most sulphonic acids; a few thio-carboxylic acids; some sulphinic acids.
  (ii) Neutral or faintly alkaline: Aliphatic sulphoxides of low mol. wt.

B. Sparingly soluble in the cold, more soluble on
warming :
  (i) Acid : Some sulphonic acids ; many sul-
      phinic acids.
  (ii) Neutral : A few sulphones.
C. Insoluble :
  (i) Acid or faintly acid : Some hydroxy-sul-
      phones ; alkyl sulphates and esters of
      sulphonic acids (slowly decomposed).
  (ii) Neutral : Mercaptans ; sulphides ; disul-
      phides ; sulphoxides and sulphones of
      high mol. wt. ; aryl esters of sulphonic
      acids.

II. Treat substances insoluble or sparingly soluble in cold
water, with warm dilute alkali.
  A. Soluble without pronounced decomposition : All
     sulphonic acids ; sulphinic acids ; sulphur com-
     pounds containing carboxyl or phenolic hydroxyl
     groups ; mercaptans.
  B. Soluble with pronounced decomposition : Alkyl
     sulphates and esters of sulphonic acids ; thio-
     carboxylic acids and esters.

III. Shake with water and HgCl$_2$ solution.
  Precipitates formed with : Mercaptans, sulphides,
  and some disulphides.

IV. Ignite with soda-lime.
  Phenols produced from most sulphonic acids ; hydrocarbons from sulphinic acids and a few sulphonic
  acids.

CARBON, HYDROGEN, and HALOGEN detected

I. Treat with cold and hot water, and test solution or mixture
with litmus.
  A. Soluble in the cold :
    (i) Acid or faintly acid : Aliphatic halogen-
        substituted carboxylic acids.
    (ii) Neutral : Halogen-substituted alcohols and
         aldehydes ; some halogen - substituted
         phenols.

B. Sparingly soluble in the cold, more soluble on warming :
 (i) Strongly acid : Simple aromatic halogen-substituted carboxylic acids.
 (ii) Faintly acid : Simple halogen-substituted phenols.

C. Insoluble :
 (i) Faintly acid : Some halogen-substituted esters ; poly-halogen-substituted phenols.
 (ii) Neutral : Halogen-substituted hydrocarbons ; esters of halogen-substituted acids ; halogen-substituted ketones ; halogen-substituted aromatic ethers.

D. Decomposed with liberation of halogen hydracid :
 (i) Rapidly : Aliphatic carboxylic halides ; aliphatic α-halogen-substituted ethers.
 (ii) Slowly : Aromatic carboxylic halides.

II. Boil under reflux with alcoholic AgNO₃.

A. Silver halide rapidly produced : Aliphatic iodo compounds ; carboxylic halides ; aliphatic α-halogen-substituted ethers.

B. Silver halide slowly produced : Aliphatic α-halogen-substituted acids, esters, aldehydes, and ketones ; some unsaturated aliphatic and some aromatic α-halogen-substituted hydrocarbons (such as allyl bromide and benzyl chloride).

C. Silver halide produced very slowly or not at all : Saturated aliphatic chloro- and bromo-substituted compounds in general ; most aromatic chloro, bromo, and iodo compounds in which halogen is attached to aromatic nucleus.

III. Boil under reflux with alcoholic KOH.

A. Potassium halide precipitated : Aliphatic chloro and bromo compounds ; aromatic chloro and bromo compounds in which halogen is not attached to aromatic nucleus.

B. No precipitate of potassium halide : Iodo compounds (KI is soluble in alcohol) ; aryl halides in general.

CARBON, HYDROGEN, NITROGEN, and SULPHUR
detected

I. **Treat with cold and hot water, and test solution or mixture with litmus.**

    A. Soluble in the cold : Thiocarbamide ; some nitro sulphonic acids ; salts of thiocyanic acid.

    B. Sparingly soluble in the cold, more soluble on warming : Many substituted thiocarbamides ; many amino sulphonic acids ; some nitro sulphonic acids, some simple and substituted sulphonamides.

    C. Insoluble : Alkyl thiocyanates ; alkyl *iso*thiocyanates ; many aromatic amino sulphonic acids ; many simple and substituted sulphonamides.

II. **Treat with cold and hot NaOH solution.**

    A. Cold. (i) Soluble : Simple and primary substituted sulphonamides ; carbosulphonimides, amino, nitro, azo, &c., sulphonic acids.

          (ii) Insoluble : Sulphonyl derivatives of secondary amines ; alkyl thiocyanates and *iso*thiocyanates.

    B. Hot. (i) Ammonia evolved : Thiocarbamide and monosubstituted thiocarbamides ; simple sulphonamides (very slowly).

          (ii) Bases produced : Substituted thiocarbamides ; sulphonyl derivatives of primary and secondary amines (very slowly).

III. **Boil under reflux with concentrated HCl.**

    Alkyl thiocyanates yield alkyl sulphides, CO_2, and NH_4Cl.

    Alkyl *iso*thiocyanates yield H_2S, CO_2, and primary amines.

    Sulphonamides yield sulphonic acids and NH_4Cl (slowly).

    Substituted sulphonamides yield primary or secondary amines and sulphonic acids.

    Thiocarbamide and substituted thiocarbamides yield H_2S and guanidine or substituted guanidines.

    Amino sulphonic acids form hydrochlorides unchanged.

IV. Boil with zinc dust and dilute HCl.
 Amino compounds produced from: Nitro and azo sulphonic acids; substituted thiocarbamides; alkyl *iso*thiocyanates (with evolution of H_2S).

METALLIC RESIDUE LEFT AFTER IGNITION
Treat with dilute HCl

Carbon and **Hydrogen** detected:
 Salts of carboxylic acids: Free acids liberated.
Carbon, Hydrogen, and **Nitrogen** detected:
 Salts of nitro carboxylic acids: Free acids liberated.
 Salts of azo carboxylic acids: Free acids liberated.
 Salts of amino carboxylic acids: Soluble hydrochlorides produced.
 Salts of nitrophenols: Free nitrophenols liberated.
 Metallic derivatives of imides of dicarboxylic acids: Free imides produced.
Carbon, Hydrogen, and **Halogen** detected:
 Salts of halogen-substituted carboxylic acids: Free acids liberated.
Carbon, Hydrogen, and **Sulphur** detected:
 Boil with solution of $BaCl_2$ in strong HCl:
   (i) SO_2 evolved: Bisulphite compounds of aldehydes or ketones.
   (ii) $BaSO_4$ slowly produced: Salts of alkyl-sulphuric acids.
   (iii) No $BaSO_4$ produced: Salts of sulphonic acids, or carbosulphonimides.
Carbon, Hydrogen, Nitrogen, and **Sulphur** detected:
 Acidify strongly with concentrated HCl: Precipitates of free acids produced from salts of many amino and azo sulphonic acids.

Carbon, Hydrogen, Nitrogen, Sulphur and **Halogen** detected.
 Salts of halogen sulphonamides.

CHAPTER II

EXAMINATION FOR RADICLES

THIS chapter is intended to serve as a guide for the detection of the various salient groups which may be present in the molecule. When one radicle has been found, it will, of course, still be necessary to search for others which may also exist in the compound under examination ; and since the great majority of organic compounds contain more than one characteristic group, the manner in which these different groups may affect the general properties of the substance must be the subject of careful consideration.

When an element other than carbon and hydrogen has been detected, the first important point to be established is the form in which this element exists. To take the case of a substance in which carbon, hydrogen, and nitrogen have been shown to exist, it must first be established whether it is a primary, secondary, or tertiary amine, anamide, a hydrazine or hydroxylamine derivative, an azo, azoxy, nitroso, or nitro body, or other type of nitrogen compound. In short, the first problem is to determine the class of the body in reference to the most uncommon element occurring therein, and not until this point is settled will it be profitable to examine the substance with a view to ascertaining the constitution of the remaining portion of the molecule.

For this reason the section dealing with substances in which only carbon and hydrogen have been detected has been reserved until the end of this chapter, so that after the ' special elements ' have been allotted to their proper classes, the substance may be examined according to the guide given for compounds in which carbon and hydrogen have been found, due allowances being made for the presence of the known 'special' groups.

When all the salient radicles have been definitely determined, reference should be made to the appended tables for the list of compounds, tabulated according to their class, and arranged in the order of boiling- and melting-points; the characteristic tests and properties of derivatives of each substance being, in so far as possible, enumerated.

Most important points, not to be neglected in the examination for radicles, are quantitative estimation of groups and preparation of derivatives. The importance of both these operations cannot be too strongly emphasised. Unfortunately the quantitative work frequently requires a comparatively long time; but many simple estimations, such as the titration of an acid or the salt of a base, or a volumetric estimation of ionised halogen, can be expeditiously carried out, and may contribute much to the certainty of an identification. In fact, owing to the absence of any definite system for the identification of organic compounds, after the establishment of the presence of the various characteristic groups in the substance the ultimate identification must occasionally depend upon such quantitative experiments The preparation of derivatives is even more important, and no excuse is valid for failure to prepare and examine at least one pure derivative.

The preliminary tests described and tabulated in the previous chapter should have led to some clue as to the nature of the group or groups present in the molecule, and the properties of the various types are therefore discussed without further reference to the general methods of distinction. The equations given in the text refer to simple typical examples of the reactions under discussion. The page references refer to the tables of organic compounds given in Chapter IV.

Types of Radicle involving the detection of
CARBON, HYDROGEN, and NITROGEN

On treatment with cold aqueous alkali, ammonia is liberated from **ammonium salts** with formation of products which may more profitably be investigated independently, with a view to identification.

Aldehyde ammonias (p. 209) also yield ammonia on gently warming with aqueous alkali. For preparation of the free aldehyde from an aldehyde-ammonia, however, decomposition by distillation with dilute sulphuric acid is advisable. Salts of organic acids may also be decomposed by means of dilute mineral acid, subsequently distilling the mixture when the acid is volatile with steam, filtering when it is insoluble or sparingly soluble in cold water, or extracting with ether. Acids which cannot be isolated by any of these methods must be examined in solution before proceeding with their isolation by some special method.

By the action of hot aqueous alkali, ammonia is liberated comparatively rapidly from **simple amides** (p. 210) and slowly from most **nitriles** (pp. 231–233).

$$CH_3 \cdot CONH_2 + NaOH = CH_3 \cdot COONa + NH_3$$
$$C_6H_5 \cdot C\!:\!N + NaOH + H_2O = C_6H_5 \cdot COONa + NH_3$$

These types of substance yield no ammonia by the action of alkali in the cold. In most cases it will be found expedient to carry out the hydrolysis by boiling under reflux with concentrated hydrochloric acid, 50 per cent. sulphuric acid or phosphoric acid, or, when possible, by heating with concentrated sulphuric acid on the water-bath.

$$CH_3 \cdot CONH_2 + HCl + H_2O = CH_3 \cdot COOH + NH_4Cl$$
$$C_6H_5 \cdot C\!:\!N + HCl + 2H_2O = C_6H_5 \cdot COOH + NH_4Cl$$

The acid formed should in every case be examined, after isolation by distillation with steam, filtration, or extraction with ether, according to the nature of the acid.

Phosphorus pentoxide reacts with amides, nitriles being produced on heating.

$$CH_3 \cdot CONH_2 = CH_3 \cdot C \vdots N + H_2O$$

These can best be isolated by distilling the nitrile from the resulting mixture, or failing this, by addition of cold water and extraction with ether.

Amides, on treatment with bromine and excess of strong alkali and subsequent distillation, yield primary amines containing one carbon atom less than the original amide.

$$CH_3 \cdot CONH_2 \longrightarrow CH_3 \cdot CONHBr \longrightarrow$$
$$CH_3 \cdot N{:}CO \longrightarrow CH_3 \cdot NH_2 + CO_2$$

The distillate should be allowed to pass at once into hydrochloric acid, the resulting solution evaporated to dryness on the water-bath, and the hydrochloride of the amine extracted from the residue with hot absolute alcohol. In the case of urea (carbamide), nitrogen is evolved without the production of an amine.

Amides may be converted into the corresponding anilides by heating with aniline, ammonia being evolved.

$$CH_3 \cdot CO \cdot NH_2 + C_6H_5 \cdot NH_2 = CH_3 \cdot CO \cdot NH \cdot C_6H_5 + NH_3$$

Imides of dicarboxylic acids (p. 210)present properties similar to those of simple amides, except that on treatment with alcoholic potash a precipitate of the potassium derivative is formed.

$$C_6H_4\genfrac{}{}{0pt}{}{CO}{CO}{>}NH + KOH = C_6H_4\genfrac{}{}{0pt}{}{CO}{CO}{>}NK + H_2O$$

On boiling with an alkaline solution of sodium hypobromite an amino acid is produced.

$$C_6H_4\genfrac{}{}{0pt}{}{CO}{CO}{>}NH \longrightarrow C_6H_4\genfrac{}{}{0pt}{}{COOH}{CO.NHBr}{} \longrightarrow C_6H_4\genfrac{}{}{0pt}{}{COOH}{NH_2}{}$$

Closely related to the amides are **urea** and its **monosubstitution products** (pp. 210, 216), which behave as amides derived from carbonic acid. On acid hydrolysis they yield carbon dioxide, an ammonium salt, and, in the case of substituted ureas, a salt of an amine. On alkaline hydrolysis ammonia is evolved, a free amine is liberated, and alkali carbonate is formed. On heating with aromatic amines, di-substituted ureas are produced, with evolution of ammonia. Thus both urea and phenylurea on heating with aniline yield carbanilide and ammonia.

$$CO(NH_2)_2 + C_6H_5 \cdot NH_2 = C_6H_5 \cdot NH \cdot CO \cdot NH_2 + NH_3$$
$$C_6H_5 \cdot NH \cdot CO \cdot NH_2 + C_6H_5 \cdot NH_2 = C_6H_5 \cdot NH \cdot CO \cdot NH \cdot C_6H_5 + NH_3$$

The same reactions may be brought about by warming the urea on the water-bath with a solution of aniline hydrochloride; in the case of urea it is possible to isolate the mono- and di-substituted derivatives by taking advantage of the solubility of the latter in hot water.

$$CO(NH_2)_2 + C_6H_5 \cdot NH_2 \cdot HCl = C_6H_5 \cdot NH \cdot CO \cdot NH_2 + NH_4Cl$$
$$C_6H_5 \cdot NH \cdot CO \cdot NH_2 + C_6H_5 \cdot NH_2 \cdot HCl =$$
$$C_6H_5 \cdot NH \cdot CO \cdot NH \cdot C_6H_5 + NH_4Cl$$

Urea and its monosubstitution products may be readily distinguished from true carboxylic amides by their ability to form, in extremely dilute solution, insoluble condensation products with xanthydrol.

$$CO(NH_2)_2 + 2HO \cdot CH {\Large\langle} {{C_6H_4} \atop {C_6H_4}} {\Large\rangle} O =$$

$$CO(NH \cdot CH {\Large\langle} {{C_6H_4} \atop {C_6H_4}} {\Large\rangle} O)_2 + 2H_2O$$

$$C_6H_5 \cdot NH \cdot CO \cdot NH_2 + 2HO \cdot CH {\Large\langle} {{C_6H_4} \atop {C_6H_4}} {\Large\rangle} O =$$

$$C_6H_5 \cdot NH \cdot CO \cdot NH \cdot CH {\Large\langle} {{C_6H_4} \atop {C_6H_4}} {\Large\rangle} O + H_2O$$

This reaction, which serves to detect minute quantities of urea in very dilute solution, is carried out by adding 1 c.c. of a 5 per cent. solution of xanthydrol in methyl alcohol to a cold solution of 0·001 gram of the urea in 10 c.c. of 50 per cent. acetic acid, when the condensation product separates in quantitative yield in the form of colourless, microcrystalline flocks.

Urethanes, or **alkyl carbamates** (p. 222), behave in many ways like true amides. Thus on boiling with dilute alkali they yield ammonia, and on boiling with dilute acids they yield ammonium salts, a carbonate (or carbon dioxide) and an alcohol being produced.

$$C_2H_5O \cdot CO \cdot NH_2 + 2NaOH = C_2H_5OH + Na_2CO_3 + NH_3$$
$$C_2H_5O \cdot CO \cdot NH_2 + HCl + H_2O = C_2H_5OH + CO_2 + NH_4Cl$$

On treatment with alcoholic potassium hydroxide, urethanes yield crystalline potassium cyanate, which may be identified by its reaction with aniline hydrochloride to form phenylurea (cf. p. 40).

$$C_2H_5O \cdot CO \cdot NH_2 + KOH = C_2H_5OH + KOCN + H_2O$$

This reaction takes place slowly in the cold and rapidly on warming. On heating with aniline, urethanes yield the corresponding alcohol, ammonia, and carbanilide.

$$C_2H_5O \cdot CO \cdot NH_2 + 2C_2H_5 \cdot NH_2 = C_2H_5OH + NH_3 + CO(NH \cdot C_5H_5)_2$$

Ammonia is also liberated from guanidine and its simple derivatives on boiling with alkali. These differ from amides and ureas in being strong bases, which are commonly met with as salts of mineral acids. On boiling with barium hydroxide solution, guanidine yields urea and ammonia:

$$NH_2 \cdot C(:NH) \cdot NH_2 + H_2O = NH_2 \cdot CO \cdot NH_2 + NH_3$$

The barium hydroxide has no action on the urea, which is hydrolysed further when sodium hydroxide is employed. On treatment with sodium hypobromite guanidine gives off two-thirds of its nitrogen in the elemental form. Guanidine and its alkyl derivatives form sparingly soluble addition products with picric acid; these crystallise well and possess characteristic melting-points.

On boiling an alcoholic solution of a **nitrile** (p. 231) under reflux with a small amount of concentrated sulphuric acid, or on passing dry gaseous hydrochloric acid into a boiling alcoholic solution of a nitrile, the corresponding ethyl ester is

produced, a precipitate of ammonium salt being simultaneously produced.

$$C_6H_5 \cdot C:N + C_2H_5OH + H_2O + HCl = C_6H_5 \cdot COOC_2H_5 + NH_4Cl$$

On reduction with tin or zinc and hydrochloric acid, or,
better, by adding sodium to a boiling absolute alcoholic
solution, primary amines are formed.

$$CH_3 \cdot C:N + 4H = CH_3 \cdot CH_2 \cdot NH_2$$

On gently warming with an alkaline solution of hydrogen
peroxide they yield the corresponding amides.

$$2C_6H_5 \cdot C:N + 2H_2O_2 = 2C_6H_5 \cdot CO \cdot NH_2 + O_2$$

Amides are also formed on warming nitriles with 50 per
cent. sulphuric acid ; the corresponding carboxylic acids
are produced if the hydrolysis is conducted at too high a
temperature or for too long a time.

Cyanohydrins (p. 232) of aldehydes and ketones present
properties differing somewhat from those of the simple
nitriles. On treatment with hot concentrated hydrochloric
acid normal hydrolysis takes place, the corresponding hydroxy-
acids being produced ; but on treatment with alkaline
reagents, hydrogen cyanide is eliminated with regeneration
of the corresponding carbonyl compounds.

$$(CH_3)_2COH \cdot C:N + 2H_2O + HCl = (CH_3)_2COH \cdot COOH + NH_4Cl$$
$$(CH_3)_2COH \cdot C:N + NaOH = CH_3 \cdot CO \cdot CH_3 + NaCN + H_2O$$

In some cases cyanohydrins are so unstable as to be decomposed merely on heating, with formation of hydrocyanic acid
and aldehydes and ketones.

If, on treatment with cold alkali, an amine is produced,
the substance is probably a **salt of an amine and an organic
acid.** The alkaline mixture should be extracted with ether
to remove the amine, and the aqueous residue acidified
and worked up for the acid by steam distillation, filtration,
or extraction with ether, as described for ammonium salts.

The majority of **substituted amides** (p. 216) yield the
corresponding amines on treatment with hot aqueous or
alcoholic alkali. As in the case of simple amides, hydrolysis

by means of acid reagents is more certain in its results, since a considerable number of substituted amides, especially in the aromatic series, are decomposed only with the greatest difficulty by boiling under reflux even with alcoholic potash. The amine and the acid may be isolated by steam distillation, filtration, or extraction with ether, after rendering the mixture after hydrolysis alternately alkaline and acid, or *vice versâ*, according to whether hydrolysis has been effected by acid or by alkaline reagents.

$$CH_3 \cdot CO \cdot NH \cdot C_6H_5 + KOH = CH_3 \cdot COOK + C_6H_5 \cdot NH_2$$
$$CH_3 \cdot CO \cdot NH \cdot C_6H_5 + HCl = CH_3 \cdot COOH + C_6H_5 \cdot NH_3 \cdot Cl$$

After isolation, both acid and amine should be examined independently.

In the same way, substituted ureas are hydrolysed on prolonged boiling with mineral acids, the corresponding amines and carbon dioxide being formed.

$$CO(NH \cdot C_6H_5)_2 + 2HCl + H_2O = CO_2 + 2C_6H_5 \cdot NH_2 \cdot HCl$$

Substituted urethanes undergo an analogous reaction,

$$C_6H_5 \cdot NH \cdot COOC_2H_5 + HCl + H_2O =$$
$$C_6H_5 \cdot NH_2 \cdot HCl + CO_2 + C_2H_5OH$$

as do also the substituted guanidines.

$$(C_6H_5 \cdot NH)_2C:NH + 3HCl + 2H_2O =$$
$$2C_6H_5 \cdot NH_2 \cdot HCl + NH_4Cl + CO_2$$
$$(C_6H_5 \cdot NH)_2C:N \cdot C_6H_5 + 3HCl + 2H_2O =$$
$$3C_6H_5 \cdot NH_2 \cdot HCl + CO_2$$

Oximes and **Hydrazones** (pp. 229, 236) are hydrolysed by boiling with concentrated hydrochloric acid or 30 per cent. sulphuric acid under reflux.

$$C_6H_5 \cdot CH:NOH + H_2O + HCl = C_6H_5 \cdot CHO + HO \cdot NH_3 \cdot Cl$$
$$(CH_3)_2C:N \cdot NH \cdot C_6H_5 + H_2O + HCl =$$
$$CH_3 \cdot CO \cdot CH_3 + Cl \cdot NH_3 \cdot NH \cdot C_6H_5$$

After hydrolysis, the aldehyde or ketone may be isolated by distillation with steam, filtration, or extraction with ether, and the acid solution examined for hydroxylamine or a hydrazine. Many substituted hydrazines, especially in the aromatic series, are precipitated as oils or solids on the addition of alkali, hydroxylamine and unsubstituted hydrazine remaining, however, in aqueous solution. Hydroxylamine and hydrazines possess powerful reducing properties, which can be shown by testing with Fehling's solution or ammoniacal silver nitrate. Oximes and hydrazones, on reduction with sodium amalgam in moist ethereal or absolute alcoholic solution, yield primary amines, which should be isolated and identified.

$$C_6H_5 \cdot CH:NOH + 4H = C_6H_5 \cdot CH_2 \cdot NH_2 + H_2O$$
$$(CH_3)_2C:N \cdot NH \cdot C_6H_5 + 4H = (CH_3)_2CH \cdot NH_2 + C_6H_5 \cdot NH_2$$

Oximes dissolve in dilute caustic alkalies, from which solution they may be liberated by saturating with carbon dioxide.

On dehydration with phosphorus pentachloride **aldoximes** are converted into nitriles.

$$C_6H_5 \cdot CH:NOH + PCl_5 = C_6H_5 \cdot C:N + POCl_3 + 2HCl$$

while **ketoximes** are caused by this reagent to undergo Beckmann's rearrangement, substituted amides being produced on treating the reaction product with water.

$$C_6H_5(C_7H_7)C:NOH \longrightarrow C_6H_5 \cdot CO \cdot N \cdot C_7H_7 \text{ or } C_7H_7 \cdot CO \cdot NH \cdot C_6H_5$$

This method serves for the distinction between isomeric ketoximes, different substituted amides being formed in the two cases. To distinguish between aldoximes and ketoximes the procedure is as follows :—An excess of phosphorus pentachloride is added to a solution of the oxime in dry ligroin, the ligroin distilled off on the water-bath, and the residue treated with cold water. An aldoxime will give rise to a nitrile (probably an oil), while a ketoxime will produce a substituted amide (probably a solid). These substances should be extracted with ether or filtered off, and purified for identification.

Hydrazides, (p. 236) or acyl derivatives of hydrazines, undergo hydrolysis on boiling with concentrated hydrochloric acid or alcoholic potash under reflux, with formation of the corresponding acids and hydrazines.

$$CH_3 \cdot CO \cdot NH \cdot NH \cdot C_6H_5 + H_2O + HCl =$$
$$CH_3 \cdot COOH + C_6H_5 \cdot NH \cdot NH_3 \cdot Cl$$

The resulting acids and hydrazines should be isolated in the manner indicated for amides and hydrazones.

*Iso*cyanides have all characteristic and unpleasant odours. On warming with hydrochloric acid they are hydrolysed, with formation of the hydrochlorides of primary amines and formic acid.

$$C_6H_5 \cdot N:C + 2H_2O + HCl = C_6H_5 \cdot NH_3 \cdot Cl + H \cdot COOH$$

*Iso*cyanides are readily oxidised by mercuric oxide to the corresponding *iso*cyanates, with production of metallic mercury.

$$C_6H_5 \cdot N:C + HgO = C_6H_5 \cdot N:CO + Hg$$

*Iso*cyanates (p. 234) possess pungent odours, the vapours irritating the mucous membranes. They are extremely reactive, reacting with water to form symmetrical disubstituted carbamides and carbon dioxide

$$2C_6H_5 \cdot N:CO + H_2O = C_6H_5 \cdot NH \cdot CO \cdot NH \cdot C_6H_5 + CO_2;$$

with alcohols and phenols, giving rise to substituted carbamic esters (substituted urethanes)

$$C_6H_5 \cdot N:CO + C_2H_5 \cdot OH = C_6H_5 \cdot NH \cdot COOC_2H_5;$$

with ammonia and with primary or secondary amines, forming substituted carbamides

$$C_6H_5 \cdot N:CO + C_6H_5 \cdot NH_2 = C_6H_5 \cdot NH \cdot CO \cdot NH \cdot C_6H_5;$$

and with carboxylic acids with production of substituted amides.

$$C_6H_5 \cdot N:CO + CH_3 \cdot COOH = C_6H_5 \cdot NH \cdot CO \cdot CH_3 + CO_2$$

By the action of hot acid or alkaline hydrolytic reagents, primary amines are produced from *iso*cyanates, owing to the initial formation of substituted carbamides or urethanes and subsequent hydrolysis of these with elimination of carbon dioxide.

If the substance should fail to undergo hydrolysis on treatment with acid or alkaline reagents, yet enter into solution in aqueous mineral acids, tests must be applied to determine whether it belongs to the family of **amines** (pp. 191–209). These are almost without exception compounds possessing pronounced basic properties, and are frequently met with in the form of a salt of an inorganic acid. In the free state they turn red litmus paper blue, or, when too feebly basic to show this colour-change distinctly, they may be tested with Congo paper previously coloured blue by very dilute hydrochloric acid. Amines in which the nitrogen atom is directly attached to one or more aromatic nuclei are as a rule far weaker bases than aliphatic amines, and solutions of their salts give an acid reaction with litmus, though not (unless more than one aromatic radicle is attached to the nitrogen atom) with Congo Red. Strong bases having a dissociation constant of 5×10^{-9} or greater are absorbed from dilute aqueous solutions of their salts by Permutite and similar exchange silicates ; whereas weaker bases, such as aromatic amines, are not so taken up. The bases may be liberated from the silicate by means of sodium hydroxide.

Salts of aliphatic amines are usually neutral or only faintly acid to litmus ; for the separation of the free bases a concentrated solution of the salt is saturated with solid potassium hydroxide, since organic bases are only slightly soluble in concentrated alkali. Hydrochlorides of most secondary and tertiary amines are soluble in chloroform, while salts of primary amines are insoluble.

Amines of all classes form definite compounds with phosphotungstic acid, with platinic chloride, and with picric acid, the latter two types of compound constituting valuable aids to identification. Platinichlorides are precipitated on the addition of platinic chloride to solutions of the base in hydrochloric acid ; after recrystallisation from alcohol their melting-point and platinum-content should be determined (cf. p. 317). The picrates are as a rule insoluble in water and sparingly soluble in cold alcohol ; they are conveniently prepared by mixing concentrated alcoholic solutions of the free base and picric acid. Their melting-points are generally sharp and characteristic.

Primary aliphatic amines may be distinguished from ammonia by placing a drop of an aqueous solution of the base upon a test paper prepared by moistening filter paper with a saturated alcoholic solution of pure 2.4-dinitrochlorobenzene; an intense yellow coloration is produced by the amines, but not by ammonia. Many secondary amines also give this test (in particular dimethylamine, which responds as readily as methylamine), but the higher members, such as diethylamine, produce the colour more slowly and less intensely. Tertiary amines give only a faint reaction or none at all. With pyridine and aromatic amines the test fails entirely. This reaction may also be employed (by treating the base in alcoholic solution with dinitrochlorobenzene) for the preparation of characteristic derivatives.

$$(NO_2)_2C_6H_3 \cdot Cl + 2CH_3 \cdot NH_2 = (NO_2)_2C_6H_3 \cdot NH \cdot CH_3 + CH_3 \cdot NH_2 \cdot HCl.$$

The same condensation may be applied to aromatic primary amines, which form, however, the 2.4-dinitrophenyl derivatives much more slowly than the aliphatic primary amines.

In order to distinguish between primary, secondary, and tertiary amines, the action of a solution of sodium nitrite upon a well-cooled solution of the substance in dilute hydrochloric acid should be tried.

Should the mixture fail to show any signs of reaction other than the possible evolution of a small amount of nitrous acid, the substance under examination may very possibly be an **aliphatic tertiary amine**—whereby it is to be noted that this definition includes compounds of the pyridine and quinoline series. Aromatic tertiary amines in which the *para*-position is occupied may likewise show no reaction towards nitrous acid, though in some instances (for example, *p*-dimethylaminophenol) oxidation may take place with formation of coloured products and evolution of gas. In such cases, the formation with an alkyl iodide of a quaternary ammonium iodide which yields no tertiary base by the action of cold aqueous alkali may be regarded as diagnostic of tertiary bases.

$$C_6H_5 \cdot N(CH_3)_2 + CH_3I = C_6H_5 \cdot N(CH_3)_3 \cdot I$$

For the identification of tertiary amines—which display but few specific reactions—analysis of the platinichloride or estimation of ionisable halogen in a sample of a suitable salt are of great value. In addition, picrates may frequently be prepared, which possess definite and characteristic melting-points; and as a general rule tertiary (in contradistinction to primary and secondary) amines yield sparingly soluble hydroferrocyanides on adding potassium ferrocyanide to their solutions in dilute hydrochloric acid.

Quaternary ammonium hydroxides, which can be produced only by the action of freshly precipitated silver oxide upon aqueous solutions of quaternary ammonium halides, are strong bases, which precipitate the hydroxides of heavy metals from solutions of their salts, liberate ammonium salts, and in general are bases as powerful as the hydroxides of the alkali metals. Many quaternary salts of quinoline and its derivatives, however, form exceptions to this rule, being converted into pseudo bases (generally insoluble in water) by the action of even weak alkalies.

A copious evolution of nitrogen on addition of the nitrite indicates the presence of an **aliphatic primary amine**.

$$CH_3 \cdot NH_3 \cdot Cl + NaNO_2 = CH_3 \cdot OH + N_2 + NaCl + H_2O$$

The resultant mixture should be rendered alkaline and distilled, and the alcohol isolated by saturating the distillate with solid potassium carbonate, or examined in solution when conditions do not appear favourable to isolation.

The formation of a diazo solution, which when added to an alkaline solution of β-naphthol yields an intensely coloured hydroxyazo compound, denotes the presence of an **aromatic primary amine**.

$$C_6H_5 \cdot NH_3 \cdot Cl + NaNO_2 + HCl = C_6H_5 \cdot N_2 \cdot Cl + NaCl + 2H_2O$$
$$C_6H_5 \cdot N_2 \cdot Cl + C_{10}H_7 \cdot ONa(2) = C_6H_5 \cdot N{:}N \cdot C_{10}H_6 \cdot OH(1{:}2) + NaCl$$

The hydroxyazo derivatives thus prepared are as a rule crystalline compounds possessing characteristic melting points.

In most cases no notable colour change occurs on adding sodium nitrite to the solution of the amine in dilute mineral acid, owing to the formation of a colourless diazonium compound. It is essential to surround the vessel with a freezing mixture while diazotising, which should be performed by gradually adding small portions of the cold dilute nitrite solution with continual stirring. The diazo solution on warming loses nitrogen with production of the corresponding phenolic compound, in some cases together with a considerable amount of tarry matter.

$$C_6H_5 \cdot N_2 \cdot OH = C_6H_5 \cdot OH + N_2$$

In order to isolate the phenol, the cold diazo solution is slowly added to a dilute solution of sulphuric acid boiling vigorously under reflux; after all has been added, the mixture is heated for a few minutes longer, rendered slightly alkaline with caustic soda, and boiled vigorously without reflux, in order to expel any volatile impurities. The alkaline mixture is then rendered acid and distilled with steam, when the phenol will in all probability pass over in the distillate. This is then extracted with ether, the ether evaporated, and the residue redistilled or recrystallised. In cases when the phenolic substance is not found to be volatile with steam, the acid solution may be extracted with ether and the extract purified by distillation or recrystallisation.

On adding the diazo solution to a solution of cuprous chloride in strong hydrochloric acid and gradually raising the temperature on the water-bath, the amino group of the original substance may be replaced by a chlorine atom (Sandmeyer's reaction).

$$C_6H_5 \cdot N_2 \cdot OH \longrightarrow C_6H_5 \cdot N_2 \cdot Cl \longrightarrow C_6H_5 \cdot Cl + N_2$$

The resultant mixture is distilled with steam and the chlorine compound separated from the distillate and purified for examination.

Many aromatic amines are readily oxidised by alkaline bleaching-powder or sodium hypochlorite solution, with formation of coloured oxidation products. They are also frequently brominated with extreme ease by the action of bromine water, precipitates of poly-bromo derivatives being formed. Such precipitates should be filtered off and purified for examination by recrystallisation from alcohol.

Characteristic of primary aromatic amines is their ability to form disubstituted thioureas by the action of carbon disulphide, preferably in the presence of alkali.

$$C_6H_5 \cdot NH_2 + CS_2 = C_6H_5 \cdot NH \cdot CSSH$$
$$2C_6H_5 \cdot NH \cdot CSSH + 2NaOH + (C_6H_5 \cdot NH)_2CS + Na_2S + CS_2 + H_2O$$

This reaction may be conveniently carried out in the following manner, using aniline as an example : to a mixture of 1·85 c.c. (0·02 mol.) of aniline and 1·5 c.c. (0·025 mol.) of carbon disulphide in a stoppered test-tube is added, in small portions, 2 c.c. (0·028 mol.) of a 40 per cent. solution of sodium hydroxide, with continual shaking and cooling. When the mixture becomes too pasty to permit of efficient agitation (owing to the separation of crystals of thiocarbanilide) 2·5 c.c. of water is added, and the mixture shaken for a few minutes longer. The product is then filtered off, washed well with water, and recrystallised from alcohol.

Aromatic primary amines may also be identified by means of the corresponding monosubstituted ureas, which are precipitated in crystalline form on adding a freshly prepared aqueous solution of potassium cyanate to a fairly concentrated solution of the hydrochloride (or other soluble salt) of the base.

$$C_6H_5 \cdot NH_2 \cdot HCl + KOCN = C_6H_5 \cdot NH \cdot CO \cdot NH_2 + NH_4Cl$$

The same derivative is formed on warming a solution of the amine hydrochloride with an excess of urea, when the corresponding disubstituted urea is formed as a by-product (cf. p. 30).

The presence of either aliphatic or aromatic primary

amines may be confirmed by warming a minute quantity with a mixture of alcoholic potash and chloroform, when the vile and characteristic odour of an *iso*cyanide will be perceptible.

$$C_6H_5 \cdot NH_2 + CHCl_3 + 3KOH = C_6H_5 \cdot N{:}C + 3KCl + 3H_2O$$

This test is so sensitive that it is given by some derivatives of primary amines, such as their acetyl derivatives, from which the base is formed during the reaction. The resulting *iso*cyanides are as a rule not very stable (they polymerise readily) and do not lend themselves to the identification of the primary amines from which they are formed. A specific reaction, which in many cases yields crystalline derivatives, is the condensation of primary amines with benzaldehyde, which on shaking with solutions of the base in dilute acetic acid causes the precipitation of the benzal derivative.

$$C_6H_5 \cdot CHO + C_6H_5 \cdot NH_2 = C_6H_5 \cdot CH{:}N \cdot C_6H_5 + H_2O$$

The aliphatic benzalamines are generally stable oils which may be distilled under atmospheric pressure without decomposition, those of the aromatic series being crystalline.

For the identification of the simpler aromatic primary amines, advantage may be taken of the fact that their hydro-chlorides (which possess definite melting points) can be distilled under atmospheric pressure without decomposition ; the boiling points, which are quite definite, differ enough to enable even isomers (such as the toluidines) to be distinguished in this way.

The formation with nitrous acid of an insoluble compound points to the presence of a **secondary amine, either** aliphatic or aromatic.

$$C_6H_5 \cdot NH \cdot CH_3 + HNO_2 = C_6H_5 \cdot N(NO) \cdot CH_3 + H_2O$$

The resulting nitrosoamines are oils or low-melting solids, only sparingly soluble in water or in dilute acid. They may best be isolated by extraction with ether. On warming a nitrosoamine with tin and hydrochloric acid, the secondary amine from which it was produced is regenerated.

$$C_6H_5 \cdot N(NO) \cdot CH_3 + 6H = C_6H_5 \cdot NH \cdot CH_3 + NH_3 + H_2O$$

Aromatic nitroso-amines in which the *para*-position is not occupied can be converted into the *para*-nitroso derivative of the original secondary amine by the action of alcoholic or ethereal hydrochloric acid.

$$C_6H_5 \cdot N(NO) \cdot CH_3 \longrightarrow NO \cdot C_6H_4 \cdot NH \cdot CH_3 (1 \cdot 4)$$

The presence of a nitroso-amine should be confirmed by Liebermann's test : on mixing with phenol and concentrated sulphuric acid, diluting with water, and neutralising with caustic soda, a blue colour is produced.

The presence of primary or secondary amines should always be established by benzoylation or acetylation. Benzoylation is effected by shaking the amine in a corked flask with an excess of benzoyl chloride and a considerable excess of cold dilute aqueous sodium hydroxide until the odour of benzoyl chloride is no longer perceptible in the mixture (Schotten-Baumann process).

$$C_6H_5 \cdot NH_2 + C_6H_5 \cdot COCl + NaOH =$$
$$C_6H_5 \cdot NH \cdot CO \cdot C_6H_5 + NaCl + H_2O$$
$$C_6H_5 \cdot COCl + 2NaOH = C_6H_5 \cdot COONa + NaCl + H_2O$$

It will be noted that the excess of the benzoyl chloride not utilised for the benzoylation is hydrolysed by the alkali, with formation of sodium chloride and sodium benzoate. The resulting precipitate—if any—is to be filtered off and recrystallised from alcohol. Should no precipitate appear on completion of benzoylation, as may be the case on treatment of some aliphatic primary and secondary amines, the mixture is to be extracted with ether and the ethereal extract purified by recrystallisation or distillation.

Acetylation of all types of primary and secondary amines may be effected by boiling with acetic anhydride.

$$(CH_3 \cdot CO \cdot)_2O + C_6H_5 \cdot NH \cdot CH_3 =$$
$$C_6H_5 \cdot N(CH_3) \cdot CO \cdot CH_3 + CH_3 \cdot COOH$$

or in many cases (particularly those of the simpler aromatic primary amines) by boiling with acetic acid.

$$CH_3 \cdot COOH + C_6H_5 \cdot NH_2 = CH_3 \cdot CO \cdot NH \cdot C_6H_5 + H_2O$$

The most convenient method of acetylation consists in shaking a suspension of the base in water, or a solution in dilute acetic acid, with acetic anhydride in the cold, when the acetyl compound as a rule separates in nearly pure, crystalline form. Acetyl chloride may also be employed, particularly for the acetylation of feebly basic compounds, but its use is complicated by the simultaneous formation of hydrochlorides of the amines.

It is of advantage to determine the percentage of the acyl group in the pure acetyl or benzoyl derivative by one of the methods described on pages 317–319.

The action of benzenesulphonyl chloride in the presence of aqueous alkali, as in the Schotten-Baumann process, towards primary and secondary amines is instructive in that it affords a distinction between the two classes of compound. Primary amines on treatment with this reagent yield primary substituted benzenesulphonamides.

$$C_6H_5 \cdot SO_2Cl + C_6H_5 \cdot NH_2 + NaOH = $$
$$C_6H_5 \cdot SO_2 \cdot NH \cdot C_6H_5 + NaCl + H_2O$$

These are soluble in alkali, the N-hydrogen atom being replaceable by an alkali metal.

$$C_6H_5 \cdot SO_2 \cdot NH \cdot C_6H_5 + NaOH = C_6H_5 \cdot SO_2 \cdot NNa \cdot C_6H_5 + H_2O$$

On shaking the resultant alkaline solution with ether, however, the free sulphonamide passes into the ether, from which it can be isolated. Secondary amines form secondary substituted benzenesulphonamides, which, having no replaceable hydrogen atom, are insoluble in alkali.

$$C_6H_5 \cdot SO_2Cl + C_6H_5 \cdot NH \cdot CH_3 + NaOH = $$
$$C_6H_5 \cdot N(CH_3) \cdot SO_2 \cdot C_6H_5 + NaCl + H_2O$$

The p-bromobenzenesulphonyl derivatives may be prepared in the same way, using p-bromobenzenesulphochloride. Many of these, however, such as those of the toluidines and the naphthylamines, differ from the corresponding unsubstituted derivatives in being insoluble in 10 per cent. sodium hydroxide solution. Characteristic derivatives can similarly be obtained by the use of m-nitrobenzenesulphochloride.

The presence of primary and secondary amines may also be demonstrated by their behaviour towards phenyl *iso*cyanate in dry benzene solution, derivatives of phenylurea being produced.

$$(C_6H_5)_2\cdot NH + C_6H_5\cdot N{:}CO = C_6H_5\cdot NH\cdot CO\cdot N(C_6H_5)_2$$

Tertiary amines are not affected by acetic anhydride or boiling acetic acid, and yield no benzoyl derivative when subjected to the Schotten-Baumann process. This failure to react may be noted by the absence of any rise in temperature on adding acetic anhydride to the pure base. Aromatic tertiary amines in which alkyl groups are attached to the nitrogen atom nevertheless react when mixed alone with benzoyl chloride, a benzoyl group taking the place of an alkyl radicle, with simultaneous formation of a quaternary ammonium salt.

$$2C_6H_5\cdot N(CH_3)_2 + C_6H_5\cdot COCl =$$
$$C_6H_5\cdot CO\cdot N(CH_3)\cdot C_6H_5 + C_6H_5\cdot N(CH_3)_3\cdot Cl$$

Such a mixture, when heated above 180°, loses alkyl chloride ; so that if enough benzoyl chloride has been employed, all of the tertiary amine is ultimately coverted into the benzoyl derivative of the corresponding secondary amine.

$$C_6H_5\cdot COCl + C_6H_5\cdot N(CH_3)_3 = C_6H_5\cdot CO\cdot N(CH_3)\cdot C_6H_5 + CH_3Cl$$

Many aromatic tertiary amines, on treatment with nitrous acid, yield the corresponding *para*-nitroso derivatives when the *para*-position is not already occupied.

$$C_6H_5\cdot N(CH_3)_2 + HNO_2 = NO\cdot C_6H_5\cdot N(CH_3)_2(1\cdot 4) + H_2O$$

The hydrochlorides of these substances are usually of a yellow colour and soluble in water, though insoluble in strong hydrochloric acid ; alkali liberates the free bases as greenish solids, which on reduction with zinc dust and acid yield the corresponding derivatives of the *para*-diamines.

$$(CH_3)_2N\cdot C_6H_4\cdot NO(1\cdot 4) + 4H = (CH_3)_2N\cdot C_6H_4\cdot NH_2(1\cdot 4) + H_2O$$

On passing hydrogen sulphide into a solution of such a diamine derivative in dilute hydrochloric acid, and then oxidising the mixture by the addition of a few drops of ferric chloride solution, a deep blue or violet coloration will be produced, owing to the formation of a thionine dye of the methylene blue type.

$$2(CH_3)_2N \cdot C_6H_4 \cdot NH_2(1 \cdot 4) \longrightarrow (CH_3)_2N.$$

On boiling these *para*-nitroso compounds with alcoholic potash the corresponding secondary amines and *para*-nitroso-phenols are produced.

$$(CH_3)_2N \cdot C_6H_4 \cdot NO(1 \cdot 4) \xrightarrow{\text{KOH}} (CH_3)_2NH + HO \cdot C_6H_4 \cdot NO(1 : 4)$$

In **aliphatic amino acids** (p. 223) the functional characteristics of the amino group, while present, are to some extent masked by the association of the carboxyl radicle. Thus the free compounds are practically neutral to litmus, and the simpler members possess a sweet taste. Acyl groups may be introduced by treatment with acetic anhydride or with benzoyl chloride in presence of sodium carbonate (or, less satisfactorily, sodium hydroxide) solution, with the formation of strongly acidic products. Similarly, addition products with aromatic *iso*cyanates can be prepared which serve for the identification of the amino acids. The latter reaction is most conveniently carried out with α-naphthyl *iso*cyanate : a solution of 0·5 gram of the amino acid in 30 c.c. of water together with 5 c.c. of normal potassium hydroxide is shaken for 2 to 3 minutes with 1·0 gram of the *iso*cyanate ; the mixture is allowed to stand for 30 to 45 minutes, filtered from the insoluble dinaphthylurea (which results from the action of water on the excess of the reagent), and acidified, when the resulting α-naphthylhydantoic acid is precipitated.

$$C_{10}H_7 \cdot N{:}CO + NH_2 \cdot CH_2 \cdot COOH + KOH =$$
$$C_{10}H_7 \cdot NH \cdot CO \cdot NH \cdot CH_2 \cdot COOK + H_2O$$

The product is recrystallised from alcohol. The melting-points of these derivatives are sharp and fairly characteristic. Amino acids may also be identified by the hydantoic acids formed by boiling them with 2 to 3 times their weight of urea in dilute barium hydroxide solution.

$$2CO(NH_2)_2 + (NH_2 \cdot CH_2 \cdot COO)_2Ba =$$
$$(NH_2 \cdot CO \cdot NH \cdot CH_2 \cdot COO)_2Ba + 2NH_3$$

Boiling is continued until evolution of ammonia ceases (6 to 10 hours), when the excess of barium is precipitated by passing in carbon dioxide, and the filtrate concentrated and acidified with acetic acid. The resulting hydantoic acids vary in their solubility in cold water from 3 per cent. down to 0·06 per cent. In the above derivatives, as well as the benzenesulphonyl and β-naphthalenesulphonyl derivatives, which are also valuable for identification purposes, the basic function of the amino group is neutralised; the same effect is brought about by the addition of excess of formaldehyde to amino acids in aqueous solution, whereby acidic methylene derivatives are formed which may be titrated with standard alkali. This last reaction furnishes a convenient procedure for estimating the equivalent weight of the amino acid under examination.

If the substance is hydrolysed by the action of alkaline reagents, yet yields no basic product, it may possibly be an ester of nitric acid or of nitrous acid.

Alkyl nitrates (p. 257), on hydrolysis with aqueous potash under reflux, yield potassium nitrate and the corresponding alcohol.

$$C_2H_5 \cdot O \cdot NO_2 + KOH = C_2H_5 \cdot OH + KO \cdot NO_2$$

This normal hydrolysis is nevertheless always accompanied to a greater or less degree by an abnormal reaction, whereby the alkyl group is partially oxidised at the expense of the nitrate, potassium nitrite being produced. Alkyl nitrates are reduced on treatment with tin and hydrochloric acid, with formation of hydroxylamine.

$$C_2H_5 \cdot O \cdot NO_2 + 6H = C_2H_5 \cdot OH + NH_2OH + H_2O$$

Care must be exercised when purifying by distillation or determining the boiling-point of an alkyl nitrate, as these esters are liable to undergo explosive decomposition on rapid heating, this property being forcibly exemplified in the case of nitroglycerol (glyceryl trinitrate) and nitro-cellulose.

Alkyl nitrites (p. 257), on hydrolysis with alkaline reagents, yield the corresponding alcohols and a metallic nitrite.

$$C_5H_{11}O \cdot NO + KOH = C_5H_{11} \cdot OH + KO \cdot NO$$

They are readily reduced, even by hydrogen sulphide, yielding the corresponding alcohol and ammonia,

$$C_5H_{11} \cdot O \cdot NO + 3H_2S = C_5H_{11} \cdot OH + NH_3 + H_2O + 3S$$

the same effect being also produced by more powerful reducing agents. On treatment of one molecular proportion of aniline dissolved in absolute alcohol in presence of one-and-one-quarter molecular proportions of sulphuric acid with a slight excess of an alkyl nitrite, diazobenzene hydroxide is produced.

$$C_6H_5 \cdot NH_2 + C_5H_{11} \cdot O \cdot NO = C_6H_5 \cdot N_2 \cdot OH + C_5H_{11} \cdot OH$$

By the action of sodium ethoxide or gaseous hydrochloric acid, they can be caused to react with ketones containing a methylene group adjacent to the carbonyl group, with formation of an *iso*nitroso derivative.

$$CH_3 \cdot CO \cdot CH_2 \cdot CH_3 + C_5H_{11} \cdot O \cdot NO =$$
$$CH_3 \cdot CO \cdot C(:NOH) \cdot CH_3 + C_5H_{11} \cdot OH$$

Care should be taken not to inhale the vapours of alkyl nitrites, since they distend the blood-vessels and thus stimulate the action of the heart.

When the substance is insoluble in aqueous mineral

acids, and remains unaffected by the action of hydrolytic
reagents, the behaviour towards reducing agents should
be investigated. It is to be borne in mind that certain
aromatic amines in which a large number of aromatic or
unsaturated groups are attached to the nitrogen atom are
so weakened in basicity by the aggregation of unsaturated
groups that they possess no salt-forming properties, and
are therefore insoluble in hydrochloric acid. Examples
of this type of compound are triphenylamine and phenyl-
pyrrole. Certain other amines, such as diphenylamine,
benzidine and the naphthylamines, are readily soluble only
in hydrochloric acid, the concentration of which lies within
definite limits, since the hydrochlorides of such bases are
liable to be salted out when the acid is too concentrated, and
hydrolysed when it is too dilute.

Suitable reducing agents, arranged in the order of their
efficacy, are the following : sodium hydrosulphite in weak
alkaline solution, tin with hydrochloric acid, zinc with hydrochloric acid, stannous chloride with hydrochloric acid, zinc
dust with acetic acid. Alcoholic ammonium sulphide and
zinc dust with alkali or with aqueous ammonia and ammonium
chloride also behave as reducing agents, but their effect is
frequently anomalous, allowing occasionally of the formation of intermediate reduction products. The use of sodium
hydrosulphite is especially to be recommended, since the
only non-volatile by-products produced on acidifying the
resulting solution with hydrochloric acid are sulphur and
sodium chloride. When the compound to be reduced is
insoluble in water, the reaction may be carried out in aqueous
alcohol.

Aromatic hydrazo compounds (p. 236), though belonging
to the class of substituted hydrazines, differ from the majority
of the members of this latter class in that they are insoluble
in aqueous acids. Their most interesting property is that
of undergoing intramolecular rearrangements when treated
with concentrated mineral acids. Thus, hydrazobenzene,

on warming with strong hydrochloric acid, is converted into benzidine (benzidine transformation).

$$C_6H_5 \cdot NH \cdot NH \cdot C_6H_5 \longrightarrow (4) \ NH_2 \cdot C_6H_4 \cdot C_6H_4 \cdot NH_2(4)$$

The products obtained by this reaction may readily be isolated by addition of alkali to the mixture. Hydrazo compounds readily yield the corresponding amino compounds on treatment with sodium hydrosulphite, while with powerful acid reducing agents—such as tin or stannous chloride with hydrochloric acid—the reduction to the amine takes place more rapidly than the intramolecular rearrangement.

$$C_6H_5 \cdot NH \cdot NH \cdot C_6H_5 + 2H = 2C_6H_5 \cdot NH_2$$

Hydrazo compounds are oxidised on standing in moist air or in alcoholic solution, but more readily by the action of oxidising agents such as alkaline solutions of potassium permanganate, ferricyanide, or hypobromite, to the corresponding azo compound.

$$C_6H_5 \cdot NH \cdot NH \cdot C_6H_5 + O = C_6H_5 \cdot N{:}N \cdot C_6H_5 + H_2O$$

They may be acylated in the same manner as primary and secondary amines, with formation of mono- and di-acyl derivatives.

Aromatic azo compounds (p. 251) are generally deeply coloured. They are extremely stable, and can be brominated, nitrated, or sulphonated, without fundamental change in the molecule. They are not attacked on warming with sulphuric acid nor on heating with iron filings. They may be reduced to hydrazo compounds by the action of zinc dust in glacial acetic acid

$$C_6H_5 \cdot N{:}N \cdot C_6H_5 + 2H = C_6H_5 \cdot NH \cdot NH \cdot C_6H_5,$$

while more powerful reducing agents, such as sodium hydrosulphite, or tin in hydrochloric acid, cause complete reduction with disruption of the nitrogen atoms.

$$C_6H_5 \cdot N{:}N \cdot C_6H_4 \cdot OH + 4H = C_6H_5 \cdot NH_2 + HO \cdot C_6H_4 \cdot NH_2$$

Aromatic azoxy compounds (p. 253) are in general far less intensely coloured than the corresponding azo compounds. They may be reduced to azo compounds by the action of alkaline reducing agents—which do not favour the benzidine transformation nor lead to the more completely reduced derivatives—such as zinc dust in aqueous or alcoholic alkali, or stannous chloride in alkaline solution:

$$C_6H_5 \cdot NO:N \cdot C_6H_5 + 2H = C_6H_5 \cdot N:N \cdot C_6H_5 + H_2O$$

The same change can be effected, in the cases of the lower and more volatile members, by distillation with iron filings. By the action of zinc dust in glacial acetic acid or of ammonium sulphide they yield the corresponding hydrazo compounds

$$C_6H_5 \cdot NO:N \cdot C_6H_5 + 4H = C_6H_5 \cdot NH \cdot NH \cdot C_6H_5 + H_2O,$$

while with tin in hydrochloric acid they are completely reduced to primary amines.

$$C_6H_5 \cdot NO:N \cdot C_6H_5 + 6H = 2C_6H_5 \cdot NH_2 + H_2O$$

On warming with concentrated sulphuric acid they are transformed into the isomeric hydroxyazo compounds.

$$C_6H_5 \cdot NO:N \cdot C_6H_5 \longrightarrow C_6H_5 \cdot N:N \cdot C_6H_4 \cdot OH(4)$$

Nitroso compounds (pp. 249–251) in which the nitroso group is directly attached to carbon possess green colours in solution or in the fused state, though in the solid state they may exist in the colourless dimolecular form. They may be reduced by acid-reducing agents to the corresponding amines.

$$C_6H_5 \cdot NO + 4H = C_6H_5 \cdot NH_2 + H_2O,$$

and may be condensed with aromatic primary amines, yielding azo compounds.

$$C_6H_5 \cdot NO + C_6H_5 \cdot NH_2 = C_6H_5 \cdot N:N \cdot C_6H_5 + H_2O$$

Oxidation with alkaline hydrogen peroxide, nitric acid, or sometimes potassium permanganate converts them into nitro compounds.

Many aromatic nitroso compounds containing one or more hydroxyl groups behave in some reactions as quinone-monoximes, with which they are in fact identical. The *p*-nitroso derivatives of aromatic secondary and tertiary amines have already been discussed in the section dealing with aromatic tertiary amines.

Aliphatic nitro compounds (p. 237), the majority of which are colourless liquids, on reduction yield aliphatic primary amines.

$$CH_3 \cdot NO_2 + 6H = CH_3 \cdot NH_2 + 2H_2O$$

When treated in alcoholic solution with sodium ethylate they give precipitates of the sodium derivatives.

$$CH_3 \cdot NO_2 + NaO \cdot C_2H_5 = CH_2 : NO \cdot ONa + C_2H_5OH$$

These precipitates should be carefully handled, since on coming into contact with a trace of water they are liable to decompose with explosive violence. They may, however, be dissolved by successively adding small quantities to cold water with continual stirring, such solutions yielding highly explosive precipitates with solutions of salts of heavy metals. Metallic derivatives are not produced from tertiary nitro-paraffins, in which no labile hydrogen atom is present.

Aromatic nitro compounds (pp. 238–249), like aliphatic nitro compounds, yield primary amines on treatment with acid-reducing agents. By the action of alkaline reducing agents the reduction may be carried to various intermediate stages. On boiling under reflux with alcoholic sodium ethoxide or methoxide, azoxy compounds are produced.

$$4C_6H_5 \cdot NO_2 + 3CH_3 \cdot ONa =$$
$$2C_6H_5 \cdot NO : N \cdot C_6H_5 + 3H \cdot COONa + 3H_2O$$

Azo compounds are formed on treatment with zinc dust in aqueous or alcoholic alkali, with sodium amalgam in alcohol, or with stannous chloride in sodium hydroxide solution.

$$2C_6H_5 \cdot NO_2 + 8H = C_6H_5 \cdot N : N \cdot C_6H_5 + 4H_2O$$

Many aromatic nitro compounds, especially those containing more than one nitro group, on boiling with concentrated sodium hydroxide solution, undergo profound decomposition with evolution of ammonia.

The majority of simple aromatic nitro compounds are

either colourless or faintly yellow, but on introducing certain substituents into the molecule, such as hydroxyl or amino groups, a distinct colour is sometimes acquired. Thus all the nitroanilines possess brilliant yellow colours; while in the case of the nitrophenols, some are colourless and some distinctly yellow, but all form intensely coloured solutions in alkali. Thus p-nitrophenol is colourless, and forms a yellow sodium salt; o-nitrophenol is pale yellow, and forms a red sodium salt; while picric acid, which has a lemon yellow colour, yields an intensely yellow solution in alkali but colourless solutions in ligroin and in mineral acids. Nitrophenols also differ from simple phenols in that they are far more strongly acidic and are acylated with greater difficulty; this latter observation is applicable to aromatic nitro-amines in contrast to other aromatic amino compounds.

The quantitative estimation of the nitro group is often of value in deciding doubtful cases. This can be done by warming an alcoholic solution of the nitro compound with a known excess of a standard solution of stannous chloride in dilute hydrochloric acid in an atmosphere of carbon dioxide for two hours on the water-bath; the excess of stannous chloride is then determined by titrating the cooled solution with standard iodine.

As many dyes (pp. 285–289) contain nitrogen in the form of amino, azo, or nitro groups, these will naturally fall into their appropriate sections, though their analysis is complicated by the fact that the majority contain sulphonic acid groups. A tabular classification of dyestuffs from an analytical standpoint will, however, be found at the conclusion of the series of tables of organic compounds.

Finally, mention is here made of the three ill-defined classes of naturally occurring nitrogenous compounds: the purines (p. 228), the proteins and the alkaloids (pp. 279–285). The purines all respond to the murexide test: on evaporating a small quantity of the substance in a porcelain basin on the water-bath with chlorine water or nitric acid, and then adding a drop of ammonia or soda solution to the residue after cooling, a purple colour is produced.

Proteins, which frequently contain sulphur and phosphorus in addition to carbon, hydrogen, and nitrogen, on hydrolysis by boiling with concentrated hydrochloric acid yield a mixture of amino acids, the majority of which are optically active. On rendering a small portion of the mixture after hydrolysis alkaline with soda and adding a drop of a dilute solution of copper sulphate, a pink coloration is produced (biuret reaction). Solutions of the proteins themselves also give the biuret reaction. Proteins may be distinguished and separated by means of their different solubilities in acid or alkali or ammonium sulphate solutions of varying concentrations. They are all insoluble in alcohol, but soluble to a greater or less extent in pure water. On addition of Millon's reagent (mercurous nitrate in dilute nitric acid) to an aqueous solution of a protein, a precipitate is formed which turns red on heating. Proteins also give the Adamkiewicz reaction: on adding a small quantity of a solution of glyoxylic acid (which may be prepared by treating a solution of oxalic acid with sodium amalgam) and then pouring concentrated sulphuric acid under the surface, a violet ring is formed.

Alkaloids differ considerably among themselves in chemical constitution and behaviour, but solutions in dilute mineral acid of the salts of almost all yield sparingly soluble precipitates with the following reagents: gallic acid, potassium mercuri-iodide, a solution of iodine in aqueous potassium iodide, and a solution of bismuth tri-iodide in aqueous potassium iodide. Picric acid also yields precipitates with many such solutions, while solutions of phosphomolybdic acid and phosphotungstic acid yield precipitates of double compounds with acid solutions of all nitrogenous substances in which the nitrogen exists in the amino form. Tables classifying the commoner purines and alkaloids will be found at the conclusion of the tabular lists of compounds.

Types of Radicle involving the detection of
CARBON, HYDROGEN, and SULPHUR

If the substance shows an acid reaction to litmus after
warming with water, it may be a sulphonic acid, a sulphinic
acid, a thiocarboxylic acid, an alkyl sulphate or sulphite,
or an alkyl ester of a sulphonic acid. It is to be noted, however, that this evidence must not be relied upon with too
much assurance, as carboxyl or phenolic hydroxyl groups
may be present in the molecule.

When a metallic residue has also been detected in a sulphur-
containing substance which gives an acid reaction on boiling
with water, it may possibly be a bisulphite compound of
an aldehyde or a ketone, or a salt of an alkyl-sulphuric
acid.

Bisulphite compounds of aldehydes or ketones, on heating
alone, yield water, sulphur dioxide, a metallic sulphite, and
the free aldehyde or ketone.

$$2(CH_3)_2C(OH)\cdot SO_2\cdot ONa =$$
$$2CH_3\cdot CO\cdot CH_3 + Na_2SO_3 + SO_2 + H_2O$$

On warming with dilute aqueous acids or sodium carbonate
they yield the free carbonyl compound, together with sulphurous acid or a sulphite. For the purpose of isolating
the aldehyde or ketone it is advisable to add dilute sodium
carbonate and to distil with or without injection of steam,
or, after warming, to extract with ether, as may appear
most convenient from the volatility or solubility of the
desired compound.

Salts of alkyl-sulphuric acids are slowly decomposed on
boiling with dilute hydrochloric acid, yielding a sulphate and
the corresponding alcohol.

$$C_2H_5O\cdot SO_2\cdot OK + H_2O = C_2H_5\cdot OH + HO\cdot SO_2\cdot OK$$

They are mild alkylating agents, reacting with aliphatic
primary and secondary amines on long boiling in aqueous

solution, with formation of sulphates of secondary or tertiary amines.

$$2C_6H_5 \cdot NH_2 + C_2H_5O \cdot SO_2OK =$$
$$(C_6H_5 \cdot NH \cdot C_2H_5)_2 \cdot H_2SO_4 + K_2SO_4$$

They react readily on boiling with aqueous sodium sulphide to form the corresponding alkyl sulphides, together (especially in the cases of the higher alkyl derivatives) with some mercaptan.

$$2C_2H_5O \cdot SO_2OK + Na_2S = (C_2H_5)_2S + Na_2SO_4 + K_2SO_4$$
$$2C_2H_5O \cdot SO_2OK + 2Na_2S + 2H_2O =$$
$$2C_2H_5 \cdot SH + K_2SO_4 + Na_2SO_4 + 2NaOH$$

They are also hydrolysed on boiling with alkalies, with formation of the corresponding alcohol, but (with the exception of the case of the methyl derivative) this reaction is too slow for the purpose of identification.

On heating with dry salts of carboxylic acids they yield the corresponding esters.

$$C_2H_5O \cdot SO_2 \cdot OK + CH_3 \cdot CO \cdot ONa = CH_3 \cdot CO \cdot OC_2H_5 + NaKSO_4$$

Aromatic sulphonic acids pp. (266–269) are strong acid which cannot be extracted with ether from their aqueous solutions. For isolation, their sodium salts may be precipitated by ample addition of sodium chloride and the dry salts converted into the insoluble chlorides by means of phosphorus pentachloride. These chlorides can then be hydrolysed by boiling with water, and the solution concentrated. In many cases the free sulphonic acids can be precipitated by the addition of a sufficient quantity of concentrated hydrochloric or sulphuric acid. They may be prepared in a pure condition by the action of hydrogen sulphide upon their lead salts.

Many sulphonic acids (or their salts) are deprived of their sulphonic group by dissolving them in 50 per cent. sulphuric acid and distilling in a current of steam over a free flame, gradually raising the temperature by increasing the concentration of the sulphuric acid.

$$C_6H_5 \cdot SO_2OH + H_2O = C_6H_6 + H_2SO_4$$

Sulphonic acids derived from simple hydrocarbons, on reaching their decomposing temperature, gradually give up the parent hydrocarbon which condenses with the steam. The temperature at which the rate of hydrolysis becomes appreciable is characteristic of the sulphonic acid ; as a general rule, those hydrocarbons which are readily sulphonated are regenerated at the lowest temperatures.

Crystalline salts possessing characteristic melting-points may in many cases be obtained with benzyl-*iso*-thiourea (the hydrochloride of which is prepared by warming equimolecular quantities of benzyl chloride and thiourea in 40 per cent. alcohol). These salts are formed on adding to a solution of 1·0 gram of the sulphonic acid in 20 c.c. of boiling 1·8 per cent. hydrochloric acid a solution of 1·0 gram of the reagent in 5 c.c. of the same solvent ; they crystallise out on cooling and are recrystallised from 1·8 per cent. hydrochloric acid.

Most sulphonic acids (in the form of their sodium or potassium salts) yield phenols on fusion with potassium hydroxide in a nickel or iron crucible.

$$C_6H_5 \cdot SO_2 \cdot OK + KOH = C_6H_5 \cdot OH + K_2SO_3$$

The phenols can be isolated by dissolving the cooled melt in water, acidifying with dilute sulphuric acid, and extracting with ether or distilling with steam. Aliphatic sulphonic acids are completely destroyed by this treatment.

By the action of phosphorus pentachloride upon a salt of a sulphonic acid, or in some instances of thionyl chloride upon the free acid, the chlorides are produced.

$$C_6H_5 \cdot SO_2 \cdot ONa + PCl_5 = C_6H_5 SO_2 \cdot Cl + POCl_3 + NaCl$$
$$C_6H_5 \cdot SO_2 \cdot OH + SOCl_2 = C_6H_5 \cdot SO_2 \cdot Cl + SO_2 + HCl$$

These sulphonic chlorides can be purified by distillation under reduced pressure, or recrystallisation, when feasible, from some non-hydroxylic solvent such as benzene or ligroin. They are as a rule but slowly decomposed by cold water, and may be employed for acylation of phenols by the Schotten-Baumann process.

$$C_6H_5 \cdot SO_2Cl + C_6H_5 \cdot ONa = C_6H_5 \cdot SO_2 \cdot OC_6H_5 + NaCl$$

With aqueous ammonia they yield sulphonamides

$$C_6H_5 \cdot SO_2Cl + 2NH_3 = C_6H_5 \cdot SO_2NH_2 + NH_4Cl$$

and with aniline they yield the corresponding anilides

$$C_6H_5 \cdot SO_2Cl + 2C_6H_5 \cdot NH_2 =$$
$$C_6H_5 \cdot SO_2 \cdot NH \cdot C_6H_5 + C_6H_5 \cdot NH_2 \cdot HCl$$

On treatment with aqueous sodium sulphite they are converted into sulphinic acids:

$$C_6H_5 \cdot SO_2 \cdot Cl + Na_2SO_3 + H_2O =$$
$$C_6H_5 \cdot SO \cdot OH + NaCl + NaHSO_4,$$

while on boiling with zinc in hydrochloric acid they are completely reduced to mercaptans:

$$C_6H_5 \cdot SO_2Cl + 6H = C_6H_5 \cdot SH + HCl + 2H_2O,$$

sulphonic acids themselves resisting this treatment.

Aromatic sulphinic acids (p. 272) may be detected by Smiles's test: on dissolving in cold concentrated sulphuric acid and adding one drop of phenetole or anisole a blue colour is produced, due to the formation of a *para*-substituted aromatic sulphoxide by elimination of water:

$$C_6H_5 \cdot SO \cdot OH + C_6H_5OC_2H_5 = C_6H_5 \cdot SO \cdot C_6H_4OC_2H_5(4) + H_2O$$

and on further addition of an excess of phenetole the blue colour is discharged, owing to the formation of the sulphate of a sulphonium base.

$$C_6H_5 \cdot SO \cdot C_6H_4OC_2H_5 + C_6H_5OC_2H_2 + H_2SO_4 =$$
$$C_6H_5 \cdot S(\cdot O \cdot SO_3H):(\cdot C_6H_4OC_2H_5)_2 + H_2O$$

Aromatic sulphinic acids on fusion with potash yield hydrocarbons.

$$C_6H_5 \cdot SO \cdot OK + KOH = C_6H_6 + K_2SO_3$$

They may be oxidised by permanganate to sulphonic acids, and reduced by zinc with hydrochloric acid to mercaptans.

Alkyl sulphates (p. 271) are in general water-insoluble liquids, which on boiling with water are converted into the corresponding alcohols and sulphuric acid, alkyl-sulphuric acids being formed as intermediate products.

$$CH_3O)_2SO_2 + H_2O = CH_3O \cdot SO_2 \cdot OH + CH_3OH$$
$$CH_3O \cdot SO_2 \cdot OH + H_2O = H_2SO_4 + CH_3OH$$

They are more powerful alkylating agents than salts of alkyl-sulphuric acids, and can be employed, in the presence of alkali, for the alkylation of phenols, amines, and similar compounds.

$$2C_6H_5ONa + (CH_3O)_2SO_2 = 2C_6H_5OCH_3 + Na_2SO_4$$
$$2C_6H_5 \cdot NH_2 + 2(CH_3O)_2SO_2 =$$
$$C_6H_5 \cdot N(CH_3)_2 \cdot CH_3O \cdot SO_2OH + C_6H_5 \cdot NH_2 \cdot CH_3O \cdot SO_2OH$$

Alkyl sulphites resemble carboxylic esters rather than alkyl sulphates in that they possess no alkylating properties. On hydrolysis with alkali they yield the corresponding alcohol and a sulphite.

$$(C_2H_5O)_2SO + 2NaOH = 2C_2H_5OH + Na_2SO_3$$

Alkyl esters of sulphonic acids (p. 270) exhibit properties similar to those of the alkyl sulphates, being hydrolysed to alcohols and sulphonates on boiling with aqueous alkalies

$$C_6H_5 \cdot SO_2OCH_3 + NaOH = C_6H_5 \cdot SO_2ONa + CH_3OH$$

and acting as vigorous alkylating agents towards amines

$$2C_6H_5 \cdot SO_2OCH_3 + 3C_6H_5 \cdot NH_2 =$$
$$C_6H_5 \cdot N(CH_3)_2 + 2C_6H_5 \cdot SO_2OH \cdot NH_2 \cdot C_6H_5$$

and phenols in alkaline solution.

$$C_6H_5 \cdot SO_2OCH_3 + C_6H_5 \cdot ONa = C_6H_5 \cdot OCH_3 + C_6H_5 \cdot SO_2ONa$$

Aryl esters of sulphonic acids (p. 270) are much more stable towards hydrolytic reagents than the foregoing, resisting the action of boiling 10 per cent. sodium hydroxide solution. They may, however, be broken up by heating with highly concentrated alkali to about 200°.

$$C_6H_5 \cdot SO_2 \cdot OC_6H_5 + 2NaOH = C_6H_5 \cdot SO_2ONa + C_6H_5 \cdot ONa + H_2O$$

On warming with alcoholic sodium ethoxide they yield a phenolic ether and a sulphonate.

$$C_6H_5 \cdot SO_2 \cdot OC_6H_5 + C_2H_5ONa = C_6H_5 \cdot SO_2ONa + C_6H_5 \cdot OC_2H_5$$

They do not react in an analogous manner with amines, and can be boiled with aniline without change. For their identification, they may be nitrated by the action of concentrated nitric acid upon a solution in concentrated sulphuric acid, when they yield dinitro derivatives which are readily broken up by alkalies into salts of nitro sulphonic acids and (generally *para*) nitrophenols.

$$\langle\ \rangle-SO_2\cdot O-\langle\ \rangle\ +\ 2HNO_3\ =$$

$$\langle\ \rangle-SO_2\cdot O-\langle\ \rangle\ -\ NO_2\ +\ 2H_2O$$
$$\overset{|}{NO_2}$$

Thiocarboxylic acids (p. 273), on boiling with water, yield the corresponding carboxylic acids and hydrogen sulphide.

$$CH_3\cdot CO\cdot SH\ +\ H_2O\ =\ CH_3\cdot CO\cdot OH\ +\ H_2S$$

They may be employed as acylating agents; reacting with amines, such as aniline with production of substituted amides and hydrogen sulphide.

$$CH_3\cdot CO\cdot SH\ +\ C_6H_5\cdot NH_2\ =\ CH_3\cdot CO\cdot NH\cdot C_6H_5\ +\ H_2S$$

They do not yield thio-esters on treatment with alcohols in the usual manner, but lose hydrogen sulphide with formation of carboxylic esters.

$$CH_3\cdot CO\cdot SH\ +\ C_2H_5OH\ =\ CH_3\cdot CO\cdot OC_2H_5\ +\ H_2S$$

On treatment with salts of heavy metals in watery solution they yield coloured precipitates which decompose into the sulphides on boiling.

$$2CH_3\cdot COSH\ +\ CuSO_4\ =\ (CH_3\cdot CO\cdot S)_2Cu\ +\ H_2SO_4$$
$$(CH_3\cdot CO\cdot S)_2Cu\ +\ H_2O\ =\ 2CH_3\cdot COOH\ +\ H_2S\ +\ CuS$$

If the substance is strongly alkaline, or is the salt of a strong base which is not liberated by aqueous alkali, it may possibly be a sulphonium compound. **Sulphonium hydroxides** are frequently more strongly basic than the hydroxides of the alkali metals; the free bases cannot for this reason be prepared by the action of caustic soda upon solutions of their salts. The process commonly employed for this purpose involves the action of silver oxide upon a solution of sulphonium halide.

$$2(CH_3)_3S\cdot I\ +\ Ag_2O\ +\ H_2O\ =\ 2(CH_3)_3S\cdot OH\ +\ 2AgI$$

Sulphonium salts in acetone solution dissolve mercuric

iodide with formation of addition compounds, which crystallise out on evaporation of the solvent.

$$2(CH_3)_3SI + HgI_2 = (CH_3)_3SI \cdot HgI_2$$

For determination of the equivalent of the base the platinichloride may be isolated and treated in the manner described
on p. 317. This may readily be prepared by the action
of platinic chloride upon a concentrated aqueous solution of
the sulphonium chloride, precipitation (if necessary) by
gradual addition of alcohol, and recrystallisation from a suitable solvent such as epichlorohydrin.

$$2(CH_3)_3SCl + PtCl_4 = [(CH_3)_3S]_2PtCl_6$$

If the substance is practically neutral to litmus, it may
be a sulphone, a sulphoxide, a sulphide or a disulphide, or a
mercaptan. Due allowance must be made for the possible
presence of carboxyl groups, and the fact is to be borne in
mind that the presence of the molecule of a sulphone group-
ing considerably augments the acidic character of phenolic
hydroxyl groups.

Sulphones (p. 265) exhibit no specific reactions, being
extremely stable. They are unattacked by the action of the
most powerful acids, alkalies, or oxidising or reducing agents.
Aromatic sulphones may thus be boiled with fuming nitric
acid with no further effect than nitration, while the simpler
aliphatic members of this class are unaffected even by this
violent treatment. They are, however, broken up into sul-
phinates and hydrocarbons on treatment with sodium in
boiling toluene.

$$2C_6H_5 \cdot SO_2 \cdot C_6H_5 + 2Na = 2C_6H_5 \cdot SOONa + C_6H_5 \cdot C_6H_5$$

The simpler sulphones may be distilled unchanged under
atmospheric pressure ; some disulphones such as sulphonal,
on the other hand, break down on strongly heating, yielding carboxylic acids, mercaptans, sulphur dioxide, and other
products.

Sulphoxides (p. 265) may exhibit faintly basic properties.

Many give Smiles's test (cf. aromatic sulphinic acids),[1] and are far less stable than the sulphones. They may be oxidised by nitric acid, or better, by adding finely powdered potassium permanganate to a solution in glacial acetic acid, with formation of sulphones ; and may be reduced to the corresponding sulphides by boiling with tin or zinc in hydrochloric acid.

Sulphides and **mercaptans** (pp. 262, 264) may be characterised by the fact that they give precipitates of solid double compounds when shaken with aqueous mercuric chloride.

$$(C_2H_5)_2S + HgCl_2 = (C_2H_5)_2S(Cl)\cdot Hg\cdot Cl$$
$$C_2H_5SH + HgCl_2 = C_2H_5S\cdot Hg\cdot Cl + HCl$$

These compounds may be recrystallised from alcohol, and possess definite melting-points. It is to be noted that hydrochloric acid is liberated by the action of mercuric chloride upon mercaptans, so that the production of a strongly acid solution on addition of the sublimate solution is indicative of the presence of a mercaptan.

Sulphides, on oxidation by standing with the calculated amount of hydrogen peroxide in acetone solution, yield sulphoxides, while on treatment with stronger oxidising agents, such as nitric acid or potassium permanganate in glacial acetic acid, they are oxidised to sulphones.

Mercaptans, on oxidation with dilute nitric acid, are converted into the corresponding sulphonic acids

$$C_2H_5\cdot SH + 3O = C_2H_5\cdot SO_2OH,$$

milder oxidising agents, such as bromine water, iodine, or ferric chloride, giving rise to disulphides.

$$2C_6H_5SH + 2FeCl_3 = C_6H_5S\cdot SC_6H_5 + 2FeCl_2 + 2HCl$$

On treatment with cold concentrated sulphuric acid they are oxidised with evolution of sulphur dioxide.

Mercaptans exhibit their close relationship to hydrogen sulphide in their ability to form metallic derivatives, yielding

[1] It is to be observed that aromatic sulphoxides which contain hydroxyl and similar groups dissolve in concentrated sulphuric acid with a more or less pronounced blue colour.

(generally yellow) precipitates with dilute silver nitrate and entering into solution in aqueous sodium hydroxide. With the exception of that of methyl mercaptan, the sodium salts of the simple aliphatic mercaptans are so readily hydrolysed that on boiling their alkaline solutions the free mercaptans are liberated and pass out with the steam. Like the corresponding sulphides, the alkali mercaptides of the aliphatic series yield intense purple colours on treatment with sodium nitroprusside solution ; in the aromatic series these colours are extremely transitory, owing to the oxidation of the mercaptan to the disulphide.

Mercaptans may be acetylated by the action of acetyl chloride in dry chloroform or benzene solution, with formation of thioacetic esters.

$$C_2H_5SH + CH_3 \cdot COCl = CH_3 \cdot CO \cdot SC_2H_5 + HCl$$

The simpler sulphides and mercaptans possess powerful and somewhat unpleasant odours.

Disulphides (p. 264) exhibit properties similar to those of the sulphides. They may, however, be reduced to the mercaptans by treatment with zinc dust in dilute mineral acids

$$C_2H_5S \cdot SC_2H_5 + 2H = 2C_2H_5SH$$

and yield sulphonic acids on oxidation with nitric acid. Solutions of aromatic disulphides in concentrated sulphuric acid, on treatment in the cold with phenetole, yield mixed *p*-phenetyl sulphides with evolution of sulphur dioxide.

$$C_2H_5S \cdot SC_2H_5 + 2C_6H_5OC_2H_5 + H_2SO_4 =$$
$$2C_2H_5S \cdot C_6H_4OC_2H_5(1:4) + H_2O + SO_2$$

Types of Radicle involving the detection of
CARBON, HYDROGEN, and HALOGEN

Throughout the series of organic halogen compounds it may be taken that the chlorine compounds part less readily with their halogen than do the corresponding bromine compounds, and that iodine compounds are the most reactive of their class. Thus alkyl iodides are rapidly decomposed on warming with alcoholic silver nitrate, the alkyl chlorides and bromides being decomposed by this reagent far less readily, if at all. The only iodo compounds which are not decomposed in this way are those in which the iodine atom is directly attached to an aromatic nucleus, an example of this type being iodobenzene.

On boiling the substance with alcoholic potash, all types of halogen compounds, with the exception of the majority of those in which the halogen atom is united to an aromatic nucleus, yield potassium halide. This, if formed in considerable quantity, is precipitated from the alcoholic solution, or if formed in only small amount, can be detected by dilution, acidification with dilute nitric acid, removal of by-products by filtration or extraction with ether, and addition of silver nitrate to the clear aqueous solution. Aromatic halogen compounds in which a nitro group is present in the positions *ortho* or *para* to the halogen atom are, unlike other aryl halides, decomposed with replacement of the halogen atom by a hydroxyl or alkoxyl group. Halogen compounds may thus be divided into two large classes, which comprise organic derivatives of all three halogens.

Organic compounds containing chlorine and bromine may further be roughly subdivided according to their relative reactivity towards halogen-eliminating reagents.

On treatment with water, warming if the substance does not enter into solution, and decanting the aqueous portion, solutions of halogen hydracids will be present in the case of carboxylic acid halides and aliphatic halogen-substituted ethers in which the halogen atom is attached to the same carbon atom as the alkoxyl group.

Carboxylic acid halides (p. 185) react with water, yielding the corresponding carboxylic acid and hydrochloric acid or one of its analogues.

$$CH_3 \cdot COCl + H_2O = CH_3 \cdot COOH + HCl$$

This reaction takes place rapidly in the cold with the halides of the lower fatty acids, but increasingly slowly with increasing molecular weight, possibly on account of decreasing solubility in water. On treatment with alcohols, in which they are soluble, they rapidly yield esters.

$$C_6H_5 \cdot COCl + CH_3OH = C_6H_5 \cdot COOCH_3 + HCl$$

A similar reaction takes place, rather more slowly, on warming with phenols.

$$CH_3 \cdot COCl + C_6H_5OH = CH_3 \cdot CO \cdot OC_6H_5 + HCl$$

On slowly adding an acid halide to an excess of concentrated ammonia solution, with efficient agitation and cooling, the amide is formed.

$$C_6H_5 \cdot COCl + 2NH_3 = C_6H_5 \cdot CONH_2 + NH_4Cl$$

The amides of acids of high molecular weight, being insoluble in water, separate out during the reaction; those of low molecular weight, which dissolve more readily, frequently remain in solution, so that it is often convenient to carry out the reaction in the presence of a relatively large volume of ether; the ammonium chloride solution is separated and the ether distilled, when the amide remains as a residue. An analogous reaction takes place with amines such as aniline or diphenylamine.

$$CH_3 \cdot COCl + 2C_6H_5 \cdot NH_2 = CH_3 \cdot CO \cdot NH \cdot C_6H_5 + C_6H_5 \cdot NH_2 \cdot HCl$$

If the base be dissolved in ether, the amine hydrochloride is precipitated and may be filtered off, leaving the substituted amide in solution.

Similar in general behaviour are the **alkyl chloroformates** (or **chlorocarbonates**), (p. 185), which react slowly with cold water, yielding hydrochloric acid, carbon dioxide, and alcohols.

$$Cl \cdot COOC_2H_5 + H_2O = HCl + CO_2 + C_2H_5OH$$

On warming with alcohols they yield alkyl carbonates and hydrogen chloride :

$$C_2H_5OH + Cl \cdot COOC_2H_5 = (C_2H_5O)_2CO + HCl$$

and react similarly on shaking with cold alkaline solutions of phenols.

$$C_6H_5ONa + Cl \cdot COOC_2H_5 = C_6H_5O \cdot COOC_2H_5 + NaCl$$

When slowly added to cold concentrated ammonia, preferably covered with a large volume of ether, alkyl carbamates (urethanes) are formed and may be isolated by distilling the ethereal solution.

$$2NH_3 + Cl \cdot COOC_2H_5 = NH_2 \cdot COOC_2H_5 + NH_4Cl$$

An analogous reaction takes place with aniline, alkyl carbanilates being produced.

$$2C_6H_5 \cdot NH_2 + Cl \cdot COOC_2H_5 =$$
$$C_6H_5 \cdot NH \cdot COOC_2H_5 + C_6H_5 \cdot NH_2 \cdot HCl$$

α-Halogen-substituted aliphatic ethers (p. 177), on treatment with water, and in some cases with alcohol, yield the corresponding alcohols, aldehydes, and halogen hydrides.

$$CH_2Cl \cdot OCH_3 + H_2O = CH_2O + CH_3OH + HCl$$

On treatment with anhydrous potassium or sodium acetate, the halogen may be replaced by an acetoxyl group, the resulting esters being in most cases sufficiently stable for characterisation.

$$CH_3 \cdot CH(OCH_3) \cdot Cl + CH_3 \cdot COOK =$$
$$CH_3 \cdot CH(OCH_3) \cdot O \cdot CO \cdot CH_3 + KCl$$

Observation of the effects on boiling with a solution of pyridine in aqueous alcohol [1] under reflux, cooling, diluting with distilled water, acidifying with dilute nitric acid, filtering if necessary, and adding silver nitrate to the clear solution, is of service in distinguishing some of the remaining types of halogen compounds. Chlorine compounds should be boiled with the pyridine solution for about thirty minutes and bromine compounds for about five minutes.

As a general rule, **halogen-substituted ketones, acids, and esters, in which the halogen atom is attached to the carbon atom next to the carbonyl or similar group,** give rise to solutions containing considerable quantities of ionised halogen, as evi-

---

[1] About 0·5 gram of the substance with a similar amount of pyridine is sufficient, the volume of solvent being about 20 c.c. Pure alcohol may be employed should the substance fail to dissolve to a sufficient extent in aqueous alcohol.

denced by the formation of a distinct precipitate of silver halide. Similarly, the **halides of such radicles as allyl and benzyl** part with their halogen fairly readily to pyridine.

$$C_6H_5N + C_6H_5 \cdot CH_2 \cdot Cl = C_6H_5N \begin{smallmatrix} CH_2 \cdot C_6H_5 \\ Cl \end{smallmatrix}$$

Other classes of aliphatic chlorine and bromine compounds may yield a faint turbidity on the addition of silver nitrate, while aryl halides yield none whatever.

Simple **alkyl halides** (pp. 167–173) may bedistinguished from other types of organic halogen compounds by their complete insolubility in concentrated sulphuric acid. Unsaturated and aromatic halogenated hydrocarbons may dissolve in hot sulphuric acid, with formation of acidic products, but this action takes place with increasing difficulty as the proportion of halogen in the molecule increases.

Characteristic derivatives of all **aliphatic halogen compounds** (pp. 167–173, 178, 179, 182–188, 189)—which definition includes aromatic compounds containing halogen-substituted side-chains—may be prepared by boiling under reflux (*a*) with an alcoholic or aqueous-alcoholic solution of potassium cyanide, when nitriles are formed :

$$C_6H_5 \cdot CH_2 \cdot Br + KCN = C_6H_5 \cdot CH_2 \cdot CN + KBr$$

(*b*) with primary or secondary amines, such as aniline or ethylaniline, secondary or tertiary bases being formed :

$$2C_6H_5 \cdot NH_2 + C_2H_5Br = C_6H_5 \cdot NH \cdot C_2H_5 + C_6H_5 \cdot NH_2 \cdot HBr$$

or (*c*) with anhydrous sodium acetate, or better with silver acetate, producing acetic esters, this last reaction being especially applicable in the case of alkyl iodides, the dry silver salt being treated with the iodo compounds in dry ether.

$$CH_3 \cdot I + CH_3 \cdot COOAg = CH_3 \cdot COOCH_3 + AgI$$

On boiling the substance with an alcoholic solution of a phenol containing an equivalent amount of alkali, phenolic ethers are produced. The most suitable phenol is β-naphthol, since the ethers formed from it are generally solids possessing characteristic melting points.

$$C_{10}H_7ONa + C_2H_5Br = C_{10}H_7 \cdot OC_2H_5 + NaBr$$

Alkyl halides react in dry ethereal solution with metallic magnesium, forming the ether-soluble alkyl-magnesium halides (Grignard reagents).

$$C_2H_5 \cdot Br + Mg = C_2H_5 \cdot Mg \cdot Br$$

These addition products are highly reactive, yielding the parent hydrocarbon with any substance containing a replaceable hydrogen atom (such as water, alcohols, amines, amides, acids, etc.), forming secondary alcohols with aldehydes and tertiary alcohols with ketones and esters, and regenerating the alcohol corresponding to the original halide on exposure to atmospheric oxygen. For purposes of identification the most suitable derivative is the carboxylic acid formed on passing carbon dioxide into the ethereal alkyl-magnesium halide and decomposing the resulting salt with dilute mineral acid.

$$C_2H_5 \cdot Mg \cdot Br + CO_2 = C_2H_5 \cdot COOMg \cdot Br$$
$$C_2H_5 \cdot COOMg \cdot Br + HCl = C_2H_5 \cdot COOH + MgBrCl$$

The resulting acid may be identified as its amide or anilide, and its identity definitely locates the position of the original halogen atom.

Chloroform, bromoform, iodoform, and chloral hydrate may be detected in very small amounts by the following test: to 4 c.c. of 20 per cent. sodium hydroxide solution are added enough pyridine to form a layer 2 mm. deep and a drop of the liquid suspected to contain one of these compounds, The mixture is heated just to boiling and allowed to stand; should one of the above substances be present the pyridine layer assumes a red colour.

Aromatic halogen compounds (pp. 173–176, 178, 181, 188) may be treated according to the methods suggested for the examination of aromatic hydrocarbons—namely nitration sulphonation, oxidation, etc. (pp. 73–76), when characteristic derivatives can be prepared in the same ways. As stated above, halogen atoms directly united to an aromatic nucleus are incapable of undergoing the general metathetical reactions characteristic of alkyl halides ; there is however one exception to this rule, and this is the formation of Grignard reagents with magnesium in dry ether. This reaction takes place as readily as it does with the aliphatic halogen compounds, and it also can best be adapted to identification by the formation of carboxylic acids by the action of carbon dioxide.

$$C_6H_5 \cdot Br \longrightarrow C_6H_5 \cdot Mg \cdot Br \longrightarrow C_6H_5 \cdot COOMg \cdot Br \longrightarrow C_6H_5 \cdot COOH$$

It may also be of advantage to prepare the parent hydrocarbon by the cautious addition of water or alcohol.

$$C_6H_5 \cdot Mg \cdot Br + C_2H_5OH = C_6H_6 + MgBr \cdot OC_2H_5$$

Iodine compounds differ from the corresponding chloro- and bromo-derivatives in their behaviour towards chlorine. Aliphatic iodides on treatment with chlorine are converted into the corresponding chlorides, with elimination of iodine. An analogous reaction takes place with bromine. Aromatic iodo compounds, on the other hand, lose no iodine but form yellow, crystalline dichlorides.

$$C_6H_5 \cdot I + Cl_2 = C_6H_5 \cdot ICl_2$$

The halogen atom directly attached to an aromatic nucleus may be partially or even quantitatively obtained as sodium halide by dissolving the compound in alcohol and adding excess of sodium in small portions (see p. 309, Stepanow's method).

Types of Radicle in which
CARBON, HYDROGEN, NITROGEN, and SULPHUR
occur in conjunction

Under this head are included the Thiocyanates, Isothio-cyanates, Thioamides and Thioureas, and Sulphonamides. In other types of compounds in which carbon, hydrogen, nitrogen, and sulphur have been detected, the groups involving the nitrogen and the sulphur atoms may be considered independently. Thus, for example, in the case of sulphanilic acid, the nitrogen may be demonstrated to be present in the form of an aromatic primary amino radicle by the formation of a diazo solution, and other characteristic reactions, while the sulphur may be shown to be in the form of a sulphonyl group by the fact that the substance forms neutral salts with alkalies, cannot be reduced to a sulphide or a mercaptan, and so forth. The effect of the two groups upon each other is of course to be taken into consideration, as this frequently causes very considerable changes from the usual reactions of the individual types. Thus sulphanilic acid, on fusion with potash, instead of yielding potassium sulphite and an amino-phenol, yields aniline and potassium sulphate.

In the types discussed in this section the sulphur and nitrogen atoms are so dependent upon each other that no selective examination of either is possible, the whole group being considered as one individual radicle.

In the aliphatic and aromatic **thiocyanates** (p. 278), the fact that the alkyl or aryl radicle is attached to sulphur is shown by reduction with zinc dust in hydrochloric acid.

$$C_2H_5 \cdot S \cdot CN + 2H = C_2H_5 \cdot SH + HCN$$

The resulting mercaptan should be isolated and examined, and hydrocyanic acid should be carefully tested for by passing the evolved gases into alkali and treating the solution for the ' Prussian blue ' test. On oxidation by boiling with nitric acid they yield sulphonic acids.

$$C_2H_5 \cdot S \cdot CN + 2O + H_2O = C_2H_5 \cdot SO_2OH + HCN$$

On boiling with alcoholic potash, potassium thiocyanate is formed :

$$CH_3 \cdot S \cdot CN + KOH = CH_3OH + KSCN,$$

which may be tested for by diluting with water, acidifying with dilute nitric acid, and adding a drop of ferric chloride solution, when a red coloration of ferric thiocyanate will appear. Some thiocyanates whose boiling-points lie above 160° are converted partially or entirely into the corresponding *iso*thiocyanates on distillation under atmospheric pressure.

*Iso*thiocyanates (p. 278), or 'Mustard oils,' possess properties analogous to those of the *iso*cyanates, though they are somewhat less reactive. Like the latter, they possess irritating odours. On long boiling with concentrated hydrochloric acid they break down into primary amines, with evolution of hydrogen sulphide, which should be tested for by placing in the evolved vapours a piece of filter paper moistened with lead acetate solution.

$$CH_2{:}CH{\cdot}CH_2{\cdot}N{:}C{:}S + HCl + 2H_2O =$$
$$CH_2{:}CH{\cdot}CH_2{\cdot}NH_2{\cdot}HCl + CO_2 + H_2S$$

On reduction with zinc dust in dilute mineral acid they yield primary amines with evolution of thioformaldehyde, which is recognisable by its leek-like odour.

$$C_3H_5{\cdot}N{:}C{:}S + HCl + 4H = C_3H_5{\cdot}NH_3{\cdot}Cl + CH_2S$$

On treatment with ammonia or with primary or secondary amines, derivatives of thiocarbamide are produced.

$$C_3H_5{\cdot}N{:}C{:}S + C_6H_5{\cdot}NH_2 = C_3H_5{\cdot}NH{\cdot}CS{\cdot}NH{\cdot}C_6H_5$$

On warming in alcoholic solution with mercuric oxide or chloride, a derivative of urethane is produced, with precipitation of mercuric sulphide.

$$C_3H_5{\cdot}N{:}C{:}S + HgO = C_3H_5{\cdot}N{:}C{:}O + HgS$$
$$C_3H_5{\cdot}N{:}C{:}O + C_2H_5OH = C_3H_5{\cdot}NH{\cdot}CO{\cdot}OC_2H_5$$

Sulphonamides (pp. 274, 275)—simple, primary, and secondary—have been discussed in the section dealing with amines (p. 43). Substituted sulphonamides may be produced by treating the sodium derivatives of simple sulphonamides with alkylating agents. Simple sulphonamides, on heating to about 120° with 70–80 per cent. sulphuric acid, yield the free sulphonic acid and ammonium sulphate.

$$C_6H_5{\cdot}SO_2{\cdot}NH_2 + H_2O + H_2SO_4 = C_6H_5{\cdot}SO_2OH + NH_4SO_4H$$

while primary and secondary substituted sulphonamides on hydrolysis yield the corresponding sulphonic acid and amine. If the mixture be heated to boiling, the parent hydrocarbon, sulphuric acid, and ammonia are formed.

$$C_6H_5{\cdot}SO_2OH + H_2O + H_2SO_4 = C_6H_6 + H_2SO_4 + NH_4SO_4H$$

Thioamides and thiocarbamides (p. 275) on hydrolysis with alcoholic potash under reflux, yield the potassium salt of the carboxylic acid or carbonic acid, potassium sulphide, and ammonia or an amine.

$$CH_3 \cdot CS \cdot NH_2 + 3KOH = CH_3 \cdot COOK + NH_3 + K_2S + H_2O$$
$$(C_6H_5 \cdot NH)_2CS + 4KOH = 2C_6H_5 \cdot NH_2 + K_2CO_3 + K_2S + H_2O$$

Simple thioamides on treatment with mercuric oxide yield the nitriles with formation of mercuric sulphide.

$$C_6H_5 \cdot CS \cdot NH_2 + HgO = C_6H_5 \cdot C \vdots N + HgS + H_2O$$

Thiocarbamide and its derivatives on warming with strong hydrochloric acid yield primary amines or ammonia, guanidine or substituted guanidines, and hydrogen sulphide.

$$(C_6H_5 \cdot NH)_2CS + HCl = C_6H_5 \cdot N:C:S + C_6H_5 \cdot NH_3 \cdot Cl$$
$$C_6H_5 \cdot N:C:S + HCl + 2H_2O = C_6H_5 \cdot NH_3 \cdot Cl + CO_2 + H_2S$$
$$(C_6H_5 \cdot NH)_2CS + C_6H_5 \cdot NH_2 = (C_6H_5 \cdot NH)_2C:N \cdot C_6H_5 + H_2S$$

In many cases it is possible to isolate the *iso*thiocyanate which is formed as an intermediate product. The guanidine derivative may be decomposed by boiling with alcoholic potash.

$$C_6H_5 \cdot N:C(NH \cdot C_6H_5)_2 + 2KOH + H_2O = 3C_6H_5 \cdot NH_2 + K_2CO_3$$

Simple and monosubstituted thiocarbamides on treatment with mercuric oxide yield simple and substituted cyanamides :

$$C_6H_5 \cdot NH \cdot CS \cdot NH_2 + HgO = C_6H_5 \cdot NH \cdot C \vdots N + HgS + H_2O,$$

while symmetrically disubstituted thiocarbamides are converted by mercuric oxide into the corresponding derivatives of carbamide.

$$CS(NH \cdot C_6H_5)_2 + HgO = CO(NH \cdot C_6H_5)_2 + HgS.$$

Types of Radicle involving the detection of CARBON and HYDROGEN only

In this section are set forth the principles to be followed in the examination of the remaining portion of the molecule of substances in which elements other than carbon and hydrogen have been detected. Such examination can of course be carried out only after the allotment of the compound into its proper class with respect to the nitrogen, sulphur, or halogen contained therein. For the purposes in view, however, it is assumed throughout that in the types of compound described no elements other than carbon and hydrogen have been detected; for were the discussion not thus restricted, an unwieldy mass of exceptions and special cases would require to be described. All such exceptions and special cases will be found in the tables of compounds. The preliminary tests, if rigorously and completely carried out, will have greatly limited the range of possibilities, if they have not definitely established the class of the substance under examination; hence doubt should but rarely arise from this restriction of the field of discussion.

If the substance is readily soluble in water, the presence of oxygen in the molecule is certain. Hydrocarbons and ethers, and the majority of esters, acid anhydrides, and many substances of high molecular weight containing but few hydroxyl groups are insoluble or but sparingly soluble in water. Other types of compound, especially those of low molecular weight, such as alcohols, some phenols, aldehydes, ketones, carboxylic acids, sugars, and glucosides, frequently dissolve in cold water.

When the substance is insoluble in water, the action of metallic sodium should be tried upon a solution of the dry substance in absolutely dry ether, which should be drawn from a stock maintained permanently in contact with this metal. As a general rule, evolution of hydrogen ensues in all cases except those of hydrocarbons and ethers and some esters, such as ethyl benzoate, in which no replaceable hydrogen atom is present.

Hydrocarbons may be distinguished from ethers—and in fact from all oxygen-containing compounds which are sufficiently soluble in benzene—by taking advantage of the observation that solutions of iodine in oxygen-free liquids are violet in colour, while solutions of iodine in liquids containing oxygen (combined either in the solvent or in some other solute present in sufficient quantity) possess a brown tint. The test may be performed by mixing in a test-tube 5 c.c. of a 0·005 per cent. solution of iodine in pure benzene with 5 c.c. of a 5–10 per cent. solution in the same solvent of the substance under examination. The colour of the resulting mixture, viewed through the length of the tube, is compared with that of a mixture of the same volumes of the iodine solution and pure benzene.

Hydrocarbons (p. 104), unless unsaturated or aromatic, do not exhibit a wide scope of reactions. Saturated hydrocarbons may be distinguished from unsaturated and aromatic hydrocarbons by their failure to rise in temperature when treated with a cold mixture of concentrated nitric and sulphuric acids. They are also completely insoluble in concentrated sulphuric acid, while unsaturated hydrocarbons are as a rule either dissolved or polymerised to higher-boiling products. Aromatic hydrocarbons vary among themselves in their reactivity towards strong sulphuric acid ; benzene is only slowly sulphonated at its boiling temperature ; toluene and ethylbenzene are dissolved rapidly on boiling, though slowly in the cold ; *ortho* and *meta* xylenes are sulphonated rapidly in the cold, while *para* xylene requires long treatment at the boiling temperature for complete sulphonation ; mesitylene and pseudocumene are very rapidly sulphonated in the cold ; naphthalene and anthracene, on the other hand, are sulphonated only slowly in comparison with the highly methylated derivatives of benzene.

On account of the lack of reactivity of saturated hydrocarbons, their identification must generally rest upon determinations of boiling point and density.

Aromatic hydrocarbons may frequently be oxidised by different reagents such as nitric acid, chromic acid mixture,[1]

---

[1] Prepared either by dissolving 10 grams of chromic anhydride in 60 c.c. of water, and adding 6 c.c. of concentrated sulphuric acid ; or by adding 11 c.c. of sulphuric acid to a solution of 15 grams of potassium bichromate in 60 c.c. of water.

a solution of chromic acid in glacial acetic acid or sulphuric acid of fairly high concentration, or potassium permanganate in acid, neutral, or alkaline solution ; different end-products are frequently obtained by varying the oxidising agent. As a general rule, side-chains are thus oxidised to aldehydic or carboxyl groups directly united to the aromatic nucleus. Thus toluene or ethylbenzene yield benzoic acid, naphthalene yields phthalic acid, and p-xylene or cymene yields terephthalic acid.

$$C_6H_5 \cdot CH_3 + 3O = C_6H_5 \cdot COOH + H_2O$$
$$C_6H_4(CH_3)_2 + 6O = C_6H_4(COOH)_2 + 2H_2O$$

The procedure for oxidation with alkaline permanganate—which is the method most generally applicable to all types of aromatic compounds, as well as hydrocarbons—is as follows : Between one and two grams of the substance is boiled under reflux with very dilute alkali, some pieces of porous earthenware or capillary glass tubes sealed at one end being added to facilitate ebullition. A solution containing the exact amount of potassium permanganate—calculated from the equation

$$2KMnO_4 + H_2O = 2MnO_2 + 2KOH + 3O,$$

sufficient to produce the required effect—is gradually added to the boiling solution, and the heating continued until the original red colour of the permanganate has disappeared. The precipitated hydrated peroxide of manganese is then filtered off, the filtrate concentrated to small bulk, filtered if necessary, acidified with hydrochloric acid, and the resulting acid filtered off or extracted with ether. It is inadvisable to employ more than the calculated quantity of permanganate, since the oxidation products themselves are frequently destroyed to some extent by the oxidising agent. Similarly, on oxidising with chromic acid mixture, the amount of oxidising agent is to be calculated from the equation

$$2CrO_3 + 3H_2SO_4 = Cr_2(SO_4)_3 + 3H_2O + 3O,$$

the action being continued until the original yellow colour has been entirely superseded by the green colour of the

chromic salt. In addition to oxidation, sulphonation, bromination, and especially nitration, are of the greatest advantage
for the purpose of preparing characteristic derivatives of aromatic hydrocarbons and other types of aromatic compounds.

Sulphonation may be effected either by warming with
concentrated sulphuric acid or by the action of fuming sulphuric acid, according to the ease with which the compound
is sulphonated. The resulting sulphonic acids frequently
crystallise out on slightly diluting the sulphonation mixture
at the end of the reaction ; or the sodium salts may be thrown
out by adding the mixture to a relatively large volume of
saturated sodium chloride solution.

For the preparation of sulphonic derivatives the most
satisfactory procedure, however, is to add the hydrocarbon
gradually to about five times its weight of chlorosulphonic
acid, with efficient cooling and agitation. On pouring the
resulting mixture into crushed ice the corresponding sulphochloride (or mixture of isomeric sulphochlorides) separates as
an oil or low-melting solid, which can be extracted with chloroform and distilled under reduced pressure or filtered off and
recrystallised from light petroleum.

$$(CH_3)_2C_6H_4 + 2Cl \cdot SO_3H = (CH_3)_2C_6H_3 \cdot SO_2Cl + HCl + H_2SO_4$$

A small proportion of sulphone is frequently formed simultaneously ; such sulphones are less soluble in light petroleum
than the sulphochlorides, or remain as residues on distillation.
For further characterisation, the sulphochlorides may be
converted into the corresponding sulphonamides by treatment
with ammonia (cf. p. 57).

Bromination is best carried out by slowly adding the
requisite amount of bromine to the hydrocarbon, to which
a small quantity of iodine or iron filings has been added.
After washing it with water, the product is fractionally distilled in order to separate unchanged hydrocarbon and dibromo derivatives from the principal monobromo product.   If
the bromine is added at 100–150° in the absence of catalyst,
bromination takes place in the side-chain ; thus the xylenes

yield xylyl bromides and xylylene bromides, and ethylbenzene yields a–bromo and αβ–dibromo derivatives. The preparation of these compounds is not recommended since they are often very strongly lachrymatory.

For the preparation of mononitro derivatives, a mixture of concentrated nitric and sulphuric acids is added, with vigorous stirring, to the hydrocarbon alone or in solution in carbon tetrachloride, the temperature being held below 40°. In order to obtain more highly nitrated derivatives, fuming (90–95 per cent.) nitric acid is substituted for the ordinary (65–70 per cent.) acid, and the temperature is raised towards the end of the reaction. Great care should be taken in nitrating unknown compounds, as the reaction is sometimes explosively violent and a splash of acid may cause serious injuries to the eyes or skin.

Many aromatic hydrocarbons, and aromatic compounds generally, form well-defined addition products with picric acid, produced by mixing saturated solutions of the substance under examination and of picric acid in 95 per cent. alcohol, warming, and allowing to cool slowly. The picrates, which crystallise out on cooling, may be recrystallised from the same solvent, and possess melting-points characteristic of the hydrocarbon.

Unsaturated compounds, as stated in the chapter on examination for approximate constitution, yield addition-products with bromine, and may be readily oxidised with formation of a variety of different end-products, according to the degree of violence with which the oxidation is carried out. Unlike saturated and many aromatic hydrocarbons, they dissolve — at least partially — in concentrated sulphuric acid, from which, however, they cannot be recovered unchanged on dilution with water. The simpler aliphatic unsaturated hydrocarbons dissolve in cold 80–90 per cent sulphuric acid, giving water-soluble alkylsulphuric acids which on distillation with steam break up into secondary or tertiary alcohols.

$$CH_3 \cdot CH : C(CH_3)_2 + H_2SO_4 = CH_3 \cdot CH_2 C(CH_3)_2 \cdot O \cdot SO_3H$$
$$CH_3 \cdot CH_2 \cdot C(CH_3)_2 \cdot O \cdot SO_3H = CH_3 \cdot CH_2 \cdot C(CH_3)_2 \cdot OH + H_2SO_4$$

The higher the molecular weight of the hydrocarbon the more readily does this reaction take place and the lower the necessary concentration of the acid; but the higher members display an increasing tendency to polymerise to high-boiling hydrocarbons which do not dissolve in the acid mixture.

Unsaturated, like aromatic, hydrocarbons react with fuming nitric acid, occasionally with considerable violence. This test serves to distinguish saturated paraffin hydrocarbons which alone are unattacked by this powerful reagent.

Ethers (pp. 110–113) may be differentiated from saturated and aromatic hydrocarbons by the fact that they dissolve in cold concentrated sulphuric acid. On pouring the resulting solution very slowly into ice-cold water, the ether is thrown out of solution, and can be recovered unchanged. They may be oxidised by warming with a solution of chromic acid in concentrated sulphuric acid, with production, in the case of aliphatic or aliphatic-aromatic ethers, of carboxylic acids or of aldehydes. The aliphatic-aromatic ethers may be decomposed by boiling with constant-boiling (48 per cent.) hydrobromic acid, which breaks them up into phenols and alkyl bromides.

$$C_6H_5 \cdot OCH_3 + HBr = C_6H_5 \cdot OH + CH_3Br$$

A similar effect may be brought about with concentrated hydriodic acid (cf. p. 320) or by carefully warming the ether with anhydrous aluminium chloride.

If the substance shows an acid reaction to litmus when examined in presence of water or aqueous alcohol, it may be a carboxylic acid or an acid anhydride. Some phenols and a few easily hydrolysable esters, such as methyl oxalate, may also present acid properties towards litmus. In the case of phenols, the acid reaction is generally extremely faint and often barely perceptible, while in the case of esters it is more the exception than the rule for an acid reaction to be obtained. In order to distinguish these classes, a small quantity—about 0·05 gram—of the substance, finely powdered if solid, is suspended or dissolved in pure water or aqueous alcohol, a drop of phenolphthalein solution added, and decinormal sodium or potassium hydroxide run in from a burette. Sharp end-points will be given readily only by acids and very easily hydrolysable anhydrides and esters.

Carboxylic acids (pp. 136–149) are the most strongly acidic class of compound among substances containing only carbon, hydrogen, and oxygen, and their alkali salts are not decomposed by the action of carbon dioxide. The lower members of the series are miscible with water, and only few acids exist which are insoluble in boiling water.

On warming on the water-bath with an excess of methyl or ethyl alcohol in presence of a small amount of concentrated sulphuric acid, or on passing a current of dry hydrogen chloride into a boiling solution of the acid in the alcohol, esters are produced.

$$CH_3 \cdot COOH + C_2H_5OH = CH_3 \cdot COOC_2H_5 + H_2O$$

When sulphuric acid has been employed for esterification, the mixture should be poured into cold water and ether added, the extract separated from the aqueous portion by a separating funnel, washed with dilute sodium carbonate solution and again with pure water, and finally distilled. When gaseous hydrochloric acid has been employed as a catalyst, the same process may be applied for isolation; but when the boiling-point of the ester is high, the resultant mixture may be fractionally distilled without further treatment. Care must be taken, however, that the reaction has been given sufficient time to come to completion, otherwise the ester will be contaminated with unchanged acid. For this reason it is preferable, whenever possible, to wash the final product with sodium carbonate solution before distilling.

On warming on the water-bath at 50–60° with phosphorus trichloride or with thionyl chloride, carboxylic acids yield the corresponding chlorides.

$$3CH_3 \cdot COOH + PCl_3 = 3CH_3 \cdot COCl + H_3PO_3$$
$$C_6H_5 \cdot COOH + SOCl_2 = C_6H_5 \cdot COCl + HCl + SO_2$$

These may be employed, without necessarily purifying before further conversion, for the preparation of esters, amides, or substituted amides.

On boiling an acid with an equivalent quantity of aniline or p-toluidine for several hours, the anilide or p-toluidide is produced.

$$CH_3 \cdot COOH + C_6H_5 \cdot NH_2 = CH_3 \cdot CO \cdot NH \cdot C_6H_5 + H_2O$$

The lower members of the fatty acid series may rapidly be distinguished by testing firstly with acid permanganate, which is decolorised by formic acid but by none of its homologues ; the latter differ in the solubility of their ferric and cupric salts in organic liquids. A 1–2 per cent. solution of the acid in water is accurately neutralised (to phenolphthalein) with seminormal alkali,[1] and 2 c.c. of the resulting solution is mixed with 1 c.c. of *iso*amyl alcohol (preferably diluted with half its volume of methyl alcohol), and one or two drops of 2 per cent. ferric chloride or copper sulphate are added. The mixture is well shaken and allowed to stand until it separates into layers. In the case of acetic acid (and formic acid) the aqueous layer is coloured and the *iso*amyl alcohol colourless ; with propionic acid and higher homologues the colour is entirely in the alcohol. In the latter case the test is repeated, substituting ethyl ether for the *iso*amyl alcohol, when the colour is taken up by the ether only with butyric and higher acids. These can be distinguished by employing benzene as the organic solvent, which becomes coloured only with valeric and higher acids. It is to be noted that the heavy-metallic salts of butyric acid and its higher homologues are precipitated from aqueous solution, while with formic, acetic and propionic acids they are soluble in water.

The addition of ferric chloride solution serves roughly to distinguish simple acids from **aliphatic hydroxy-acids** (p. 145) While simple acids form dull reddish colorations or precipi-

---

[1] Sodium or potassium, not alkaline earth metal, salts of the acids must be employed.

tates when treated in aqueous solution with a few drops of
this reagent, hydroxy-acids, and in particular α-hydroxy-
acids, form intensely yellow-coloured solutions on addition of
a drop of ferric chloride. This last test may also be applied
in the following manner : to a dilute aqueous solution of
phenol a few drops of ferric chloride are added. On adding
a small quantity of the resulting violet-coloured solution to
a solution of the α-hydroxy-acid in water, the violet coloration is discharged, a deep yellow tint taking its place. The
majority of aliphatic hydroxy-acids are extremely soluble in
water.

Many **aromatic hydroxy-acids** (p. 147), in particular
those in which the hydroxyl group is in the position *ortho*
to the carboxyl group, give the violet or bluish colours produced by phenolic compounds on treatment with ferric chloride
solution.

It has been shown by Reid that many carboxylic acids
yield esters possessing characteristic melting-points on treating their sodium or potassium salts with *p*-nitrobenzyl bromide, or with phenacyl bromide (bromoacetophenone) or
certain halogen derivatives of the latter. A weighed amount
of the acid is dissolved in water or aqueous alcohol and titrated
with normal alcoholic potassium hydroxide ; the resulting
solution is evaporated to dryness after adding a trace of acid
to neutralise any excess of alkali. An amount of the dry
salt corresponding to slightly more than 5 c.c. of normal
alkali is dissolved in 5 c.c. of water, and 10 c.c. of alcohol
and 1·0 gram of the reagent are added to the solution, which
is then boiled under reflux for one to two hours. A clear
solution usually results on heating ; should a sparingly
soluble product separate it is necessary to add more alcohol.
The mixture is then rapidly chilled, with the addition of
small amounts of water if no separation of crystals occurs ;
the product is washed successively with dilute alcohol and
water, and finally recrystallised from dilute alcohol until no
further change in melting-point occurs on recrystallisation.

Acid anhydrides (p. 150) are, as a rule, but sparingly soluble in cold water, being more or less rapidly hydrolysed with formation of the corresponding acids on boiling with water or dilute alkali. On warming with aniline or p-toluidine they yield the anilides or p-toluidides even more readily than do the free acids.

$$CH_3 \cdot CO \cdot)_2 O + C_6H_5NH_2 = CH_3 \cdot CO \cdot NH \cdot C_6H_5 + CH_3 \cdot COOH$$

They may be converted into the esters on boiling with alcohols or phenols.

Esters (pp. 150–160), the majority of which are liquids insoluble in water, may be hydrolysed by boiling under reflux with aqueous or alcoholic alkali, with concentrated hydrochloric acid, or with 40 per cent. sulphuric acid, or, better, syrupy phosphoric acid. In many cases in which the free acid is stable towards concentrated sulphuric acid, esters may be hydrolysed by warming with this reagent for about fifteen minutes to 100° on the water-bath.

$$CH_3 \cdot CO \cdot OC_2H_5 + H_2O = CH_3 \cdot COOH + C_2H_5OH$$

Whenever possible, however, it is advisable to perform the hydrolysis with an excess of aqueous alkali, continuing the heating until all the ester has entered into solution. The mixture is then distilled with steam, and the alcohol which has passed over with the steam is isolated by fractionation of the distillate and salting out the alcohol by the addition of solid potassium carbonate. The alcohol may, however, also be examined in solution. Alcohols are of course not present in the distillate obtained after hydrolysis of esters of most phenols and non-volatile alcohols such as glycols or glycerol; in such cases the reaction mixture should be saturated with carbon dioxide, when any phenol present may be isolated by distillation with steam or by extraction with ether, while polyhydroxylic alcohols can be separated only by evaporation to complete dryness on the water-bath and extraction of the residue with a mixture of alcohol and ether. The alkaline solution containing the salt of the acid should be acidified with dilute sulphuric acid and filtered, extracted with ether, or distilled, in order to isolate the free acid.

On standing with concentrated aqueous ammonia, many esters are converted into amides.

$$CH_3 \cdot CO \cdot OC_2H_5 + NH_3 = CH_3 \cdot CO \cdot NH_2 + C_2H_5OH$$

Phenols (pp. 120–125 exhibit, as stated above, slightly acid properties, being almost always soluble in solutions of alkali hydroxides, and occasionally in ammonia. The resultant alkali salts are, in contradistinction to the salts of carboxylic acids, decomposed by an excess of carbon dioxide.

$$C_6H_5 \cdot ONa + CO_2 + H_2O = C_6H_5 \cdot OH + NaHCO_3$$

Phenols may be recognised by the violet, blue, or green colours which are frequently imparted to their aqueous or alcoholic solutions by addition of one or two drops of ferric chloride. The permanence of such colorations varies greatly with individual phenols—some persisting indefinitely, some disappearing only after several minutes, and some changing in tint almost immediately. Some phenols, also, give colorations in alcoholic solution while giving none in water. It is to be observed that similar colorations are produced by ferric chloride with certain keto-enolic substances, such as acetoacetic esters. Such compounds also form solutions in dilute aqueous alkalies, and may be precipitated therefrom by the action of carbon dioxide. They lack, however, that stability towards acid and alkaline hydrolytic reagents which is characteristic of phenols, and no doubt should exist as to their complete difference in class.

Phenols may be acylated by warming under reflux with acetic anhydride, by the action of acetyl chloride alone or in indifferent or basic (e.g. pyridine) solution, or in solution in dilute alkali by benzoyl chloride according to the Schotten-Baumann method.

$$CH_3 \cdot COCl + C_6H_5OH = CH_3 \cdot COOC_6H_5 + HCl$$
$$C_6H_5 \cdot COCl + C_6H_5ONa = C_6H_5 \cdot COOC_6H_5 + NaCl$$

Similar treatment with sulphonic chlorides, particularly benzenesulphochloride and p-toluenesulphochloride, leads to the formation of sulphonic esters.

$$C_6H_5 \cdot SO_2Cl + C_6H_5 \cdot ONa = C_6H_5 \cdot SO_2OC_6H_5 + NaCl$$

With phenyl *iso*cyanate, carbanilates are formed.

$$C_6H_5 \cdot N{:}CO + C_6H_5 \cdot OH = C_6H_5 \cdot NH \cdot COOC_6H_5$$

All of the above reactions lead in general to the production of crystalline derivatives possessing characteristic melting-points.

The majority of phenols are readily brominated on treatment with bromine water, with immediate formation of poly-bromo derivatives, which may be recrystallised from alcohol ; they also may often be nitrated or sulphonated, with formation of characteristic derivatives. These reactions all take place with extreme readiness.

A sensitive test for phenols in very dilute solution is afforded by the development of a red colour on adding alkali and a small quantity of a cold solution of p-nitroaniline in dilute hydrochloric acid which has been decolorised (diazotised) by sodium nitrite. The following test is also applicable to the detection of small quantities of phenols : to 10 c.c. of the phenol solution is added one drop of a 10 per cent. solution of sodium nitrite, then 2 to 5 c.c. of concentrated sulphuric acid is run under the surface ; a ring, green below and red above, forms at the zone of contact.

Reid's method for the identification of acids (p. 80) may also be applied to phenols, which are thus converted into characteristic p-nitrobenzyl ethers : to 25 c.c. of 0·2 N alcoholic potassium hydroxide 1·0 gram of the phenol is added (a larger quantity being taken if it be suspected that the molecular, or rather equivalent, weight be above 200), and the solution boiled for one hour under reflux with 1·0 gram of the reagent. The product is isolated in the same manner as the esters of carboxylic acids.

The remaining types included in this section exhibit no
acid properties towards indicators.

Alcohols (pp. 113–120) may be acylated by treatment
with acid chlorides or anhydrides, or by heating with acids
in presence of sulphuric acid or hydrogen chloride. The
lower members of the series, and almost all polyhydroxylic
alcohols, are readily soluble in water.

Primary and secondary alcohols, both simple and polyhydroxylic, can be converted into esters by boiling with acetic
acid in presence of sulphuric acid or hydrogen chloride, or,
preferably, by warming with acetic anhydride. They also
yield benzoates on shaking them in alkaline solution with
benzoyl chloride.

On boiling with excess of 48 per cent. hydrobromic acid,
preferably in the presence of sulphuric acid, alcohols of almost
all types yield alkyl bromides.

$$C_2H_5OH + HBr = C_2H_5Br + H_2O$$

Simple primary, secondary, and tertiary alcohols may be
differentiated by their reactivity towards strong hydrochloric
acid.   Primary alcohols as a rule are considerably more soluble
in this reagent than in pure water but do not enter into
reaction with it, even on long boiling ;   secondary alcohols
yield the corresponding chlorides, but only on warming ;
while tertiary alcohols react so readily with concentrated
hydrochloric acid that the chlorides separate in the cold.
Exception to this rule must be made in the cases of alcohols
of the benzyl type and of glycols, which are (although primary
alcohols) converted into their chlorides on boiling with
concentrated hydrochloric acid. The analogous reaction
takes place rather more readily with hydrobromic acid and
hydriodic acid.   Addition of zinc chloride markedly promotes
the esterification of alcohols by hydrochloric acid, so that
by its use primary chlorides may be prepared in good yields.

Reid's method of identification (p.80) has been extended
to alcohols, by treating them with phthalic anhydride and

submitting the sodium salts of the resulting acid phthalic esters to the action of p-nitrobenzyl bromide.

$$C_6H_4\diagup{\begin{matrix}CO\\CO\end{matrix}}\diagdown O + C_2H_5OH = C_6H_4\diagup{\begin{matrix}COOC_2H_5\\COOH\end{matrix}}$$

$$NO_2 \cdot C_6H_4 \cdot CH_2Br + C_6H_4\diagup{\begin{matrix}COOC_2H_5\\COONa\end{matrix}} =$$

$$C_6H_4\diagup{\begin{matrix}COOC_2H_5\\COOCH_2 \cdot C_6H_4 \cdot NO_2\end{matrix}} + NaBr$$

The procedure in this case is somewhat more laborious : 1·0 gram of phthalic anhydride and 1 c.c. of the alcohol are sealed up in a small tube with fairly stout walls and not less than 10 c.c. capacity, and the tube heated for an hour in a boiling water-bath, or in an oil-bath at 140° when the alcohol is suspected to be secondary. In cases when the boiling-point of the alcohol lies above the reaction temperature, the mixture may be heated in a loosely stoppered test-tube fitted with a rod for stirring. When the reaction is complete, the product is dissolved in about 15 c.c. of ether and the solution shaken with 10 c.c. of water to which 5 c.c. of normal sodium hydroxide have been added. The liquids are then separated ; the ether layer is shaken with a small quantity of water, and the united aqueous portion shaken out once with a little fresh ether, after which it is evaporated to dryness on the water-bath. The residue is treated with p-nitrobenzyl bromide in the same way as the sodium salts of other acids. It may be pointed out that by the above procedure all the phthalic anhydride is esterified, so that no fear need be entertained of encountering the p-nitrobenzyl ester of phthalic acid among the final products.

The simpler alcohols may also be identified by the preparation of their 3:5-dinitrobenzoyl esters, which form crystalline solids of definite melting-point.[1]

[1] The procedure for the preparation of these esters, according to the method recommended by Mulliken (*Identification of Pure Organic*

Alcohols yield characteristic carbanilates and α-naphthylurethanes on treating them with phenyl *iso*cyanate and with α-naphthyl *iso*cyanate.

$$C_{10}H_7 \cdot N:CO + C_2H_5OH = C_{10}H_7 \cdot NH \cdot COOC_2H_5$$

Primary alcohols as a rule react vigorously, secondary alcohols require heating, while tertiary alcohols furnish poor yields or none at all. The presence of water, either in the alcohol originally or formed in a by-reaction, leads to the simultaneous formation of disubstituted ureas (cf. p. 35); these are removed by recrystallising the product from light petroleum, in which the above by-products are insoluble. Analogous derivatives may be prepared by treating alcohols with diphenylcarbamyl chloride in the presence of dilute alkali.

$$(C_6H_5)_2N \cdot COCl + C_2H_5OH + NaOH =$$
$$(C_6H_5)_2N \cdot COOC_2H_5 + NaCl + H_2O$$

The majority of **aldehydes** (pp. 126–130) and **ketones** (pp. 130–133) may be detected by treatment with a concentrated aqueous solution of sodium bisulphite, when a crystalline solid often separates out, its formation occasionally being accompanied by considerable evolution of heat. This precipitate consists of the sodium salt of an α-hydroxysulphonic acid, usually termed an 'aldehyde or ketone bisulphite compound.'

$$C_6H_5 \cdot CHO + NaHSO_3 = C_6H_5 \cdot CH(OH)SO_3Na$$
$$CH_3 \cdot CO \cdot CH_3 + NaHSO_3 = (CH_3)_2C(OH)SO_3Na$$

The general behaviour of this class of compound has already been discussed on p. 54. It is to be observed, however,

---

Compounds (1905), 168), is as follows : a small quantity of 3·5-dinitrobenzoic acid is converted into the chloride by gentle warming with rather more than an equal weight of phosphorus pentachloride. The mixture is then allowed to cool on a watch-glass, and the solid dinitrobenzoyl chloride separated from the adherent phosphorus oxychloride by rapidly pressing out on a porous earthenware tile. To prepare the ester, a very small quantity (0·1 to 0·2 gram) of the crude chloride is treated with a slight excess (4 to 8 drops) of the alcohol in a stoppered test-tube, and the lower end of the tube immersed in water previously warmed to a temperature of 75–85°. After the mixture has thus been warmed for about ten minutes, it is allowed to cool, and the resulting solid ester recrystallised from 60 per cent. alcohol until pure.

that the bisulphite compounds of many carbonyl compounds of these types are readily soluble in water, and may therefore produce no precipitate. An ethereal solution of an aldehyde or a ketone will nevertheless lose its solute on treatment with a saturated bisulphite solution, whether the resulting salt separates out or not. The tendency of aldehydes and of ketones in which the carbonyl group is attached to methyl or exists in a ring (as in *cyclo*hexanone) to combine with bisulphites is so pronounced that they develop free alkali on shaking with neutral sodium sulphite solution.

$$(CH_3)_2CO + Na_2SO_3 + H_2O = (CH_3)_2C(OH) \cdot SO_3Na + NaOH$$

This can be observed by the formation of a red colour with phenolphthalein. On the other hand, ketones in which higher alkyl groups are attached to the carbonyl react slowly with bisulphite or not at all.

Aldehydes and ketones containing a methyl group attached to the carbonyl readily yield iodoform on treatment with iodine and dilute alkali.

$$CH_3 \cdot CHO + 6I + 4NaOH = CHI_3 + H.COONa + 3NaI + 3H_2O$$

This reaction is not specific for carbonyl compounds, as it is given by ethyl, *iso*propyl, and other alcohols which on oxidation yield the above type of aldehyde or ketone.

Aldehydes and ketones form characteristic derivatives on treatment with hydroxylamine or with hydrazines. Oximes may be prepared by warming the substance with an excess of an aqueous or alcoholic solution of hydroxylamine.

$$C_6H_5 \cdot CHO + NH_2OH = C_6H_5 \cdot CH:NOH + H_2O$$
$$C_6H_5 \cdot CO \cdot C_6H_5 + NH_2OH = (C_6H_5)_2C:NOH + H_2O$$

The carbonyl compound is dissolved in not less than three times its weight of alcohol; to the hot solution a slight excess (1 to 1·5 molecular proportions) of solid hydroxylamine hydrochloride is added, followed at once by an excess of anhydrous sodium acetate. The mixture is then gently warmed, so as to avoid bumping, until a drop of the solution gives a clear solution in 0·5 c.c. of 10 per cent. sodium hydroxide, without odour of aldehyde or ketone. The mixture is then concentrated on the water-bath, cooled, diluted with water, and extracted with ether ; or should the oxime have separated out as a solid, this may be filtered off and recrystallised from alcohol or ligroin.

Phenylhydrazones of aldehydes and ketones may be prepared by warming the substance on the water-bath for about two hours in aqueous-alcoholic solution under reflux with either pure phenylhydrazine, phenylhydrazine acetate, or phenylhydrazine hydrochloride in presence of an excess of sodium acetate.

$$C_6H_5 \cdot CHO + C_6H_5 \cdot NH \cdot NH_2 = C_6H_5 \cdot CH:N \cdot NH \cdot C_6H_5 + H_2O$$

The product may be isolated by adding very dilute acetic acid to the solution and filtering or extracting with ether. It may be recrystallised from aqueous alcohol or from ligroin.

Since many phenylhydrazones possess inconveniently low melting points, it is frequently preferable to employ a substituted phenylhydrazine such as p-bromophenyl hydrazine, p-nitrophenylhydrazine, or 2:4-dinitrophenylhydrazine. The first two of the above-mentioned reagents may be employed in the same manner as phenylhydrazine ; the derivatives obtained by their means are generally less soluble, as well as higher-melting, than the unsubstituted phenylhydrazones. In the dinitrophenylhydrazine the basic properties of the hydrazine group have been so weakened by the presence of the nitro groups that the condensation with the carbonyl compound can be carried out in acid solution : the aldehyde or ketone is added to a dilute solution of the reagent in 2 N hydrochloric acid ; the hydrazone precipitates almost immediately and is recrystallised from alcohol. The condensation, which is especially suitable for the detection and identification of water-soluble compounds of low molecular weight, may also be effected in boiling alcohol ; this method, however, suffers from the sparing solubility of dinitrophenylhydrazine in alcohol.

Semicarbazide is of value in the identification of carbonyl

compounds as it frequently furnishes crystalline derivatives of compounds which give unsatisfactory results with hydroxylamine and phenylhydrazine. The general procedure for the preparation of semicarbazones is similar to that of oximes, the carbonyl compound being warmed in alcoholic or aqueous-alcoholic solution with a slight excess of semicarbazide hydrochloride and sodium acetate.

$$(CH_3)_2CO + NH_2 \cdot NH \cdot CO \cdot NH_2 = (CH_3)_2C:N \cdot NH \cdot CO \cdot NH_2 + H_2O$$

The resulting semicarbazones, which, with the exception of a few derivatives of low molecular weight, are sparingly soluble in cold water, may be precipitated by the addition of water and recrystallised from methyl alcohol.

Solutions of many aldehydes and ketones develop characteristic red colours when treated with sodium nitroprusside and alkali. If, instead of alkali, piperidine be employed, blue colours result. On adding a dilute solution of *m*-phenylenediamine hydrochloride to aqueous or alcoholic solutions of aldehydes or ketones, a green fluorescence is developed. Alkaline solutions of some aldehydes and ketones give red colorations on addition of *m*-dinitrobenzene. These colour reactions are given only by ketones in which at least one methyl or ethyl radicle is attached to the carbonyl group.

The simpler aldehydes and ketones, in extremely dilute aqueous solution, yield voluminous precipitates with Nessler's solution.

Aldehydes (pp. 126–130) may be distinguished from ketones by testing with Schiff's reagent.[1] On treatment of the pure substance with this solution a distinct red colour is formed within a time-limit of two minutes. In the case of water-soluble aldehydes the pink colour should appear almost

---

[1] Prepared (Mulliken, *op. cit.* 15) by dissolving 0·2 gram of rosaniline—or its acetate or hydrochloride (fuchsine)—in 10 c.c. of a cold saturated solution of sulphur dioxide in water, and, after allowing to stand until the pink colour is entirely discharged, diluting to 100 c.c. This solution should be preserved away from light in a well-stoppered bottle.

instantly. The solution should never be warmed or treated with alkaline reagents, as both of these agencies restore the pink colour in the absence of any aldehyde. The presence of mineral acids—even too great an excess of the sulphurous acid—is to be avoided, as this tends to diminish the susceptibility of the reagent to aldehydes. Since many compounds may contain traces of substances which restore the colour of the fuchsine, the appearance of a pink tint after the expiration of the time-limit is to be disregarded. Yellow to red colours are developed by aldehydes with benzidine in glacial acetic acid solution.

Aldehydes may be oxidised by nitric acid and other oxidising agents with formation of the corresponding carboxylic acids.

$$CH_3 \cdot CH:O + O = CH_3 \cdot CO \cdot OH$$

They reduce Fehling's solution on warming and precipitate metallic silver in the amorphous condition or in the form of a mirror on warming with a solution of silver nitrate in a mixture of caustic soda and strong ammonia.

On warming with concentrated potash solution, aliphatic aldehydes yield aldehyde-resins with powerful odours, while aromatic aldehydes are converted into a mixture of the corresponding acid and alcohol.

$$2C_6H_5 \cdot CHO + KOH = C_6H_5 \cdot COOK + C_6H_5 \cdot CH_2OH$$

Aromatic aldehydes react with bromine in carbon tetra-chloride or chloroform solution to form acid bromides:

$$C_6H_5 \cdot CHO + Br_2 = C_6H_5 \cdot CO \cdot Br + HBr$$

while in aliphatic aldehydes the hydrogen atoms in the alkyl radicle are substituted by bromine with formation of somewhat unstable bromo compounds.

Aromatic aldehydes, on warming with primary amines, yield condensation-products by elimination of water (cf. p. 41).

$$C_6H_5 \cdot CHO + C_6H_5 \cdot NH_2 = C_6H_5 \cdot CH:N \cdot C_6H_5 + H_2O$$

Formaldehyde differs from other aliphatic aldehydes in

some of its reactions. Thus on heating with concentrated alkali it yields methyl alcohol and a formate (but no aldehyde resin), while with dilute ammonia it forms neutral hexamethylenetetramine. Its oxime and phenylhydrazone are difficult to isolate, owing to their tendency to polymerise.

Paraldehydes and **acetals** (p. 126) behave like ethers towards alkalies, but are much more susceptible to the action of acids. Both types yield aldehydes on boiling with dilute mineral acids, the latter giving rise simultaneously to alcohols.

$$CH_3 \cdot CH \!-\!\!-\! O \!-\!\!-\! CH \cdot CH_3 = 3CH_3CHO$$
$$\qquad\qquad\quad |$$
$$\qquad\quad O \cdot CH(CH_3) \cdot O$$

$$CH_3 \cdot CH(OC_2H_5)_2 + H_2O = CH_3 \cdot CHO + 2C_2H_5OH$$

They are not attacked by Fehling's solution nor by metallic sodium.

Ketones (pp. 130–133) are far less susceptible than aldehydes to the action of oxidising agents. They do not reduce Fehling's solution nor ammoniacal silver nitrate, and do not restore the colour to Schiff's reagent. Aliphatic and aliphatic-aromatic ketones may, however, be oxidised by boiling with chromic acid mixture, with formation of carboxylic acids.

$$C_6H_5 \cdot CO \cdot CH_3 + 4O = C_6H_5 \cdot COOH + CO_2 + H_2O$$

Aliphatic and aliphatic-aromatic ketones, on treatment with an equivalent quantity of bromine, are very readily brominated with substitution of bromine in the aliphatic group adjacent to the carbonyl.

$$C_6H_5 \cdot CO \cdot CH_3 + Br_2 = C_6H_5 \cdot CO \cdot CH_2Br + HBr$$

Glucosides (p. 165) and **carbohydrates** (p. 161), while properly belonging to the classes of alcohols, aldehydes, or ketones, may be discussed independently, inasmuch as they possess many properties peculiar to themselves. They may be detected by Molisch's reaction—which is stated [1] to be so delicate that it is given by substances other than carbo-

[1] Mulliken, *op. cit.*, 26.

hydrates when contaminated by dust or by fibres from the filter paper : to a small portion (about 0·005 gram) of the substance in 1 c.c. of water, 2 drops of a 10 per cent. solution of α-naphthol in chloroform are added. On carefully adding 1 c.c. of concentrated sulphuric acid from a finely-pointed pipette so that it forms a separate layer below the water, a violet ring will be formed at the junction of the layers. On cautiously mixing the layers by shaking the test-tube in a stream of cold water, a deep purple solution results, which on dilution with cold water yields a violet precipitate. On shaking and adding a small quantity of the suspension to an excess of concentrated ammonia the colour is changed to dull brown.

On strongly heating alone, glucosides and carbohydrates, in common with some aliphatic hydroxy-acids, yield the pungent odour attributed to ' burnt sugar.'

Glucosides may be distinguished from most carbohydrates by their failure to reduce Fehling's solution or react with phenylhydrazine until they have been boiled with dilute mineral acid, which splits them up into a sugar and an alcohol, phenol, etc.

$$CH_3O \cdot CH \cdot (CHOH)_2 \cdot CH \cdot CHOH \cdot CH_2OH + H_2O =$$
$$\underset{\rule{3em}{0.4pt}\ O\ \rule{3em}{0.4pt}}{}$$

$$CH_3OH + CHO \cdot (CHOH)_4 \cdot CH_2OH$$

This inability to react with Fehling's solution before hydrolysis is also characteristic of the disaccharide sucrose (cane sugar), which is in fact a true glucoside.

Most of the complex natural glucosides yield intense colours on treatment with cold concentrated sulphuric acid.

Carbohydrates (pp. 161–165) may be roughly subdivided into : (1) monosaccharides (pentoses and hexoses) ; (2) di- and tri-saccharides (such as saccharose, maltose, raffinose) ; (3) polysaccharides (such as starch, glycogen, inulin). Cellulose may also be included in the third division. All carbohydrates, on treatment with cold concentrated sulphuric acid, give only colorations varying between yellow, brown, and black, no members of this class giving red or purple colours.

Monosaccharides are mostly colourless crystalline solids, all readily soluble in water, yielding optically active solutions. The specific rotations of the sugars are important physical characteristics, and should in all cases be determined.

Monosaccharides are unchanged on boiling with dilute mineral acids, but decomposed with formation of indefinite products on warming with concentrated alkali. They are readily oxidised : by boiling with Fehling's solution, yielding a red precipitate of cuprous oxide ; by boiling with Nylandr's solution,[1] with formation of a black precipitate ; or by warming with a solution of silver nitrate in a mixture of concentrated ammonia and caustic soda solution, with precipitation of metallic silver in the amorphous condition or in the form of a mirror.

Many monosaccharides, on treatment with phenyl-hydrazine acetate in aqueous solution at 100°, react with formation of osazones.

$$CH_2OH \cdot (CHOH)_4 \cdot CHO + C_6H_5 \cdot NH \cdot NH_2 =$$
$$CH_2OH \cdot (CHOH)_4 \cdot CH:N \cdot NH \cdot C_6H_5 + H_2O$$
$$CH_2OH \cdot (CHOH)_3 \cdot CO \cdot CH_2OH + C_6H_5 \cdot NH \cdot NH_2 =$$
$$CH_2OH \cdot (CHOH)_3 \cdot C(\cdot CH_2OH):N \cdot NH \cdot C_6H_5 + H_2O$$
$$\left. \begin{array}{l} CH_2OH \cdot (CHOH)_3 \cdot CHOH \cdot CH:N \cdot NH \cdot C_6H_5 \\ \text{or } CH_2OH \cdot (CHOH)_3 \cdot C(CH_2OH):N \cdot NH \cdot C_6H_5 \end{array} \right\} + 2C_6H_5 \cdot NH \cdot NH_2$$
$$= CH_2OH \cdot (CHOH)_3 \cdot C(:N \cdot NH \cdot C_6H_5) \cdot CH:N \cdot NH \cdot C_6H_5 +$$
$$C_6H_5 \cdot NH_2 + NH_3 + H_2O$$

The phenylhydrazones formed as intermediate products are, except in the one instance of the hexose mannose, extremely soluble in water, and readily reduce a further molecule of phenylhydrazine, thus paving the way for the formation of an osazone. The yield of osazone varies greatly with the concentration of the reacting substances ; the maximum yield of glucosazone is obtained when a mixture of 1·8 gram of glucose, 3·24 gram of phenylhydrazine, and 5 c.c. of acetic

---

[1] A solution of 2 grams of basic bismuth nitrate and 4 grams of Rochelle salt in 100 c.c. of 10 per cent. sodium hydroxide solution.

acid is diluted to 25 c.c. On increasing the dilution the yield falls rapidly.

Maquenne has pointed out that each individual monosaccharide has its own time-interval through which it must be heated before the yellow osazone makes its appearance. In order to utilise this discovery it is necessary to conduct the reaction under standard conditions. Maquenne's procedure is therefore here set forth in detail: a solution of 1 gram of the sugar in 100 c.c. of water is heated to 100° in a loosely corked flask suspended in a beaker containing boiling water, whereupon 5 c.c. of a solution [1] of phenylhydrazine acetate is added. The time at which **a** precipitate or turbidity first makes its appearance is carefully noted. Heating should be continued for at least one hour, the mixture cooled, and the osazone filtered off and recrystallised from a small quantity of 50 per cent. alcohol. Unfortunately the melting points of the osazones of the commoner sugars not only lie in the same region (around 200°), but they are apt to vary with the rate of heating, so that they are of little value in characterisation. The form in which the crystals separate initially, as they appear when viewed through the microscope, is of more aid in identification.

In contradistinction to phenylhydrazine, which furnishes osazones, substituted hydrazines of higher molecular weight such as diphenylhydrazine, benzylphenylhydrazine, and β-naphthylhydrazine, yield sparingly soluble hydrazones on warming with sugars in aqueous-alcoholic solution. Such derivatives are more satisfactory than the phenylosazones for the identification of sugars, as they possess sharper melting points which differ considerably with different sugars. Benzylphenylhydrazones may be prepared by mixing 3 grams of the sugar in 5 c.c. of water with 4 grams of benzylphenylhydrazine

---

[1] Prepared by diluting with water to 100 c.c. a mixture of 40 grams of pure phenylhydrazine and 40 grams of glacial acetic acid. This olution should be preserved away from light in a tightly-stoppered bottle of just sufficient capacity.

in 20 c.c. of alcohol, warming on the water-bath, adding water until a turbidity just appears, and allowing the mixture to stand, when the benzylphenylhydrazone separates in crystalline condition. This reaction is of especial value for the identification of pentoses. Analogous derivatives may be obtained with the other hydrazines above mentioned by a similar procedure.

Methylphenylhydrazine is also of value inasmuch as it yields both hydrazones and osazones ; in particular, it reacts more readily and gives a better yield of hydrazone with ketoses than with aldoses.

Ketoses may be distinguished by their resistance to the action of bromine water, their reducing power (towards Fehling's solution) being unaltered by treatment with this reagent. **Aldoses,** on the other hand, readily decolorise bromine water, the resulting solution possessing a greatly diminished reducing power or none at all.

Pentoses give several specific reactions by means of which they may be distinguished from the hexoses. On distillation with 12 per cent. hydrochloric acid they yield furfural, which possesses a characteristic odour and develops a red colour with aniline acetate paper. On warming with 18 per cent. hydrochloric acid and a small quantity of phloroglucinol a purple colour is formed ; while addition of a pentose to a boiling solution of orcinol in 18 per cent. hydrochloric acid containing a little ferric chloride causes the formation of a green colour.

Hexoses give a red colour on warming with resorcinol in hydrochloric acid ; this test takes place more rapidly with ketohexoses than with aldohexoses. They may also be distinguished by Fenton's test : a small sample is moistened with water and warmed on the water-bath with one or two drops of phosphorus tribromide until the mixture begins to darken, whereupon it is cooled and mixed with a little alcohol and a few drops of ethyl malonate ; on adding an excess of alcoholic potash and finally diluting with water a blue fluorescence appears.

A specific reaction for hexoses is the formation of levulinic acid. The sugar is heated on the water-bath for 15 to 20 hours with 4 to 5 parts of constant-boiling (20 per cent.) hydrochloric acid under reflux ; the mixture is cooled, filtered, and repeatedly shaken out with ether. After distilling off the ether the residue is tested for levulinic acid by gently warming it with a solution of iodine in dilute sodium carbonate (iodoform test) ; or if a sufficient quantity is available it may be isolated as the crystalline zinc salt by warming it in concentrated aqueous solution with zinc oxide, filtering hot, and allowing to crystallise. This salt may be dissolved in water and converted into the sparingly soluble silver salt, and the percentage of silver determined by ignition (cf. p. 315). Or the levulinic acid may be identified as its phenyl-hydrazone (p. 150).

Different hexoses may be distinguished by the formation of saccharic acid or of mucic acid on oxidation with nitric acid : a 2-gram sample of the sugar is treated with 8–12 gram of 25 per cent. nitric acid (sp. gr. 1·15) and the acid evaporated by heating on the water-bath until the syrupy residue begins to assume a brown colour. Water amounting to rather less in volume than the acid employed is then added. If a precipitate appear on thus diluting, it will in all probability consist of mucic acid, which, after cooling, should be filtered off and purified by dissolving in dilute alkali and reprecipitating by the addition of a slight excess of mineral acid. The filtrate from the mucic acid, or the clear solution if no precipitate has appeared, is then exactly neutralised in the warm by the cautious addition of potassium carbonate, and the resulting dark-coloured solution again acidified with acetic acid and evaporated to a syrup. After the further addition of a few drops of acetic acid and cooling, acid potassium saccharate separates out in those cases where saccharic acid is formed. This should be dried on a porous tile and recrystallised from a small quantity of water in order to remove any oxalic acid. The silver salt, which may be prepared by neutralising the acid salt with ammonia, boiling to remove any excess, adding silver nitrate solution, and filtering off and drying the precipitate at 110°, should be ignited (see p. 315) in order to determine the equivalent of the acid.

Di- and **Tri-saccharides** behave like glucosides in that when warmed with dilute mineral acids they are hydrolysed with formation of monosaccharides. They vary, however, in their stability towards oxidising agents and phenylhydrazine. Thus, sucrose does not reduce Fehling's solution on boiling, and forms no compound when warmed with aqueous phenylhydrazine acetate; maltose and lactose, on the other hand, resemble the monosaccharides in their behaviour towards both of these reagents; with the difference, however, that the osazones formed do not separate from solution until the reaction mixture is allowed to cool. Di- and tri-saccharides resemble the monosaccharides in their ready solubility in water.

Polysaccharides are far less soluble in cold water than the sugars, but solutions of some of them can be obtained on boiling with water. Such solutions are, however, never entirely clear. On hydrolysis by boiling with dilute mineral acids they yield monosaccharides. They do not react with Fehling's solution nor with phenylhydrazine. On treatment with a cold solution of iodine in aqueous potassium iodide characteristic colours are produced, which are discharged on heating but reappear on cooling. Cellulose, on prolonged warming with concentrated hydrochloric acid, may be partially or entirely hydrolysed, with formation of dextrose, It is, however, insoluble in pure water, and develops no colour with iodine solution. Much information as to the nature and source of the cellulose is afforded by microscopical examination of the fibres.

CHAPTER III

SEPARATION OF MIXTURES OF ORGANIC COMPOUNDS

WHEN it is required to identify the constituents of a mixture of organic substances, it will in all cases be necessary to separate each component from the mixture and to isolate it in a pure state before proceeding with the examination. To identify the constituents of a mixture without separating them is at best an extremely difficult, and in most cases an almost impracticable, feat.

Owing to the great number of possibilities, no definite rule for procedure can be laid down; but in the first instance it is advisable to ascertain what elements are present, whether an acid or an alkaline reaction is given, and whether any residue remains after ignition.

Should the mixture appear to contain some volatile liquid, it may be heated on the water-bath in a distilling flask attached to a condenser until no more of the liquid passes over. The distillate should be redistilled, employing a thermometer, in order to ascertain whether it is homogeneous. Should this not be the case, it must be further investigated with a view to separation by chemical methods. Fractional distillation in the ordinary way is generally not well adapted to the separation of mixtures available in only small amounts.

The residue in the flask may then be treated with an excess of dry ether, any insoluble portion being filtered off and washed with the same solvent, the washings being added to the filtrate. By this means the majority of salts, carbohydrates and other polyhydroxylic compounds, sulphonic acids, and similar substances insoluble in ether, may be separated from the main portion. Such a residue is to be examined independently, extraction with cold methyl alcohol being carried out as a preliminary step towards further separation.

Should the mixture have been found to contain nitrogen the ethereal solution is shaken in a separating-funnel with dilute sulphuric acid. In the absence of nitrogen this operation may be omitted. By this means basic substances are removed from the mixture on separating the aqueous and ethereal layers. The bases may be recovered by rendering the aqueous solution alkaline and again extracting with ether.

The ethereal solution after this treatment should be washed with a small quantity of water—the washings being discarded—and shaken with dilute caustic soda solution. This has the effect of removing all compounds of an acidic character. The treatment of the aqueous portion will be discussed below.

The ether now contains only neutral substances. From these any aldehydic and many ketonic compounds can be removed by shaking with a concentrated solution of sodium bisulphite. The aldehydes and ketones can be recovered from the resulting precipitate or aqueous solution by acidification with dilute sulphuric acid followed by distillation, extraction, or filtration.

The alkaline solution containing the acidic substances should be saturated with carbon dioxide and extracted with ether. By this procedure all phenolic compounds which contain no carboxyl or nitro groups, oximes, and similar weak acids are liberated and pass into the ether. On adding dilute sulphuric acid until evolution of carbon dioxide ceases, carboxylic acids and nitrophenols are liberated, and can be isolated by extraction, filtration, or distillation.

At this stage all ethereal solutions should be evaporated, the ether—if only for the sake of safety from conflagrations—being efficiently condensed and thus recovered. All residues

should be tested afresh for constituent elements, and tests
for homogeneity applied.

The results of the above operations are briefly summarised
in the following scheme :—

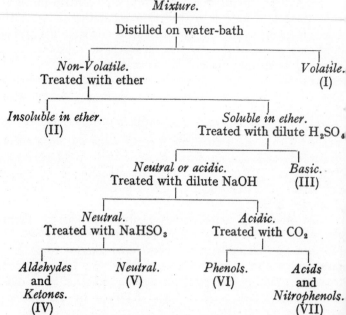

Mixture.

Distilled on water-bath

Non-Volatile.
Treated with ether

Volatile.
(I)

Insoluble in ether.
(II)

Soluble in ether.
Treated with dilute H_2SO_4

Neutral or acidic.
Treated with dilute NaOH

Basic.
(III)

Neutral.
Treated with $NaHSO_3$

Acidic.
Treated with CO_2

Aldehydes
and
Ketones.
(IV)

Neutral.
(V)

Phenols.
(VI)

Acids
and
Nitrophenols.
(VII)

The various fractions, denominated I, II, &c., may contain
the following types of compound :—

I. Hydrocarbons, ethers, alcohols, ketones, esters, aliphatic
   halogen compounds ; and conceivably aldehydes,
   acetals, nitriles, aliphatic amines, mercaptans, sulphides, and alkyl nitrates and nitrites whose boiling-
   points lie below 100°.

II. Metallic salts, salts of organic bases with mineral acids,
    carbohydrates and other polyhydroxylic compounds,
    amino acids, sulphonic acids of all types.

III. Aliphatic and aromatic primary, secondary, and
     tertiary amino compounds ; possibly some amides.

IV. Aldehydic and ketonic compounds, containing no groups which would have placed them in another fraction.

V. Hydrocarbons, ethers, alcohols, higher ketones, esters, and aliphatic or aromatic halogen compounds, not included in other fractions. Also nitriles; nitro-hydrocarbons, -ethers, -alcohols; simple azoxy, azo hydrazo compounds; sulphides, disulphides, sulph-oxides, sulphones, sulphonamides and a few non-reactive anhydrides, ketones, and esters of mineral acids.

VI. Simple and substituted phenols, keto-enolic substances, mercaptans, some thioamides.

VII. Carboxylic acids; nitrophenols in which the nitro groups are present in either *ortho* or *para* position.

Any obvious decompositions produced by the action of water on the mixture, such as in the case of acid halides, will have been observed in the preliminary investigation of the mixture. Much information as to the nature of the constituents may be obtained by the mere performance of the above separations.

Steam distillation from acid and from alkaline solutions, while constituting an excellent means of separation in place of extraction with ether, has not been recommended in the above scheme on account of the fact that many substances, such as esters or amides, are decomposed by hot acid or alkaline aqueous solutions, but preserve their identity when treated in ethereal solution with these reagents in the cold.

For the further separation of the individual substances contained in the different fractions no definite scheme can be drawn up, but a few general suggestions may be offered.

Separation can in many cases be effected by treatment of the fraction with different liquids which exert selective solvent effects. Water, ethyl alcohol, ligroin, benzene acetone, chloroform, or glacial or dilute acetic acid may be employed for this purpose. This method may also be applied by dissolving the mixture in one solvent and precipitating one of the components by the addition of another liquid in which it is insoluble.

Distillation with steam, when feasible, occasionally serves for the separation of substances—even of isomers—of differing volatility. Neutral, basic, and acidic substances which volatilise with steam may be separated very cleanly by alternate distillation from acid and alkaline solutions. This method should however be applied with caution, owing to possibilities of hydrolysis.

Finally, fractional crystallisation and fractional distillation under atmospheric or reduced pressure may be employed when all other methods have failed. Both of these operations are, however, often extremely tedious, and should be regarded only as a last resort. The criterion of purity in the case of fractional distillation is the isolation of a fraction of constant boiling-point, while solid substances must be recrystallised until no rise in melting-point is observable on further recrystallisation of any fraction.

For the ultimate identification of solids it is frequently of great value to prepare an intimate mixture of small quantities of the substance under examination and of a specimen from another source of the compound with which it is suspected to be identical. Should such a mixture melt at the same temperature as its components, except in a comparatively small number of cases, such as for example some d- and l- forms of optically active compounds, or where the compound decomposes at or slightly above its melting point, there is every likelihood that the two compounds are identical.

CHAPTER IV

CLASSIFIED TABLES OF THE COMMONER ORGANIC COMPOUNDS

In the following tables compounds are classified according to the radicles present in them, the individuals of each class being arranged, so far as is convenient, in progressive order of boiling-points in the case of liquids, and melting-points in the case of solids. It will be noted that the order in which the various classes appear is dependent upon the elements present, and that, as a general rule, these classes are further arranged in increasing order of oxygenation.

Thus hydrocarbons appear at the outset, followed by ethers, alcohols, phenols, aldehydes, ketones, and carboxylic acids. The lists of compounds in which only carbon and hydrogen can be detected are followed by those of organic halogen compounds, then by derivatives of nitrogen, succeeded by organic compounds containing sulphur.

At the conclusion of the tables will be found a brief account of the general methods of qualitative examination of alkaloids, together with a list of the common alkaloids in which the general properties and reactions of each are detailed. In addition to this, an abridgment of Rota's scheme for the investigation of dyes is appended. Owing to the complicated nature of this class of substances, as well as to the paucity of typical reactions which are not at once evident from the formulæ of the majority of dyes, no detailed list of dyes is given.

The following abreviations are employed throughout the tables :—

B.P.	Boiling-point.	*tert.*-	Tertiary.
M.P.	Melting-point.	*o*-	Ortho.
Subl.	Sublimes.	*m*-	Meta.
d.	*After a figure :* Boils or melts with decomposition at the specified temperature.	*p*-	Para.
		s.	Symmetrical.
		as.	Asymmetrical.
		d-	Dextro-.
	Before a figure : Decomposes at or near the specified temperature.	*l*-	Levo-.
		dl-	Racemic.
		Soln.	Solution.
		ppte.	Precipitate.
D.	Specific gravity of liquid at specified temperature, referred to water at 4°.	Sol.	Soluble.
		Insol.	Insoluble.
		Deriv.	Derivative.
		Compd	Compound.
$[a]_D^t$	Specific rotation for sodium D light at temperature t°.	Conc.	Concentrated.
		Dil.	Dilute.
		Mol.	Molecular proportion.
n-	Normal.		
sec.-	Secondary.	Alc.	Alcohol.

HYDROCARBONS

LIQUID

B.P.

21°   *iso*Propylethylene $(CH_3)_2CH\cdot CH:CH_2$
D. 0·648 (0°). Unsaturated. Dibromide decomposes on boiling under atm. press.; B.P. 65°/10 mm. or 75°/20 mm. Insol. in 75–80% H_2SO_4 at 0°.

30°   *iso*Pentane $(CH_3)_2CH\cdot CH_2\cdot CH_3$
D. 0·639 (0°).

36°   *n*-Pentane $CH_3(CH_2)_3CH_3$
D. 0·647 (0°).

38°   Trimethylethylene (Amylene) $(CH_3)_2C:CH\cdot CH_3$
D. 0·678 (0°). Unsaturated. Dibromide M.P. 7°; B.P. 173°d., 59°/10 mm., 65°/16 mm. Sol. in 75–80% H_2SO_4 at 0°; soln yields *tert.*-amyl alc. B.P. 102° on dilution and distillation. Technical ' Amylene ' is usually a mixture boiling between 25° and 40°.

68°   *n*-Hexane $CH_3(CH_2)_4CH_3$
D. 0·668 (11°).

B.P.
80°   *cyclo*Hexane $CH_2 \cdot CH_2 \cdot CH_2$

$CH_2 \cdot CH_2 \cdot CH_2$

M.P. 4°. D. 0·790 (20°). Unattacked by cold fuming HNO_3; on boiling, adipic acid M.P. 149° is
formed.

80°   Benzene C_6H_6
M.P. 5°. D. 0·874 (20°). On nitration yields nitrobenzene B.P. 209° and *m*-dinitrobenzene M.P. 90°.
On bromination yields bromobenzene B.P. 157° and
p-dibromobenzene M.P. 89°. With $ClSO_3H$ yields
benzenesulphonyl chloride M.P. 14°, B.P. 251°d. and
diphenyl sulphone M.P. 128°. Sulphonated slowly on
boiling with conc. H_2SO_4. Picrate M.P. 84°.

83°   *cyclo*Hexene   CH:CH—CH_2

$CH_2 \cdot CH_2 \cdot CH_2$

D. 0·809 (0°). Unsaturated. On oxidation by HNO_3
yields adipic acid M.P. 149°. Dibromide B.P. 101°/13
mm., 116°/29 mm. Dichloride B.P. 188°.

110°   Toluene $C_6H_5 \cdot CH_3$
D. 0·871 (13°). On oxidation yields benzoic acid M.P.
121°. 2:4-Dinitro deriv. M.P. 70°. 2:4:6-Trinitro
deriv. M.P. 82°. Sulphonated rapidly on warming
with conc. H_2SO_4. *p*-Sulphonyl chloride M.P. 69°.
p-Sulphonamide M.P. 137°.

136°   Ethylbenzene $C_6H_5 \cdot C_2H_5$
D. 0·876 (10°). On oxidation yields benzoic acid
M.P. 121°. Readily sulphonated on warming with
conc. H_2SO_4. With Br_2 (2 mols.) at 130° yields styrene
dibromide M.P. 73°. 2:4:6-Trinitro deriv. M.P. 37°.
p-Sulphochloride M.P. 12°. *p*-Sulphonamide M.P.
109°.

137°   *p*-Xylene $C_6H_4(CH_3)_2$ (1:4)
M.P. 15°. D. 0·866 (14°). On oxidation yields
terephthalic acid (*q.v.*). Very slowly sulphonated by
warm conc. H_2SO_4. With Br_2 (2 mols.) at 130° yields
p-xylylene bromide M.P. 144°. With fuming HNO_3
at 0° yields 2-nitro deriv. B.P. 239°. On warming with
conc. HNO_3 in conc. H_2SO_4 yields 2:3:6-trinitro deriv.
M.P. 137°. Sulphochloride M.P. 24°. Sulphonamide
M.P. 147°.

139°   *m*-Xylene $C_6H_4(CH_3)_2$ (1:3)
D. 0·878 (4°). On oxidation yields *iso*phthalic acid

B.P.

($q.v.$). Very readily sulphonated by cold conc. H_2SO_4. With Br_2 (2 mols.) at 130° yields *m*-xylylene bromide M.P. 76°. With conc. HNO_3 in conc. H_2SO_4 at 0° yields 2:4-dinitro deriv. M.P. 83°; on warming yields 2:4:6-trinitro deriv. M.P. 182°. Sulphochloride is an oil. Sulphonamide M.P. 137°.

142°   *o*-Xylene $C_6H_4(CH_3)_2$ (1:2)

D. 0·890 (4°). On oxidation yields phthalic acid M.P. 195°. Very readily sulphonated by cold conc. H_2SO_4. With Br_2 (2 mols.) at 130° yields *o*-xylylene bromide M.P. 93°. Dinitro deriv. MP. 71°. Trinitro deriv. M.P. 178°. Sulphochloride M.P. 51°. Sulphonamide M.P. 144°.

146°   Styrene $C_6H_5 \cdot CH{:}CH_2$

D. 0·925 (0°). Unsaturated. Polymerises with a drop of conc. H_2SO_4 to glassy mass. On oxidation by acid $KMnO_4$ yields benzaldehyde B.P. 179°; by alkaline $KMnO_4$ or chromic acid yields benzoic acid M.P. 121°. Dibromide M.P. 73°.

152°   Cumene $C_6H_5 \cdot CH(CH_3)_2$

D. 0·875 (4°). On oxidation yields benzoic acid, M.P. 121°. Readily sulphonated. 2:4:6-Trinitro deriv. M.P. 109°. Sulphonamide M.P. 107°.

155°   Pinene $C_{10}H_{16}$

D. 0·858 (20°). Unsaturated. Optically active; *d.* or *l.* Dibromide M.P. 164°. Hydrochloride M.P. 125°.

158°   Propylbenzene $C_6H_5 \cdot CH_2 \cdot CH_2 \cdot CH_3$

D. 0·861 (21°). On oxidation yields benzoic acid M.P. 121°. *p*-Bromo deriv. B.P. 220°.

164°   Mesitylene $C_6H_3(CH_3)_3$ (1:3:5)

D. 0·877 (4°). On oxidation yields trimesic acid (M.P. about 300°, subl. 200°; methyl ester M.P. 143°; ethyl ester M.P. 133°). Very readily sulphonated; sulphonic acid (crysts. from sulphonation mixture) regenerates mesitylene on boiling with conc. HCl. On warming with 25% HNO_3 yields nitro deriv. M.P. 41°, B.P. 255°. With fuming HNO_3 in the cold yields dinitro deriv. M.P. 86°. With conc. HNO_3 in conc. H_2SO_4 in the cold yields trinitro deriv. M.P. 230°. Sulphochloride M.P. 57°. Sulphonamide M.P. 141°.

168°   Pseudocumene $C_6H_3(CH_3)_3$ (1:2:4)

D. 0·889 (4°). Readily sulphonated on warming with

B.P.

an equal vol. of conc. H_2SO_4; sulphonic acid crystallizes on slightly diluting. With fuming HNO_3 at 0° yields 5-nitro deriv. M.P. 71°. On warming with conc. HNO_3 in conc. H_2SO_4 yields 3:5:6-trinitro deriv. M.P. 185°. Sulphochloride M.P. 61°. Sulphonamide M.P. 181°.

175° Cymene $CH_3 \cdot C_6H_4 \cdot CH(CH_3)_2$ (1:4)

D. 0·872 (0°). Sulphonated slowly by warm conc. H_2SO_4. On oxidation yields terephthalic acid (q.v.). Oxidised by conc. HNO_3 to p-tolyl methyl ketone B.P. 224°. Nitration satisfactory only below 15"; 2-nitro deriv. B.P. 264°. Bromination in presence of Fe in cold yields 2-bromo deriv. B.P. 234°. Sulphonamide M.P. 115°.

176° Limonene $C_{10}H_{16}$

D. 0·846 (20°). Unsaturated. Optically active, $[a]_D$ = + 107° or − 105°. Tetrabromide M.P. 104°. Dihydrochloride M.P. 50°.

176° Sylvestrene $C_{10}H_{16}$

D. 0·851 (16°). Unsaturated. Optically active, $[a]_D$ = + 66°. Tetrabromide M.P. 135°. Dihydrochloride M.P. 72°.

181° Dipentene $C_{10}H_{16}$

D. 0·850 (15°). Optically inactive. Unsaturated. Tetrabromide M.P. 124°. Dihydrochloride M.P. 50°.

182° Indene

$$C_6H_4 \underset{CH_2}{\overset{CH}{\diagdown}}\hspace{-1.2em}\diagup CH$$

M.P.−2°. D. 0·997 (15°). Gradually polymerises on heating. Yields Na deriv. on heating to 140° with sodium. Oxidised by HNO_3 to phthalic acid M.P. 195°. With alc. KOH and benzaldehyde in cold yields a product M.P. 135°. Picrate M.P. 98° (v. explosive).

192° Decahydronaphthalene

$$\begin{array}{ccc} CH_2 \cdot CH_2 \cdot CH \cdot CH_2 \cdot CH_2 \\ | \qquad\quad | \qquad\quad | \\ CH_2 \cdot CH_2 \cdot CH \cdot CH_2 \cdot CH_2 \end{array}$$

D. 0·894 (20°). No rise in temp. with conc. H_2SO_4 + HNO_3. On boiling with 33% HNO_3 yields a nitro deriv. (insol. in alc. KOH) B.P. 96°/2 mm. and a dinitro deriv. M.P. 164° d. The mononitro deriv. with Zn dust + acetic acid yields an amine B.P. 98°/15 mm. (benzoyl deriv. M.P. 148°).

B.P.
206°　Tetrahydronaphthalene

$$C_6H_4 \begin{cases} CH_2 \cdot CH_2 \\ \quad | \\ CH_2 \cdot CH_2 \end{cases}$$

D. 0·971 (20°). On oxidation yields phthalic acid
M.P. 195°. With (2 mols.) bromine at 100° yields a
dibromo deriv. M.P. 70°, which with alc. KOH yields
naphthalene M.P. 80°. On nitration at 0° with (1 mol.)
HNO$_3$ in conc. H$_2$SO$_4$ yields mixture of 1-nitro deriv.
M.P. 34°, B.P. 157°/13 mm. and 2-nitro deriv. M.P.
31°, B.P. 169°/13 mm.

240°　a-Methylnaphthalene　　$C_{10}H_7 \cdot CH_3$ (1)
D. 1·00 (19°). On oxidation by long boiling with dil.
HNO$_3$ yields a-naphthoic acid M.P. 160°. Nitro
deriv. B.P. 194°/27 mm. Picrate M.P. 141°.

SOLID

M.P.
15°　p-Xylene B.P. 137°. See Hydrocarbons (Liquid)

26°　Diphenylmethane　　$(C_6H_5)_2CH_2$
B.P. 261°. Faint orange-like odour. Oxidised by
chromic acid to benzophenone M.P. 48°. Nitration
with conc. HNO$_3$ + H$_2$SO$_4$ yields tetranitro deriv.
M.P. 172°.

32°　β-Methylnaphthalene　　$C_{10}H_7 \cdot CH_3$ (2)
B.P. 240°. Oxidised by conc. HNO$_3$ to β-naphthoic
acid M.P. 182°. Nitro deriv. M.P. 81°. Picrate
M.P. 115°.

51°　l-Camphene　　$C_{10}H_{16}$
B.P. 160°. Unsaturated. Optically active. Dibromide M.P. 89°. Hydrochloride M.P. 149°.

52°　Dibenzyl　　$(C_6H_5 \cdot CH_2)_2$
B.P. 284°. Easily oxidised to benzoic acid M.P. 121°.
On boiling with KClO$_3$ in HCl yields stilbene M.P.
125°. With cold fuming HNO$_3$ yields dinitro deriv.
M.P. 180°.

70°　Diphenyl　　$(C_6H_5)_2$
B.P. 254°. Oxidised by chromic acid in glacial acetic
acid to benzoic acid M.P. 121°. With bromine in
presence of Fe yields pp′-dibromo deriv. M.P. 169°.
On warming with fuming HNO$_3$ yields pp′-dinitro
deriv. M.P. 233°.

80°　Naphthalene　　$C_{10}H_8$
B.P. 218°. Characteristic odour. Green colour de-

veloped on adding dry $AlCl_3$ to soln in $CHCl_3$. Oxidised to phthalic acid M.P. 195°. Picrate M.P. 149°. With *m*-dinitrobenzene in C_6H_6 (not alc.) forms a compd M.P. 52°. Compd with 2:4-dinitrochlorobenzene M.P. 78°. Compd with 2:4:6-trinitrotoluene M.P. 97°.

92° Triphenylmethane $(C_6H_5)_3CH$

B.P. about 359°. Nitration with fuming HNO_3 in cold yields trinitro deriv. M.P. 206°. Reduction of this yields triamino deriv. M.P. 148°, which on oxidation with PbO_2 gives intense red colour of rosaniline. With Br_2 at 130° yields triphenylbromomethane M.P. 152°. Forms compd with benzene M.P. 78°.

95° Acenaphthene

$$C_{10}H_6 \begin{cases} CH_2 \ (1) \\ | \\ CH_2 \ (8) \end{cases}$$

B.P. 277°. Oxidised by chromic acid to naphthalic acid (d. 180° giving anhydride M.P. 266°) and acenaphthenequinone M.P. 261°. Picrate M.P. 161°. Compd with 2:4-dinitrotoluene M.P. 60°. Compd with 2:4:6-trinitrotoluene M.P. 109°.

98° Retene (8-Methyl-2-*iso*propylphenanthrene)

B.P. 390°. Resists oxidation by $KMnO_4$ in water. With $K_2Cr_2O_7 + H_2SO_4$ yields retenequinone M.P. 197°. With Br_2 at 90–100° yields dibromo deriv. M.P. 180°. Forms unstable picrate M.P. 124°.

100° Phenanthrene

$$\begin{array}{c} C_6H_4 \cdot C_6H_4 \\ | \quad\quad | \\ CH = CH \end{array}$$

B.P. 340°. Oxidised to phenanthrenequinone M.P. 202° and diphenic acid M.P. 229°. Picrate M.P. 143°. Compd with 2:4-dinitrochlorobenzene M.P. 44°. Compd with 2:4:6-trinitrotoluene M.P. 87°.

113° Fluorene

$$\begin{array}{c} C_6H_4 \\ | \quad\quad \diagdown CH_2 \\ C_6H_4 \diagup \end{array}$$

B.P. 295°. Dissolves in conc. H_2SO_4 on warming with blue colour. Oxidation with chromic acid in acetic acid yields fluorenone M.P. 84°, with alkaline $KMnO_4$ yields phthalic acid M.P. 195°. Forms unstable picrate M.P. 79° in ethereal soln.

125° Stilbene $C_6H_5 \cdot CH:CH \cdot C_6H_5$

B.P. 306°. Unsaturated, but decolorises bromine

only on warming. Oxidised by acid $KMnO_4$ to benzaldehyde B.P. 179°. Dibromide M.P. 237°. Compd with picryl chloride M.P. 70°.

216°   Anthracene $C_6H_4{\Large\diagdown}{\begin{matrix}CH\\|\\CH\end{matrix}}{\Large\diagup}C_6H_4$

B.P. 351°. Oxidised by chromic acid in acetic acid to anthraquinone M.P. 273°. With Br_2 in CCl_4 yields dibromo deriv. M.P. 221°. Picrate M.P. 138°.

ALIPHATIC ETHERS

LIQUID

B.P

35°   Ethyl Ether $(C_2H_5)_2O$
D. 0·719 (15°). Characteristic odour. Sol. in 11 vols. of cold water. Sol. unchanged in cold conc. H_2SO_4; insol. in 50% H_2SO_4.

42°   Methylal. See Aldehydes and Acetals.

64°   Dimethylacetal. See Aldehydes and Acetals.

89°   Ethylal. See Aldehydes and Acetals.

104°   Acetal. See Aldehydes and Acetals.

124°   Paraldehyde. See Aldehydes and Acetals.

140°   *n*-Butyl Ether $(C_4H_9)_2O$
D. 0·784 (0°).

169°   Benzyl Methyl Ether $C_6H_5 \cdot CH_2 \cdot OCH_3$
D. 0·981 (4°). Insol. in water. On boiling with 48% HBr yields benzyl bromide B.P. 198° and methyl bromide B.P. 4°. On warming with conc. H_2SO_4 and glacial acetic acid yields benzyl acetate B.P. 206°. Bromine reacts in the cold yielding benzaldehyde B.P. 179°, benzyl bromide, benzoyl bromide and other products.

170°   *iso*Amyl Ether $[(CH_3)_2CH \cdot CH_2 \cdot CH_2]_2O$
D. 0·781 (15°).

176°   Cineole $C_{10}H_{18}O$
D. 0·927 (20°). Optically inactive. Possesses weak basic properties; forms a sparingly soluble ferro-cyanide on shaking with a conc. soln. of $K_4Fe(CN)_6$ in 7% HCl. On shaking with a saturated iodine-Kl soln, crystals of iodine addition-product separate. Soln. in an equal vol. of petroleum ether yields with dry HCl a crystalline hydrochloride, from which

cineole is regenerated with water. With dry HCl at
40–50° yields dipentene dihydrochloride M.P. 50°.

185°   Benzyl Ethyl Ether $C_6H_5 \cdot CH_2 \cdot OC_2H_5$
Insol. in water. On boiling with 48% HBr yields
benzyl bromide. B.P. 198° and ethyl bromide B.P.
38°. Reacts with bromine like benzyl methyl ether
(q.v.). Yields benzyl acetete B.P. 206° on warming
with conc. H_2SO_4 and glacial acetic acid.

294°   Apiole M.P. 30°. See Phenolic Ethers (solid).

295°   Benzyl Ether $(C_6H_5 \cdot CH_2)_2O$
D. 1·036 (16°). On boiling with 48% HBr yields
benzyl bromide B.P. 198°. With acetic acid + conc.
H_2SO_4 yields benzyl acetate B.P. 206°.

PHENOLIC ETHERS

LIQUID

154°   Anisole $C_6H_5 \cdot OCH_3$
D. 0·988 (21°). On boiling with 48% HBr yields
phenol M.P. 42°, B.P. 181°, and methyl bromide B.P.
4°. With conc. $HNO_3 + H_2SO_4$ in cold yield
dinitroanisole M.P. 86°.

171°   o-Cresyl methyl Ether $CH_3 \cdot C_6H_4 \cdot OCH_3$ (1:2)
D. 0·996 (0°). On boiling with 48% HBr yields o-
cresol M.P. 31°, B.P. 180°, and methyl bromide B.P.
4°. Oxidation by alkaline $KMnO_4$ yields methylsalicylic acid M.P. 98°.

172°   Phenetole $C_6H_5 \cdot OC_2H_5$
D. 0·979 (4°). On boiling with 48% HBr yields
phenol M.P. 42°, B.P. 181°, and ethyl bromide B.P. 38°.
On gentle nitration yields p-nitrophenetole M.P. 58°.

176°   p-Cresyl Methyl Ether $(CH_3)C_6H_4 \cdot OCH_3$ (1:4)
D. 0·985 (0°). On boiling with 48% HBr yields
p-cresol M.P. 35°, B.P. 201°. Oxidised by $K_2Cr_2O_7 +$
H_2SO_4 to anisic acid M.P. 184°.

177°   m-Cresyl Methyl Ether $(CH_3)C_6H_4 \cdot OCH_3$ (1:3)
D. 0·985 (4°). On boiling with 48% HBr yields
m-cresol B.P. 202°. With fuming HNO_3 yields
trinitro deriv. M.P. 91°. Oxidised by $KMnO_4$ to
m-methoxybenzoic acid, M.P. 106°.

207°   Veratrole M.P. 15°. See Phenolic Ethers (Solid).

214°   Resorcinol Dimethyl Ether $C_6H_4(OCH_3)_2$ (1:3)
D. 1·080 (0°). On boiling with 48% HBr yields

B.P.

resorcinol M.P. 118°. On nitration with HNO_3 + H_2SO_4 yields trinitro deriv. M.P. 124°. With (2 mols.) bromine yields a dibromo deriv. M.P. 141°.

216°   Thymol Methyl Ether $(CH_3)_2CH \cdot C_6H_3(CH_3) \cdot OCH_3$
(1:4:2)
D. 0·954 (0°). On boiling with 48 % HBr yields thymol M.P. 50°. Nitration in conc. H_2SO_4 with fuming HNO_3 yields a trinitro deriv. M.P. 92°.

232°   Safrole $CH_2:CH \cdot CH_2 \cdot C_6H_3(O_2CH_2)$ (1:3:4)
D. 1·114 (0°). Unsaturated. With excess of bromine yields a pentabromo deriv. M.P. 169°. Oxidised by alkaline $KMnO_4$ to piperonylic acid M.P. 228°.

232°   Anethole M.P. 21°. See Phenolic Ethers (Solid).

243°   Resorcinol Monomethyl Ether. See Phenols (Liquid).

244°   Eugenol Methyl Ether $CH_2:CH \cdot CH_2 \cdot C_6H_3(OCH_3)_2$
(1:3:4)
Unsaturated. Dibromide M.P. 77°. Oxidised by $K_2Cr_2O_7$ in glacial acetic acid to veratric acid M.P. 180°.

246°   *iso*Safrole $CH_3 \cdot CH:CH \cdot C_6H_3(O_2CH_2)$ (1:3:4)
D. 1·125 (14°). Unsaturated. With (5 parts) bromine in CS_2 yields a tribromo deriv. M.P. 109°. Oxidised by acid $KMnO_4$ to piperonal M.P. 37°, B.P. 263°, by alkaline $KMnO_4$ to piperonylic acid M.P. 228°.

247°   Eugenol. See Phenols (Liquid).

252°   Phenyl Ether M.P. 28°. See Phenolic Ethers (Solid).

263°   α-Naphthyl Methyl Ether. $C_{10}H_7 \cdot OCH_3$ (1).
D. 1·096 (14°). On boiling with 48 % HBr yields α-naphthol M.P. 94° and methyl bromide B.P. 4°.

267°   *iso*Eugenol. See Phenols (Liquid).

276°   α-Naphthyl Ethyl Ether $C_{10}H_7 \cdot OC_2H_5$ (1)
D. 1·071 (4°). On boiling with 48 % HBr yields α-naphthol M.P. 94° and ethyl bromide B.P. 38°.

282°   β-Naphthyl Ethyl Ether M.P. 37°. See Phenolic Ethers (Solid).

294°   Apiole M.P. 30°. See Phenolic Ethers (Solid).

SOLID

M.P.
15°   Veratrole $C_6H_4(OCH_3)_2$ (1:2)
B.P. 207°. On boiling with 48 % HBr yields catechol M.P. 104°. With bromine yields dibromo deriv.

M.P. 91°. Nitration with fuming HNO_3 yields nitro deriv. M.P. 95°. Picrate M.P. 56°.

21° Anethole $CH_3 \cdot CH:CH \cdot C_6H_4 \cdot OCH_3$ (1:4)
B.P. 232°. Unsaturated. Oxidation with dil. HNO_3 yields anisaldehyde B.P. 248°, with chromic acid yields anisic acid M.P. 184°, and with $KMnO_4$ yields p-methoxyphenylglyoxylic acid M.P. 132°.

28° Phenyl Ether $(C_6H_5)_2O$
B.P. 252°. Not readily hydrolysed. Nitration with fuming HNO_3 yields dinitro deriv. M.P. 135°.

30° Apiole $CH_2:CH \cdot CH_2 \cdot C_6H(O_2CH_2)(OCH_3)_2$ (1:3:4:2:5)
B.P. 294°. D. 1·015. Dissolves in conc. H_2SO_4 with blood-red colour. On oxidation with chromic acid in acetic acid yields apiolaldehyde M.P. 102°. With alk. $KMnO_4$ yields apiolic acid M.P. 175° and a neutral subst. M.P. 122°.

31° Guaiacol. See Phenols (Solid).

37° β-Naphthyl Ethyl Ether $C_{10}H_7 \cdot OC_2H_5$ (2)
B.P. 282°. On boiling with 48 % HBr yields β-naphthol M.P. 122° and ethyl bromide B.P. 38°.

53° Hydroquinone Monomethyl Ether. See Phenols (Solid)

55° Hydroquinone Dimethyl Ether. $C_6H_4(OCH_3)_2$ (1:4)
B.P. 212°. Forms yellow soln in conc. H_2SO_4. On boiling with 48 % HBr yields hydroquinone M.P. 169° and methyl bromide B.P. 4°. With bromine in boiling glacial acetic acid yields dibromo deriv. M.P. 142°.

72° β-Naphthyl Methyl Ether $C_{10}H_7 \cdot OCH_3$ (2)
B.P. 274°. On boiling with 48 % HBr yields β-naphthol M.P. 122° and methyl bromide B.P. 4°.

80° Vanillin. See Aldehydes and Acetals.

ALCOHOLS

LIQUID

B.P.
65° Methyl Alcohol CH_3OH
D. 0·796 (20°). Miscible with water. Oxidised to formaldehyde (characteristic odour) by a hot Cu wire coated with oxide. With $K_2Cr_2O_7 + H_2SO_4$ in cold dil. soln yields formaldehyde (mixture on warming with orcinol gives a ppte. which dissolves in dil. NaOH with green fluorescence). On boiling with conc. HI yields iodide B.P. 43°. Acetate B.P. 57°. Benzoate

B.P. 198°. Carbanilate M.P. 47°. α-Naphthyl-carbamate M.P. 124°. Acid phthalate M.P. 82°. p-Nitrobenzyl phthalate M.P. 105°. 3:5-Dinitro-benzoate M.P. 107°.

78° Ethyl Alcohol   C₂H₅OH

D. 0·789 (20°). Miscible with water. Oxidised by hot dil. K₂Cr₂O₇ + H₂SO₄ to acetaldehyde B.P. 21°; by alkaline KMnO₄ to acetic acid B.P. 118°. With iodine and dil. NaOH yields iodoform M.P. 119°. On boiling with conc. HI yields iodide B.P. 72°. Bromide B.P. 38°. Acetate B.P. 77°. Benzoate B.P. 213°. Carbanilate M.P. 52°. α-Naphthylcarbamate M.P. 79°. Acid phthalate is an oil. p-Nitrobenzyl phthal-ate M.P. 80°. 3·5-Dinitrobenzoate M.P. 92°.

83° tert-Butyl Alcohol M.P. 25°. See Alcohols (Solid).

83° isoPropyl Alcohol   (CH₃)₂CH·OH

D. 0·789 (20°). Miscible with water. Oxidised by hot dil. K₂Cr₂O₇ + H₂SO₄ to acetone B.P. 56°. With iodine + Na₂CO₃ soln. in cold yields iodoform M.P. 119°. On warming with conc. HCl yields chloride B.P. 36°. Bromide B.P. 60°. Iodide B.P. 89°. Acetate B.P. 91°. Benzoate B.P. 218°. Carbanilate M.P. 90°. α-Naphthylcarbamate M.P. 78°. p-Nitro-benzyl phthalate M.P. 74°.

97° n-Propyl Alcohol   CH₃·CH₂·CH₂OH

D. 0·804 (20°). Miscible with water. Oxidised by hot dil. K₂Cr₂O₇ + H₂SO₄ to propionaldehyde B.P. 49°; by alkaline KMnO₄ to propionic acid B.P. 140°. On boiling with 48 % HBr yields bromide B.P. 71°. Iodide B.P. 102°. Acetate B.P. 101°. Benzoate B.P. 230°. Carbanilate M.P. 58°. α-Naphthyl-carbamate M.P. 105°. p-Nitrobenzyl phthalate M.P. 53°.

97° Allyl Alcohol   CH₂:CH·CH₂OH

D. 0·871 (0°). Miscible with water. Irritating odour. Unsaturated. Dibromide B.P. 212°. Oxidised by dil. K₂Cr₂O₇ + H₂SO₄ to acrolein B.P. 52° (very irritating odour). On boiling with 48 % HBr yields bromide B.P. 70°. Iodide B.P. 101°. Acetate B.P. 104°. Benzoate B.P. 230°. α-Naphthylcarbamate M.P. 109°. p-Nitrobenzyl phthalate M.P. 61°.

99° sec-Butyl Alcohol   CH₃·CH(OH)C₂H₅

D. 0·827 (0°). Sol. in 6 vols of cold water. Oxidised by hot dil. K₂Cr₂O₇ + H₂SO₄ to methyl ethyl ketone

B.P. 80°. With iodine + Na_2CO_3 soln in cold yields iodoform M.P. 119°. On boiling with conc. HCl yields chloride B.P. 67°. Bromide B.P. 91°. Iodide B.P. 118°. Acetate B.P. 112°. Benzoate B.P. 235°. a-Naphthylcarbamate M.P. 97°.

102° *tert*-Amyl Alcohol $(CH_3)_2C(OH)C_2H_5$
D. 0·814 (15°). Sol. in 6 vols of cold water. With conc. HCl in cold yields chloride B.P. 86°. Bromide B.P. 108° d. Iodide B.P. 127°. Dehydrated on warming with oxalic acid, yielding trimethylethylene B.P. 38°. a-Naphthylcarbamate M.P. 71° (very poor yield).

108° *iso*Butyl Alcohol $(CH_3)_2CH·CH_2OH$
D. 0·800 (18°). Sol. in 8 vols of cold water. On boiling with dil. $K_2Cr_2O_7 + H_2SO_4$ yields *iso*butyr-aldehyde B.P. 63°; on adding conc. soln. of $Na_2Cr_2O_7$ to a cooled mixture of the alcohol with conc. H_2SO_4 yields *iso*butyl *iso*butyrate B.P. 147°. On boiling with 48 % HBr yields bromide B.P. 91°. Iodide B.P. 120°. Acetate B.P. 116°. Benzoate B.P. 241°. Carbanilate M.P. 80°. a-Naphthylcarbamate M.P. 104°. *p*-Nitrobenzyl phthalate is an oil. 3:5-Di-nitrobenzoate M.P. 64°.

116° *n*-Butyl Alcohol $CH_3·CH_2·CH_2·CH_2OH$
D. 0·810 (20°). Sol. in 11 vols of cold water. On boiling with dil. $K_2Cr_2O_7 + H_2SO_4$ yields *n*-butyr-aldehyde B.P. 74°; on adding conc. soln. of $Na_2Cr_2O_7$ to a cooled mixture of the alcohol with conc. H_2SO_4 yields *n*-butyl *n*-butyrate B.P. 165°. On boiling with 48 % HBr yields bromide B.P. 100°. Iodide B.P. 130°. Acetate B.P. 126°. Benzoate B.P. 249°. a-Naphthylcarbamate M.P. 71°. *p*-Nitrobenzyl phthalate M.P. 62°. 3:5-Dinitrobenzoate M.P. 64°.

131° *iso*Amyl Alcohol $(CH_3)_2CH·CH_2·CH_2OH$
D. 0·810 (20°). Sol. in about 40 vols of cold water. On boiling with dil. $K_2Cr_2O_7 + H_2SO_4$ yields *iso*-valeraldehyde B.P. 92°; on adding conc. soln. of $Na_2Cr_2O_7$ to a cooled mixture of the alcohol with conc. H_2SO_4 yields *iso*amyl *iso*valerate B.P. 190°. On boiling with 48 % HBr yields bromide B.P. 118°. Iodide B.P. 148°. Acetate B.P. 139°. Benzoate B.P. 262°. Carbanilate M.P. 55°. a-Naphthylcarbamate M.P. 67°. *p*-Nitrobenzyl phthalate is an oil.

134° Ethylene Glycol Monoethyl Ether $C_2H_5O·CH_2·CH_2OH$
D. 0·935 (15°). Miscible with water. On boiling with

48 % HBr yields ethylene bromide B.P. 129° and ethyl bromide B.P. 38°. Acetate B.P. 158°.

160°   *cyclo*Hexanol $CH_2 \cdot CH_2 \cdot CHOH$
                       $| \qquad\qquad |$
                       $CH_2 \cdot CH_2 \cdot CH_2$

M.P. 20°. 0·947 (20°). Sol. in 28 vols of cold water. On boiling with dil. $K_2Cr_2O_7 + H_2SO_4$ yields *cyclo*hexanone B.P. 155°; on oxidation by hot conc. HNO_3 yields adipic acid M.P. 149°. On warming with conc. HCl yields chloride B.P. 143°. Acetate B.P. 175°. Carbanilate M.P. 82°. α-Naphthylcarbamate M.P. 128°. Acid phthalate M.P. 99°. On distillation with a trace of conc. H_2SO_4 yields *cyclo*hexene B.P. 83°.

169°   Furyl Alcohol $CH \cdot O \cdot C \cdot CH_2OH$
                          $\| \qquad\quad \|$
                          $CH{-}{-}CH$

D. 1·136 (20°). Sol. in 8 vols of cold water. Resinified on warming with mineral acids. Gives green colour with conc. HCl. Pine splinter moistened with conc. HCl gives blue-green colour in vapour. On oxidation with $KMnO_4$ yields furoic (pyromucic) acid M.P. 133°. Acetate B.P. 176°. Benzoate B.P. 273°. α-Naphthylcarbamate M.P. 129°. Diphenylcarbamate M.P. 97°.

171°   Pinacol M.P. 35°. See Alcohols (Solid).

175°   *n*-Heptyl Alcohol $CH_3 \cdot [CH_2]_5 \cdot CH_2OH$
D. 0·830 (16°). Almost insol. in water. On long boiling with large excess of 48 % HBr yields bromide B.P. 176°. Iodide B.P. 203°. Acetate B.P. 191°. α-Naphthylcarbamate M.P. 62°. On boiling with dil. $K_2Cr_2O_7 + H_2SO_4$ yields *n*-heptylic acid B.P. 223°.

179°   *sec*-Octyl Alcohol $CH_3 \cdot [CH_2]_5 \cdot CH(OH) \cdot CH_3$
D. 0·819 (20°). Almost insol. in water. On boiling with dil. $K_2Cr_2O_7 + H_2SO_4$ yields methyl hexyl ketone B.P. 172°. On boiling with conc. HCl yields chloride B.P. 172°. Bromide B.P. 191°. Iodide B.P. 210°. Carbanilate is an oil. α-Naphthylcarbamate M.P. 63°. Acid phthalate M.P. 55°. On slowly adding to PCl_3 is dehydrated yielding octylene B.P. 123°.

188°   Propylene Glycol $CH_3 \cdot CH(OH)CH_2OH$
D. 1·040 (20°). Miscible with water. On boiling with 48 % HBr yields dibromide B.P. 142°. Acetate B.P.

186°.   Benzoate B.P. 240°/12 mm.   On heating with ZnCl$_2$ yields propionaldehyde B.P. 49°.

197° Ethylene Glycol $CH_2OH \cdot CH_2OH$
D. 1·125 (0°).   Miscible with water.   On oxidation by conc. HNO$_3$ yields oxalic acid (q.v.).   On boiling with 48 % HBr yields dibromide B.P. 129°.   Diacetate B.P. 187°.   Dibenzoate M.P. 73°.   Dicarbanilate M.P. 157°.   a-Naphthylcarbamate M.P. 176°.   On heating with KHSO$_4$ yields acetaldehyde B.P. 21°.

197° Linalool $C_{10}H_{18}O$
D. 0·866 (15°).   Pleasant odour.   Unsaturated.   On oxidation with dil. K$_2$Cr$_2$O + H$_2$SO$_4$ yields citral B.P. 228°.   Acetate B.P. 103°/13 mm.   Carbanilate M.P. 65°.

205° Benzyl Alcohol $C_6H_5 \cdot CH_2OH$
D. 1·043 (20°).   Sol. in 25 vols of cold water.   On oxidation by chromic acid or acid KMnO$_4$ yields benzaldehyde B.P. 179°; by alkaline KMnO$_4$ yields benzoic acid M.P. 121°.   On boiling with conc. HCl. yields chloride B.P. 179°.   Acetate B.P. 206°.   Benzoate M.P. 18°, B.P. 323°.   Carbanilate M.P. 78°.   a-Naphthylcarbamate M.P. 134°.   p-Nitrobenzyl phthalate M.P. 83°.

216° Trimethylene Glycol $CH_2OH \cdot CH_2 \cdot CH_2OH$
D. 1·052 (18°).   Miscible with water.   On boiling with conc. HCl yields dichloride B.P. 120° and chlorohydrin B.P. 161°.   Dibromide B.P. 165°.   Diacetate B.P. 209°.   Dibenzoate M.P. 53°.   a-Naphthylcarbamate M.P. 164°.

218° Terpineol M.P. 35°.   See Alcohols (Solid).

220° Phenylethyl Alcohol $C_6H_5 \cdot CH_2 \cdot CH_2OH$
D. 1·023 (13°).   Sol. in about 45 vols of cold water; soln. has odour of rose oil.   On oxidation with K$_2$Cr$_2$O$_7$ + dil. H$_2$SO$_4$ yields phenylacetic acid M.P. 76°.   On boiling with 48 % HBr yields bromide B.P. 217°d.   Acetate B.P. 232°.   Carbanilate M.P. 79°.   a-Naphthylcarbamate M.P. 119°.   Acid phthalate M.P. 188°.   p-Nitrobenzyl phthalate M.P. ·84°.

222° d-Citronellol $C_{10}H_{20}O$
D. 0·857 (17°).   Pleasant odour.   Optically active, $[a]_D = + 4°$.   Unsaturated.   On oxidation first with alkaline KMnO$_4$ and then with K$_2$Cr$_2$O$_7$ + dil. H$_2$SO$_4$ yields β-methyladipic acid M.P. 89°.   Acetate B.P. 120°/15 mm.

229°   Geraniol $C_{10}H_{18}O$
        D. 0·881 (16°).   Pleasant odour.   Optically inactive.
        Unsaturated ;   forms a tetrabromide M.P. 70°.
        Acetate B.P. 128°/16 mm.   Acid phthalate M.P.
        47°.   Diphenylcarbamate M.P. 82°.

235°   Phenylpropyl Alcohol $C_6H_5 \cdot CH_2 \cdot CH_2 \cdot CH_2OH$
        D. 1·068 (18°).   Slightly sol. in water.   On boiling
        with $K_2Cr_2O_7$ + dil. H_2SO_4 yields hydrocinnamic
        acid M.P. 48° ; with alkaline $KMnO_4$ yields benzoic
        acid M.P. 121°.   Acetate B.P. 244°.   Carbanilate
        M.P. 47°.

250°   Cinnamyl Alcohol M.P. 33°.   See Alcohols (Solid).

290°   Glycerol $CH_2OH \cdot CH(OH) \cdot CH_2OH$
        M.P. 20°.   D. 1·260 (20°).   Miscible with water.   On
        heating with $KHSO_4$ yields acrolein B.P. 52° (very
        irritating odour ;   reduces ammon. $AgNO_3$).   On
        heating 2 drops with 2 drops of phenol and 2 drops of
        conc. H_2SO_4 to 120°, diluting, and adding NH_4OH,
        red colour is formed.   Triacetate B.P. 258°.   Tri-
        benzoate M.P. 76°.   Tricarbanilate M.P. 160–180°.
        α-Naphthylcarbamate M.P. 191°.

SOLID

20°   cycloHexanol B.P. 160°.   See Alcohols (Liquid).

25°   tert-Butyl Alcohol $(CH_3)_3C \cdot OH$
       B.P. 83°.   D. 0·780 (26°).   Miscible with water.
       With 4 vols of cold conc. HCl yields chloride B.P. 52°.
       Bromide B.P. 72°.   Acetate B.P. 96°.   Carbanilate
       M.P. 136°.   α-Naphthylcarbamate M.P. 100°.   On
       heating with 45 % H_2SO_4 yields isobutylene B.P. −6°
       (dibromide B.P. 149°).

33°   Cinnamyl Alcohol $C_6H_5 \cdot CH:CH \cdot CH_2OH$
       B.P. 254°.   Unsaturated ;   dibromide M.P. 74°.
       Oxidised by acid $KMnO_4$ to benzaldehyde B.P. 179°
       and benzoic acid M.P. 121°, by chromic acid to cin-
       namic acid M.P. 133°.   Carbanilate M.P. 90°.   α-
       Naphthylcarbamate M.P. 114°.   Diphenylcarbamate
       M.P. 97°.

35°   Pinacol $(CH_3)_2C(OH) \cdot C(OH)(CH_3)_2$
       B.P. 172°.   Sparingly soluble in cold water, readily
       in hot.   Hot aqueous soln on cooling deposits hydrate
       M.P. 46°.   On warming with iodine and dil. NaOH
       yields iodoform M.P. 119°.   Oxidised by chromic acid
       to acetone B.P. 56°.   With fuming HBr yields

M.P.

tetramethylethylene dibromide M.P. 192°. With PCl_3 yields tetramethylethylene dichloride M.P. 160°. On boiling with dil. H_2SO_4 yields pinacolone B.P. 106°, with some di-*iso*propenyl B.P. 70°.

35°   Terpineol $C_{10}H_{17}\cdot OH$
B.P. 172°. Optically active, *d* or *l*. Unsaturated ; dibromide is an unstable oil. With HCl gas yields dipentene dihydrochloride M.P. 50°. Acetate B.P. 195°. On heating with $KHSO_4$ yields dipentene B.P. 181°.

42°   *l*-Menthol $C_{10}H_{19}\cdot OH$
B.P. 212°. Optically active, $[a]_D = -59\cdot6°$ in alcohol. Odour of peppermint. On boiling with $K_2Cr_2O_7$ + dil. H_2SO_4 yields menthone B.P. 207°. Acetate B.P. 227°. Benzoate M.P. 54°. *a*-Naphthylcarbamate M.P. 119°. Acid phthalate M.P. 110°. *p*-Nitrobenzyl phthalate is an oil. On heating with oxalic acid to 130° yields menthene B.P. 167°.

46°   Pinacol Hydrate. See Pinacol M.P. 35°.

49°   Cetyl Alcohol $CH_3\cdot[CH_2]_{14}\cdot CH_2OH$
B.P. 189°/15 mm. On fusion with KOH or on oxidation by CrO_3 in acetic acid yields palmitic acid M.P. 62°. Acetate M.P. 22°, B.P. 200°/15 mm. Benzoate M.P. 30°. Carbanilate M.P. 73°.

116°   Terpin Hydrate $C_{10}H_{20}O_2 + H_2O$
Sol. in 250 parts of cold water, in 100 parts of cold ether, in 10 parts of cold alcohol. On heating above M.P. loses water forming *cis*-terpin M.P. 104°. Gives yellow to light red colour with conc. H_2SO_4 ; in presence of $NaHSO_3$ colour is blood-red to brown. With PCl_3 yields dipentene dihydrochloride M.P. 50°. Diacetate B.P. 147°/13 mm.

137°   Benzoin. See Ketones (Solid).

162°   Triphenylcarbinol $(C_6H_5)_3C\cdot OH$
B.P. 380°. Not attacked by cold $KMnO_4$ soln nor by dil. mineral acids ; with conc. HCl forms a yellow soln from which triphenylchloromethane M.P. 108° separates. Forms intense yellow soln. in conc. H_2SO_4. On successive nitration, reduction, and gentle oxidation by PbO_2 yields pararosaniline (cf. Triphenylmethane M.P. 92°). Acetate M.P. 99°.

166°   *d*-Mannitol $CH_2OH[CH(OH)]_4CH_2OH$
Sol. in 7 parts of cold water, almost insol. in alcohol. Optical activity barely perceptible in aqueous soln ;

M.P.

addition of NaOH causes rotation to left, while borax
causes strong rotation to right. Gives a ppte. with
ammon. $CuSO_4$ soln. On distillation with conc. HI
yields mixture of *sec*-hexyl iodides B.P. 167°. On
heating with 7 parts of PCl_5 to 145° yields hexachloro-
hexane M.P. 137°. Hexa-acetate M.P. 119°. Hexabenzoate M.P. 124°. Hexacarbanilate M.P. 303°.

203°   *d*-Borneol $C_{10}H_{17}·OH$
B.P. 203°. Odour like camphor. Optically active,
$[a]_D = + 37°$ in alcohol. On boiling with HNO_3
yields camphor M.P. 175°. On stirring with 45 %
H_2SO_4 at 60–100° yields camphene M.P. 48°, B.P.
157°. Acetate M.P. 29°, B.P. 225°. Benzoate M.P.
25°. Carbanilate M.P. 138°. α-Naphthylcarbamate
M.P. 127°. Acid phthalate M.P. 164°. *p*-Nitro-
benzyl phthalate M.P. 100°.

225°   Inositol   CHOH·CHOH·CHOH
                          | |
                    CHOH·CHOH·CHOH
Optically inactive. Sol. in 10 parts of water at 12°,
in 6 parts at 23°. Sparingly sol. in alcohol. Sweet
taste. Does not reduce Fehling's soln. On oxidation
by $KMnO_4$ yields only CO_2, by CrO_3 in cold yields CO_2
and formic acid, by boiling HNO_3 yields oxalic acid.
On boiling with acetic anhydride + Na acetate yields
hexa-acetate M.P. 216°. Hexabenzoate M.P. 258°.

253°   Pentaerythritol   . $C(CH_2OH)_4$
Sol. in 18 parts of cold water. Tetra-acetate M.P.
84°. Tetrabenzoate M.P. 99°. Tetranitrate (high
explosive) M.P. 139°.

PHENOLS

LIQUID

B.P.
196°   Salicylaldehyde. See Aldehydes and Acetals.

202°   *m*-Cresol. $CH_3·C_6H_4·OH$ (1:3)
M.P. 3°. D. 1·050 (0°). Blue-violet colour with
$FeCl_3$. With conc. H_2SO_4 + HNO_3 yields trinitro-
cresol M.P. 105°. With bromine yields tribromocresol
M.P. 84°. Yields *m*-hydroxybenzoic acid M.P. 200°
on fusion with KOH + PbO_2. Benzoate M.P. 54°.
3:5-Dinitrobenzoate M.P. 160°. *p*-Nitrobenzyl ether
M.P. 51°. Benzenesulphonate M.P. 45°. *p*-Toluene-
sulphonate M.P. 51°. Picrate M.P. 88°.

211°   1:3:4-Xylenol M.P. 26°. See Phenols (Solid).

B.P.

224°   Methyl Salicylate. See Esters of Aromatic Hydroxy Acids.

234°   Ethyl Salicylate. See Esters of Aromatic Hydroxy Acids.

237°   Carvacrol $(CH_3)_2CH\cdot C_6H_3(CH_3)\cdot OH$ (1:4:3)
M.P. 0°. D. 0·976 (20°). Transient green colour with $FeCl_3$ in alc. soln. only (ppte in aqueous soln). On gradual addition of (1 mol.) bromine in acetic acid yields monobromo deriv. M.P. 46°. Oxidised by chromic acid to thymoquinone M.P. 45°. Acetate B.P. 246°. Benzoate B.P. above 260°d. 3:5-Dinitrobenzoate M.P. 76°. Carbanilate M.P. 135°. Nitroso deriv. M.P. 153°.

237°   *iso*Propyl Salicylate. See Esters of Aromatic Hydroxy Acids.

239°   *n*-Propyl Salicylate. See Esters of Aromatic Hydroxy Acids.

243°   Resorcinol Monomethyl Ether $CH_3O\cdot C_6H_4\cdot OH$ (1:3)
D. 1·070 (4°). Faint violet colour in alc. with $FeCl_3$. On boiling with 48 % HBr yields resorcinol M.P. 118°. With bromine in acetic acid yields tribromo deriv. M.P. 104°. Acetate B.P. 255°.

247°   Eugenol $CH_2:CH\cdot CH_2\cdot C_6H_3(OCH_3)\cdot OH$ (1:3:4)
D. 1·063 (18°). Unsaturated. Odour of cloves. Blue colour with $FeCl_3$ in alc. Oxidation by $KMnO_4$ yields vanillin M.P. 80° and vanillic acid M.P. 207°. On fusion with KOH yields protocatechuic acid M.P. 194°. With (3 mols.) bromine in ether yields tetrabromo deriv. M.P. 118°. Acetate M.P. 30°, B.P. 270°. Benzoate M.P. 69°. *p*-Nitrobenzyl ether M.P. 53°.

267°   *iso*Eugenol $CH_3\cdot CH:CH\cdot C_6H_3(OCH_3)\cdot OH$ (1:3:4)
D. 1·080 (16°). Unsaturated. Green colour with $FeCl_3$ in alc. Acetate M.P. 79°. Benzoate M.P. 103°.

268°   *n*-Butyl Salicylate. See Esters of Aromatic Hydroxy Acids.

277°   *iso*Amyl Salicylate. See Esters of Aromatic Hydroxy Acids.

283°   Resorcinol Monoacetate $CH_3\cdot COO\cdot C_6H_4\cdot OH$ (1:3)
Extremely viscous. In hydrolysis with NaOH yields resorcinol M.P. 118°. With acetic anhydride yields diacetate B.P. 278°.

320°   Benzyl Salicylate. See Esters of Aromatic Hydroxy Acids.

SOLID

M.P.
26°   1:3:4-Xylenol $(CH_3)_2C_6H_3 \cdot OH$ (1:3:4)
        B.P. 211°. Transient green-blue colour with $FeCl_3$ in
        alc., blue-violet in aqueous soln (also transient).
        With excess of bromine yields tribromo deriv. M.P.
        179°. With HNO_3 in acetic acid yields 5-nitro deriv.
        M.P. 72°. Benzoate M.P. 38°. Carbanilate M.P.
        102°.

28°   Guaiacol $CH_3O \cdot C_6H_4 \cdot OH$ (1:2)
        B.P. 205°. Green-blue colour with $FeCl_3$ in alcohol.
        On boiling with 48 % HBr yields catechol M.P. 104°.
        Heated with zinc dust yields anisole B.P. 154°.
        With PCl_5 yields o-chloroanisole B.P. 195°. Acetate
        B.P. 240°. Benzoate M.P. 57°. p-Nitrobenzyl Ether
        M.P. 63°. Benzenesulphonate M.P. 51°. p-Toluene-
        sulphonate M.P. 85°. 3:5-Dinitrobenzoate M.P. 138°.
        Carbanilate M.P. 136°.

31°   o-Cresol $CH_3 \cdot C_6H_4 \cdot OH$ (1:2)
        B.P. 190°. Violet colour with $FeCl_3$ in water. With
        bromine water yields dibromo deriv. M.P. 56°.
        Benzoate B.P. 307°. p-Nitrobenzyl Ether M.P. 89°.
        Benzenesulphonate M.P. 39°. p-Toluenesulphonate
        M.P. 53°. 3:5-Dinitrobenzoate M.P. 133°. Carbanil-
        ate M.P. 145°. Picrate M.P. 88°.

35°   p-Cresol $CH_3 \cdot C_6H_4 \cdot OH$ (1:4)
        B.P. 201°. Blue colour with $FeCl_3$ in water. With
        excess bromine water yields tetrabromo deriv. M.P.
        108°d. Acetate B.P. 214°. Benzoate M.P. 71°.
        p-Nitrobenzyl Ether M.P. 88°. Benzenesulphonate
        M.P. 43°. p-Toluenesulphonate M.P. 69°. 3:5-Di-
        nitrobenzoate M.P. 180°. Carbanilate M.P. 114°.
        Forms no picrate.

42°   Phenol $C_6H_5 \cdot OH$
        B.P. 181°. Violet colour with $FeCl_3$ in water. Sol.
        in conc. NH_4OH. On nitration with hot fuming
        HNO_3 yields picric acid M.P. 122°. With bromine
        water yields tribromophenol M.P. 93° after treatment
        of ppte with Na_2CO_3 soln. Warmed with phthalic
        anhydride and a drop of conc. H_2SO_4 yields phenol-
        phthalein (red colour with alkali). Acetate B.P. 196°.
        Benzoate M.P. 68°. 3:5-Dinitrobenzoate M.P. 145°.
        p-Nitrobenzyl Ether M.P. 91°. Carbanilate M.P.
        126°. Benzenesulphonate M.P. 35°. p-Toluenesul-
        phonate M.P. 95°. Picrate M.P. 83°.

M.P.

42°   Phenyl Salicylate.   See Esters of Aromatic Hydroxy
         Acids.

50°   Thymol $(CH_3)_2CH \cdot C_6H_3(CH_3)OH$ (1:4:2)
         B.P. 230°.   Characteristic odour.   Sparingly sol.
         in hot water.   Volatile with steam and extractable
         with ether from alkaline soln.   Transient green colour
         with $FeCl_3$ in alcohol.   Trinitro deriv. M.P. 109°.
         Nitroso deriv. M.P. 164°.   Boiled with MnO_2 and dil.
         H_2SO_4 yields thymoquinone M.P. 45°.   With (1 mol.)
         bromine in acetic acid yields bromothymol M.P. 55°.
         Acetate B.P. 244°.   Benzoate M.P. 32°.   3:5-Dinitro-
         benzoate M.P. 102°.   Benzenesulphonate M.P. 55°.
         Carbanilate M.P. 107°. p-Nitrobenzyl Ether M.P. 85°.

53°   Hydroquinone Monomethyl Ether
                  $CH_3O \cdot C_6H_4 \cdot OH$ (1:4)
         B.P. 243°.   Sol. in benzene.   Not volatile with steam.
         Yields no quinhydrone with $FeCl_3$.   Reduces ammoni-
         acal $AgNO_3$ on warming.   On boiling with 48% HBr
         yields hydroquinone M.P. 169°.

58°   Orcinol (hydrated) $CH_3 \cdot C_6H_3(OH)_2 + H_2O$ (1:3:5)
         Loses water on heating to 100°, giving anhydrous
         orcinol M.P. 107°.   Sol. in water.   Blue-violet colour
         with $FeCl_3$ in water.   Soln. in NH_4OH turns red on
         standing in air.   Reduces ammoniacal $AgNO_3$.   Tri-
         bromo deriv. M.P. 98°.   Diacetate M.P. 25°.   Dibenzo-
         ate M.P. 88°.

68°   Mesitol $(CH_3)_3C_6H_2 \cdot OH$ (1:3:5:2)
         B.P. 219°.   No colour with $FeCl_3$.   Bromine in
         glacial acetic acid in presence of iodine yields dibromo
         deriv. M.P. 158°.

70°   Methyl m-Hydroxybenzoate.   See Esters of Aromatic
         Hydroxy Acids.

71°   Pseudocumenol $(CH_3)_3C_6H_2 \cdot OH$ (1:2:4:5)
         B.P. 230°.   No colour with $FeCl_3$.   With fuming
         HNO_3 yields mononitro deriv. M.P. 48°, which forms
         a nitrate M.P. 81° with HNO_3.   Bromine in glacial
         acetic acid yields monobromo deriv. M.P. 35°.   Benzo-
         ate M.P. 63°.

72°   Ethyl m-Hydroxybenzoate.   See Esters of Aromatic
         Hydroxy Acids.

74°   1:4:2-Xylenol $(CH_3)_2C_6H_3 \cdot OH$ (1:4:2)
         B.P. 212°.   No colour with $FeCl_3$.   With bromine in
         acetic acid yields dibromo deriv. M.P. 79°.   Acetate
         B.P. 237°.   Benzoate M.P. 61°.   Carbanilate M.P. 160°.

M.P.
80°   Vanillin. See Aldehydes and Acetals.

94°   α-Naphthol $C_{10}H_7 \cdot OH$ (1)

B.P. 278°. No colour with $FeCl_3$ in water, but gives white ppte. Green colour with titanic acid in conc. H_2SO_4. Warmed in dil. NaOH with pure CCl_4 + Cu powder gives blue colour (distinction from β-naphthol). With bromine in acetic acid yields 2:4-dibromo deriv. M.P. 105°. Gives violet ppte with NaOBr soln. On adding dil. HNO_3 to soln in conc. H_2SO_4 and warming yields 2:4-dinitro deriv. M.P. 138°. Acetate M.P. 46°. Benzoate M.P. 56°. Carbanilate M.P. 178°. p-Nitrobenzyl ether M.P. 140°. Picrate M.P. 189°.

95°   β-Naphthyl Salicylate. See Esters of Aromatic Hydroxy Acids.

104°   Catechol $C_6H_4(OH)_2$ (1:2)

B.P. 245°. Readily sol. in water and in hot toluene. Green colour with $FeCl_3$. Easily oxidised ; reduces Fehling's soln. Soln. in NaOH turns brown on standing in air. With bromine in CCl_4 yields tetrabromo deriv. M.P. 192°. Diacetate M.P. 63°. Dibenzoate M.P. 84°. Carbanilate M.P. 165°.

107°   Orcinol (anhydrous) B.P. 289°. See Orcinol (hydrated) M.P. 58°.

115°   p-Hydroxybenzaldehyde. See Aldehydes and Acetals.

116°   Ethyl p-Hydroxybenzoate. See Esters of Aromatic Hydroxy Acids.

118°   Resorcinol $C_6H_4(OH)_2$ (1:3)

B.P. 276°. Sol. in water. Blue-violet colour with $FeCl_3$. On nitration yields trinitro deriv. M.P. 175°. On fusion with phthalic acid and a drop of H_2SO_4 yields fluorescein (orange soln. in NaOH with green fluorescence). Warmed with NaOH soln and $CHCl_3$ gives red soln. with green fluorescence. Diacetate B.P. 278°. Dibenzoate M.P. 117°. Dibenzenesulphonate M.P. 69°. Di-p-toluenesulphonate M.P. 80°. Dicarbanilate M.P. 164°.

122°   β-Naphthol $C_{10}H_7 \cdot OH$ (2)

B.P. 285°. Insol. in water. No colour with $FeCl_3$ in water, but white opalescence. Soln. in conc. KOH gives blue colour when warmed to 50° with $CHCl_3$ (no colour with CCl_4). Gives red colour with titanic acid in conc. H_2SO_4. With (1 mol.) bromine yields 1-bromo-2-naphthol M.P. 84°. Gives yellow colour with NaOBr soln. Acetate M.P. 70°. Benzoate M.P.

M.P.

107°. Benzenesulphonate M.P. 106°. p-Toluene-
sulphonate M.P. 125°. · Carbanilate M.P. 155°. p-
Nitrobenzyl ether M.P. 106°. Picrate M.P. 156°.

124°   Toluhydroquinone $CH_3 \cdot C_6H_3(OH)_2$ (2:1:4)
        Sol. in water. Resembles Hydroquinone M.P. 169°
        in properties. Yields toluquinone M.P. 68° on
        oxidation. Diacetate M.P. 52°.

131°   Methyl p-Hydroxybenzoate. See Esters of Aromatic
        Hydroxy Acids.

133°   Pyrogallol $C_6H_3(OH)_3$ (1:2:3)
        B.P. 293°. Sol. in water. Dull yellow colour with
        $FeCl_3$. Very easily oxidised. Soln in NaOH turns
        brown in air. Blue ppte with $FeSO_4$ soln. Tri-
        acetate M.P. 161°. Tribenzoate M.P. 89°. Tribenzene-
        sulphonate M.P. 141°. Tricarbanilate M.P. 173°.

169°   Hydroquinone $C_6H_4(OH)_2$ (1:4)
        Sol. in water, insol. in benzene. Transient blue colour
        with $FeCl_3$ in water. Yields benzoquinone M.P. 116°
        on warming with excess of conc. $FeCl_3$ soln ; in cold
        yields quinhydrone M.P. 171°. Ammonia colours
        aqueous soln brown. Diacetate M.P. 123°. Di-
        benzoate M.P. 199°. Dibenzenesulphonate M.P. 120°.
        Dicarbanilate M.P. 206°.

218°   Phloroglucinol $C_6H_3(OH)_3$ (1:3:5) $+ 2H_2O$
        Loses water at 100°. Sol. in water. Transient violet
        colour with $FeCl_3$. On nitration yields trinitro deriv.
        M.P. 165°. With bromine water yields tribromo
        deriv. M.P. 151°. With NH_2OH yields trioximino-
        cyclohexane d. (expl.) 155°. Triacetate M.P. 105°.
        Tribenzoate M.P. 173°. Tribenzenesulphonate M.P.
        116°. Tricarbanilate M.P. 123°.

250°   Phenolphthalein $C_6H_4 \cdot C(C_6H_4OH)_2$
                              $\underset{\displaystyle CO \!-\! O}{|\qquad\quad|}$

        Insol. in water, sol. in alc. Sol. in dil. NaOH forming
        red soln. ; colour discharged on adding large excess of
        conc. NaOH Ppte. from alk. soln. by acid is amor-
        phous, v. sol. in ether, and melts in boiling water. On
        warming in dil. NaOH with Zn dust colour is dis-
        charged ; on acidification, phenolphthalin M.P. 225°
        is ppted. Diacetyl deriv. M.P. 143°. Dibenzoyl
        deriv. M.P. 169°.

289°   Alizarin. See Quinones.

ALDEHYDES AND ACETALS

LIQUID

21° Acetaldehyde $CH_3 \cdot CHO$

D. 0·806 (0°). Miscible with water. Characteristic odour. Extremely dil. soln. in water gives light yellow ppte with Nessler's soln ; stronger soln gives reddish ppte. which rapidly becomes grey. With dry NH_3 in dry ether yields acetaldehyde-ammonia M.P. 93°. On warming with dil. NaOH gives powerful odour of aldehyde-resin. Gives yellow colour with dil. soln of benzidine HCl. Red colour with sodium nitroprusside (blue in presence of piperidine or diethylamine). On warming with a little conc. HCl and β-naphthol in acetic acid soln. yields ethylidene di-β-naphthyl ether M.P. 173°. Semicarbazone M.P. 162°. p-Nitrophenylhydrazone M.P. 128°. 2:4-Dinitrophenylhydrazone M.P. 162°.

42° Methylal $CH_2(OCH_3)_2$

D. 0·872 (15°). Miscible with water. On boiling with dil. HCl yields formaldehyde and methyl alc. B.P. 65°.

49° Propionaldehyde $C_2H_5 \cdot CHO$

D. 0·806 (20°). Sol. in 5 vols of cold water. Odour like acetaldehyde. Phenylhydrazone B.P. 205°/180 mm. (on warming with $ZnCl_2$ gives intense fecal odour of skatole). Semicarbazone M.P. 89°. p-Nitrophenylhydrazone M.P. 123°. 2:4-Dinitrophenylhydrazone M.P. 155°.

52° Acrolein $CH_2 \colon CH \cdot CHO$

D. 0·841 (20°). Sol. in 2–3 vols of cold water. Odour very irritating. Unsaturated. Oxidised by heavy metal oxides or ammoniacal $AgNO_3$ to acrylic acid B.P. 140°. With bromine and subsequent oxidation by HNO_3 yields αβ-dibromopropionic acid M.P. 64°. With phenylhydrazine in ether yields phenylpyrazoline M.P. 51°.

63° *iso*Butyraldehyde $(CH_3)_2CH \cdot CHO$

D. 0·794 (20°). Sol. in 9 vols of cold water. Polymerises in cold with trace of H_2SO_4 to para-*iso*butyraldehyde M.P. 59°. Semicarbazone M.P. 125°. Oxime B.P. 139°. p-Nitrophenylhydrazone M.P. 131°. 2:4-Dinitrophenylhydrazone M.P. 182°.

64° Dimethylacetal $CH_3 \cdot CH(OCH_3)_2$

D. 0·879 (0°). Slightly sol. in water. On boiling with

B.P.

dil. HCl yields acetaldehyde B.P. 21° and methyl alc.
B.P. 65°.

74° *n*-Butyraldehyde $C_2H_5 \cdot CH_2 \cdot CHO$
D. 0·817 (20°). Sol. in 22 vols. of cold water. Oxime
B.P. 152°. Semicarbazone M.P. 126°. *p*-Nitrophenyl-
hydrazone M.P. 91°. 2:4-Dinitrophenylhydrazone
M.P. 122°.

88° Ethylal $CH_2(OC_2H_5)_2$
D. 0·840 (0°). Slightly sol. in water. On boiling with dil.
HCl yields formaldehyde (*q.v.*) and ethyl alc. B.P. 78°.

97–98° Formaldehyde $H \cdot CHO$ (25–30% in water).
Pungent and characteristic odour. With NH_4OH
yields hexamethylenetetramine (*q.v.*) with evolution
of heat. Gives no colour with nitroprusside. In very
dil. soln gives with Nessler's soln a reddish-brown
ppte which becomes yellowish-grey on standing. On
warming with a little conc. HCl and β-naphthol in
alcohol yields methylene di-β-naphthyl ether M.P.
190°. Gives a gelatinous ppte. with semicarbazide
hydrochloride. Benzylphenylhydrazone M.P. 41°.
p-Nitrophenylhydrazone M.P. 181°. 2:4-Dinitro-
phenylhydrazone M.P. 155°.

92° *iso*Valeraldehyde $(CH_3)_2CH \cdot CH_2 \cdot CHO$
D. 0·803 (17°). Oxime B.P. 161°. Semicarbazone
M.P. 107°. *p*-Nitrophenylhydrazone M.P. 109°. 2:4-
Dinitrophenylhydrazone M.P. 123°. Aqueous soln
with H_2S gives thio deriv. M.P. 69°.

104° Acetal $CH_3 \cdot CH(OC_2H_5)_2$
D. 0·831 (20°). Slightly sol. in water. On boiling
with dil. HCl yields acetaldehyde B.P. 21° and ethyl
alc. B.P. 78°.

104° Crotonaldehyde $CH_3 \cdot CH:CH \cdot CHO$
D. 0·860 (14°). Fairly sol. in water. Very irritating
odour. Unsaturated. Dibromide d. on heating in
vac. With HCl in cold yields β-chlorobutyraldehyde
M.P. 96°. Oxidised slowly by air, rapidly by Ag_2O,
yielding crotonic acid M.P. 72°. Forms sol. product
with $NaHSO_3$, from which it is not regenerated by
Na_2CO_3. Oxime M.P. 119°. Phenylhydrazone M.P.
56°. Semicarbazone M.P. 144°.

124° Paraldehyde $CH(CH_3) \cdot O \cdot CH \cdot CH_3$
$$| \qquad\qquad |$$
$$O \cdot CH(CH_3) \cdot O$$
D. 0·998 (15°). Slightly sol. in water. On gently

B.P.

warming with a trace of conc. H_2SO_4 yields acetaldehyde B.P. 21°.   On warming with aniline in conc. HCl yields quinaldine B.P. 246°.

154°   Heptaldehyde $CH_3 \cdot [CH_2]_5 \cdot CHO$

D. 0·825 (20°).   On oxidation with chromic acid or dil. HNO_3 yields heptylic acid B.P. 223°.   Oxime M.P. 57°.   Semicarbazone M.P. 106°; 2:4-Dinitrophenylhydrazone M.P. 106°.

161°   Furfural $\begin{matrix} CH \cdot O \cdot C \cdot CHO \\ \| \quad\quad \| \\ CH\text{---}CH \end{matrix}$

D. 1·159 (20°).   Colourless liquid, turns brown in air. A paper moistened with aniline acetate turns red in its vapour.   On oxidation with $KMnO_4$ yields furoic (pyromucic) acid M.P. 133°.   On warming with alc. KOH yields furoic acid and furyl alc. B.P. 169°.   On warming with acetone and dil. NaOH yields furfuracetone M.P. 39°.   Phenylhydrazone M.P. 97°. p-Nitrophenylhydrazone M.P. 127°.   2:4-Dinitrophenylhydrazone M.P. 202°. Semicarbazone M.P. 202°.

179°   Benzaldehyde $C_6H_5 \cdot CHO$

D. 1·050 (15°).   Sparingly sol. in water.   Odour of almond oil.   Oxidised by alkaline $KMnO_4$ to benzoic acid M.P. 121°.   On warming with conc. KOH yields benzoic acid and benzyl alcohol B.P. 205°.   On warming with aniline yields benzalaniline M.P. 54°. With p-aminophenol in dil. acetic acid yields benzalp-aminophenol M.P. 183°.   Dibenzalacetone M.P. 111° (see Acetone B.P. 56°).   Oxime M.P. 35°. Phenylhydrazone M.P. 158°.   p-Nitrophenylhydrazone M.P. 192°.   2:4-Dinitrophenylhydrazone M.P. 235°.   Semicarbazone M.P. 214°.

196°   Salicylaldehyde $HO \cdot C_6H_4 \cdot CHO$ (1:2)

D. 1·173 (13·5°).   Sparingly sol. in water.   Violet colour with $FeCl_3$.   Oxidised by alkaline $KMnO_4$ to salicylic acid M.P. 155°.   Oxime M.P. 57°.   Phenylhydrazone M.P. 142°.   p-Nitrophenylhydrazone M.P. 223°.   2:4-Dinitrophenylhydrazone M.P. 248°.   Semicarbazone M.P. 231°.   Anil M.P. 50°.   Triacetyl deriv. M.P. 100°.   Benzoyl deriv. B.P. above 360°.

77°/16 mm.   Acetaldol $CH_3 \cdot CH(OH) \cdot CH_2 \cdot CHO$

D. 1·109 (16°).   Slowly polymerises to paraldol M.P. 90°.   On distilling with solid $AlPO_4$ or trace of iodine yields crotonaldehyde B.P. 104°.   On warming with

B.P.

aniline in conc. HCl yields quinaldine B.P. 246°. Semicarbazone M.P. 194°.

203°   Citronellal $C_{10}H_{18}O$
D. 0·855 (17°). Optically active, $[a]_D = +13°$. Unsaturated. Takes up (1 mol.) bromine ; product yields cymene B.P. 175° on heating. Oxime B.P. 135°/14 mm. Semicarbazone M.P. 82°.

220°d. Cinnamaldehyde $C_6H_5 \cdot CH{:}CH \cdot CHO$
B.P. 128°/20 mm. D. 1·050 (24°). Insol. in water. Unsaturated. Odour of cinnamon. Warmed with conc. KOH yields cinnamic acid M.P. 133° and cinnamyl alcohol B.P. 254°. Oxidised by acid $KMnO_4$ to benzaldehyde B.P. 179°, by alkaline $KMnO_4$ to benzoic acid M.P. 121°. On warming with aniline yields cinnamalaniline M.P. 109°. Oxime M.P. 138°. Phenylhydrazone M.P. 168°. p-Nitrophenylhydrazone M.P. 195°. Semicarbazone M.P. 215°. With NH_3 in alc. yields hydrocinnamide M.P. 106°.

228°   Citral $C_{10}H_{16}O$
D. 0·880 (15°). Optically inactive. Odour of lemon. Forms sparingly sol. compd. with $NaHSO_3$ (decomp. on warming with water). Oxime B.P. 150°/15 mm. With semicarbazide HCl in acetic acid without sodium acetate yields a semicarbazone M.P. 164°.

248°   Anisaldehyde $CH_3O \cdot C_6H_4 \cdot CHO$ (1:4)
D. 1·123 (18°). Insol. in water. On warming with alcoholic KOH yields anisic acid M.P. 184° and anisyl alcohol M.P. 45°. Oxime M.P. 92°. Phenylhydrazone M.P. 120°. Semicarbazone M.P. 203°.

SOLID

M.P.

37°   Piperonal $(CH_2O_2){:}C_6H_3 \cdot CHO$ (1:2:4)
B.P. 263°. Sparingly sol. in water. Odour of heliotrope. On oxidation yields piperonylic acid M.P. 228°. Oxime M.P. 110°. Phenylhydrazone M.P. 100°. Semicarbazone M.P. 230°. On warming with aniline yields piperonalaniline M.P. 65°.

80°   Vanillin $CH_3O \cdot C_6H_3(OH)CHO$ (2:1:4)
B.P. 285°. Slightly sol. in water. Odour of vanilla. Blue colour with $FeCl_3$. On oxidation by alkaline $KMnO_4$ yields vanillic acid M.P. 207°. On boiling with very dil. HCl and a few drops of $FeCl_3$ soln yields dehydrovanillin M.P. 304°d. With bromine water yields bromo deriv. M.P. 160°. Oxime M.P. 117°.

O.A.   K

B.P.

Phenylhydrazone M.P. 105°. Semicarbazone M.P. 229°. Triacetyl deriv. M.P. 88°. Benzoyl deriv. M.P. 75°. Addition product with phenyl *iso*cyanate M.P. 116°.

115°   *p*-Hydroxybenzaldehyde $HO \cdot C_6H_4 \cdot CHO$ (1:4)
Sparingly sol. in water. Forms a bisulphite compd sol. in water. Faint violet colour with $FeCl_3$. Yields *p*-hydroxybenzoic acid M.P. 215° with difficulty on oxidation, but readily on fusion with KOH. On warming with aniline yields *p*-hydroxybenzalaniline M.P. 190°. Oxime M.P. 72° (anhydrous M.P. 112°). Phenylhydrazone M.P. 177°. 2:4-Dinitrophenyl-hydrazone M.P. 157°. Semicarbazone M.P. 224°. Triacetyl deriv. M.P. 93°. Benzoyl deriv. M.P. 72°.

170°   Polyoxymethylene $(CH_2O)_n$
Slightly sol. in water. Yields formaldehyde (*q.v.*) on heating.

KETONES

LIQUID

B.P.
56°   Acetone $CH_3 \cdot CO \cdot CH_3$
D. 0·819 (0°). Miscible with water. With iodine and NaOH in the cold yields iodoform M.P. 119°. On boiling with benzaldehyde and conc. $Ba(OH)_2$ soln. in dil. alc. yields dibenzalacetone M.P. 111°. Dil. soln. in water gives red colour with alkaline nitroprusside, changed in tint on adding acetic acid. Forms a bisulphite compd. with evolution of heat. Oxime M.P. 59°. Phenylhydrazone M.P. 42°. *p*-Nitro-phenylhydrazone M.P. 148°. 2:4-Dinitrophenyl-hydrazone M.P. 128°. Semicarbazone M.P. 187°.

80°   Methyl Ethyl Ketone $CH_3 \cdot CO \cdot C_2H_5$
D. 0·830 (0°). Miscible with water. Oxime B.P. 152°. Phenylhydrazone B.P. 190°/100 mm. *p*-Nitrophenylhydrazone M.P. 128°. 2:4-Dinitrophenyl-hydrazone M.P. 115°. Semicarbazone M.P. 135°.

102°   Diethyl Ketone $C_2H_5 \cdot CO \cdot C_2H_5$
D. 0·834 (0°). Sol. in 15 vols. of cold water. Forms a bisulphite compd. only with difficulty. Oxime B.P. 165°. Phenylhydrazone B.P. 162°/24 mm. *p*-Nitro-phenylhydrazone M.P. 139°. Semicarbazone M.P. 139°.

106°   Pinacolone $CH_3 \cdot CO \cdot C(CH_3)_3$
D. 0·826 (0°). Sol. in 32 vols. of cold water. Odour

peppermint-like. Oxidised by chromic acid to tri-
methylacetic acid M.P. 35°, B.P. 163°. Forms no
bisulphite compd. Oxime M.P. 74°. Phenylhydrazone B.P. 165°/32 mm. Semicarbazone M.P. 157°.

130°   Mesityl Oxide $CH_3 \cdot CO \cdot CH{:}C(CH_3)_2$
D. 0·858 (20°). Sol. in 30 vols. of cold water. Char-
acteristic odour (like peppermint). Unsaturated.
Decolorises bromine water yielding an unstable oil.
On boiling with dil. H_2SO_4 yields acetone B.P. 56°.
Forms no bisulphite compd. Oxime M.P. 49°.
Semicarbazone M.P. 156°. With phenylhydrazine
yields phenyltrimethylpyrazoline B.P. 152°/16 mm.
p-Nitrophenylhydrazone M.P. 133°.

139°   Acetylacetone $CH_3 \cdot CO \cdot CH_2 \cdot CO \cdot CH_3$
D. 0·941 (4°). Sol. in 8 vols of cold water. Exhibits
a distinct acid reaction. Gives orange-red colour with
$FeCl_3$ in water. Gives light blue ppte of Cu salt with
Cu acetate soln. Yields acetic acid and acetone on
boiling with alkali. Forms ammonium salt M.P. 65°
on passing NH_3 into ethereal soln. Nickel salt M.P.
228°. On adding gradually to an excess of hydroxylamine base in water yields a dioxime M.P. 149°; reverse
order of addition leads to dimethylisoxazole B.P. 141°.
With phenylhydrazine yields phenyldimethylpyrazole
B.P. 273°; with p-nitrophenylhydrazine HCl in water
yields corresponding deriv. M.P. 100°. With semicarbazide yields dimethylpyrazole carboxylic amide
M.P. 107°. With aniline in cold yields anil M.P. 52°.

155°   cycloHexanone $CH_2 \cdot CH_2 \cdot CO$
                        $||$
                        $CH_2 \cdot CH_2 \cdot CH_2$

D. 0·947 (20°). Sol. in 27 vols. of cold water. Oxidation by HNO_3 yields adipic acid M.P. 149°. Oxime
M.P. 88°. Phenylhydrazone M.P. 74–77°d. p-Nitrophenylhydrazone M.P. 146°. Semicarbazone M.P.
166°.

164°   Diacetone Alcohol $(CH_3)_2C(OH) \cdot CH_2 \cdot CO \cdot CH_3$
D. 0·931 (25°). Miscible with water, alc., and ether.
On distilling with dil. NaOH yields acetone B.P. 56°;
on distilling with solid $AlPO_3$ or trace of iodine yields
mesityl oxide B.P. 130°. Oxime M.P. 57°.

202°   Acetophenone $C_6H_5 \cdot CO \cdot CH_3$
M.P. 20°. D. 1·023 (25°). Sparingly sol. in water.
On oxidation with alkaline $KMnO_4$ yields benzoic acid

M.P. 121°. On reduction by Na amalgam yields methylphenyl carbinol B.P. 203°. Oxime M.P. 59°. Phenylhydrazone M.P. 105°. *p*-Nitrophenylhydrazone M.P. 184°. Semicarbazone M.P. 162°.

207°   *l*-Menthone $C_{10}H_{18}O$
D. 0·896 (20°). Optically active, $[a]_D = -28°$. Insol. in water. Odour of peppermint. On reduction by Na amalgam yields *l*-menthol M.P. 42°. Oxime M.P. 59°. Semicarbazone M.P. 184°.

224°   *d*-Carvone $C_{10}H_{14}O$
D. 0·960 (20°). Optically active, $[a]_D = +62°$. Odour of caraway. On heating with 2% of $POCl_3$ yields carvacrol B.P. 237° (violent reaction). With Na_2SO_3 soln yields very sol. bisulphite compd and NaOH. Oxime M.P. 72°. Semicarbazone M.P. 162°.

SOLID

M.P.
20°   Acetophenone B.P. 202°. See Ketones (Liquid).

28°   Phorone $(CH_3)_2C:CH\cdot CO\cdot CH:C(CH_3)_2$
B.P. 197°. Light yellow. Unsaturated. With bromine in CCl_4 yields tetrabromide M.P. 88°. On boiling with very dil. H_2SO_4 yields acetone B.P. 56°. Semicarbazone M.P. 186°.

41°   Benzalacetone $C_6H_5\cdot CH:CH\cdot CO\cdot CH_3$
B.P. 262°. Light yellow. Insol. in water. Unsaturated. Oxidised by acid $KMnO_4$ to benzaldehyde, B.P. 179°. Forms a dibromide M.P. 124°. Oxime M.P. 115°. Phenylhydrazone M.P. 156°. *p*-Nitrophenylhydrazone M.P. 166°.

48°   Benzophenone $C_6H_5\cdot CO\cdot C_6H_5$
B.P. 305°. Insol. in water. Forms yellow soln in conc. H_2SO_4. On fusion with Na gives deep blue colour. On reduction with Zn dust + NaOH in alc. yields benzhydrol M.P. 68°. On fusion with KOH yields benzoic acid M.P. 121° and benzene B.P. 80°. Oxime M.P. 141°. Phenylhydrazone M.P. 137°. *p*-Nitrophenylhydrazone M.P. 154°. 2:4-Dinitrophenylhydrazone M.P. 229°. Semicarbazone M.P. 164°.

95°   Benzil $C_6H_5\cdot CO\cdot CO\cdot C_6H_5$
B.P. 347°. Pale yellow. Insol. in water. Boiled with alcoholic KOH yields benzilic acid M.P. 150°. Oxidised by alkaline $KMnO_4$ to benzoic acid M.P. 121°. Di-phenylhydrazone M.P. 225°. Di-*p*-nitrophenylhydrazone M.P. 290°. α-Dioxime M.P. 237°.

130°   Benzoin $C_6H_5 \cdot CO \cdot CH(OH) \cdot C_6H_5$
        B.P. 343°. Insol. in water. Oxidised by Fehling's
        soln. (with alc.) to benzil M.P. 95°; by acid $KMnO_4$ to
        benzoic acid M.P. 121° and benzaldehyde B.P. 179°.
        Acetyl deriv. M.P. 83°. Benzoyl deriv. M.P. 125°.
        α-Naphthylcarbamate M.P.140°. Oxime M.P. 151°.
        Phenylhydrazone M.P. 106°.

175°   d-Camphor $C_{10}H_{16}O$
        B.P. 209°. Optically active, $[α]_D = +44°$ in alc.
        Characteristic odour. Sol. unchanged in conc. H_2SO_4.
        On reduction in alc. with Na yields borneol M.P. 203°.
        Oxidised by hot conc. HNO_3 to camphoric acid M.P.
        187°. With Br_2 in $CHCl_3$ forms an unstable cry-
        stalline addition-product which on warming yields
        bromocamphor M.P. 76°. With Na + isoamyl nitrite
        in dry ether yields isonitrosocamphor M.P. 153°,
        which on boiling with $NH_2OH \cdot HCl$ + Na acetate in
        dil. alc. yields camphorquinone dioxime M.P. 201°d.
        and on treatment in acetic acid with $NaNO_2$ yields
        camphorquinone M.P. 198°. Oxime M.P. 118°.
        Phenylhydrazone B.P. 233°d. Semicarbazone M.P.
        237°.

218°   Phloroglucinol. See Phenols (Solid).

QUINONES

SOLID

45°   Thymoquinone $CH_3 \cdot C : CH \cdot CO$
                        $CO \cdot CH : C \cdot CH(CH_3)_2$
        B.P. 232°. Yellow. Volatile with steam. Sparingly
        sol. in water. Reduced by aqueous SO_2 to hydro-
        thymoquinone M.P. 139°. Forms a compd. with
        hydroquinone M.P. 137°.

68°   Toluquinone $CH : CH \cdot CO$
                       $CO \cdot CH : C \cdot CH_3$
        Yellow. Sparingly sol. in water. Odour resembles
        that of benzoquinone. On reduction with SO_2 yields
        toluhydroquinone. M.P. 124°. Toluquinhydrone
        (blue needles, M.P. 52°) is readily sol. in water.
        With acetic anhydride containing a little conc.
        H_2SO_4 yields 2:4:5-triacetoxytoluene M.P. 114°. With
        $NH_2OH \cdot HCl$ in water yields monoxime M.P. 134°.

M.P.

95° Benzil. See Ketones (Solid).

115° Benzoquinone

$$\begin{array}{c} CH:CH\cdot CO \\ | \qquad\qquad | \\ CO\cdot CH:CH \end{array}$$

Yellow. Sparingly sol. in cold water. Characteristic odour. Soln. in alkali turns brown in air, gives brown amorphous ppte. on boiling with dil. acids. Reduces ammon. $AgNO_3$. Reduced to quinhydrone M.P. 171° by $FeSO_4$ in dil. H_2SO_4. Liberates iodine from KI soln. Yields phenoquinone M.P. 71° on addition of phenol. With small quantity conc. HCl gives black solid, converted to chlorohydroquinone M.P. 106° on warming. With acetic anhydride containing a little conc. H_2SO_4 yields hydroxyhydroquinone triacetate M.P. 96°. With $NH_2OH\cdot HCl$ in water yields p-nitrosophenol M.P. 144°d. With PCl_5 yields p-dichlorobenzene M.P. 53°.

d. 115
–120° β-Naphthoquinone

$$C_6H_4 \diagup\!\!\!\diagdown \begin{array}{l} CO\cdot CO \ (1) \\ | \\ CH:CH\,(2) \end{array}$$

Red. Insol. in water. Odourless. Not volatile with steam. Forms green soln. in conc. H_2SO_4. Oxidised by $KMnO_4$ to phthalic acid M.P. 195°. Reduced by boiling with SO_2 soln to β-hydronaphthoquinone M.P. 60°. On warming with $NH_2OH\cdot HCl$ in alc. yields β-nitroso-α-naphthol M.P. 163°d. With acetic anhydride containing a little conc. H_2SO_4 yields 1:2:4-triacetoxynaphthalene M.P. 135°.

125° α-Naphthoquinone

$$C_6H_4 \diagup\!\!\!\diagdown \begin{array}{l} CO\cdot CH \ (1) \\ \| \\ CO\cdot CH \ (2) \end{array}$$

Yellow. Sparingly sol. in water. Odour like quinone. Volatile with steam. Sol. unchanged in conc. H_2SO_4. Sol. in dil. NaOH with red-brown colour. Not reduced by SO_2 in cold, with Zn and HCl yields α-hydronaphthoquinone M.P. 173°. With phenylhydrazine HCl in 50 % acetic acid yields benzeneazo-α-naphthol M.P. 206°d. With acetic anhydride containing a little conc. H_2SO_4 yields 1:2:4-triacetoxynaphthalene M.P. 135°. On heating with aniline yields a product M.P. 190°.

171° Quinhydrone $C_6H_4O_2\cdot C_6H_4(OH)_2$ (1:4:1':4')

Dark green. Sparingly sol. in water. Readily sol. in alc. and in ether (yellow soln.) ; almost insol. in $CHCl_3$. On boiling with water yields benzoquinone

M.P.

M.P. 115° and hydroquinone M.P. 169°. Reduced by Zn and HCl to hydroquinone; oxidised by $K_2Cr_2O_7$ + dil. H_2SO_4 to benzoquinone. Reduces ammon. $AgNO_3$.

198° Camphorquinone

$$C_8H_{14} \left\langle \begin{array}{c} CO \\ | \\ CO \end{array} \right.$$

Bright yellow. Volatile with steam. Sparingly sol. in cold water and in benzene, readily sol. in alc. Reduced by Zn and HCl to α-hydroxycamphor M.P. 203°. Insol. in cold aqueous alkalies; on long boiling with alc. KOH yields camphoric acid M.P. 187°. With phenylhydrazine yields mono-phenyl-hydrazone M.P. 170°.

202° Phenanthrenequinone

$$\begin{array}{c} C_6H_4{\cdot}CO \\ | \quad\quad | \\ C_6H_4{\cdot}CO \end{array}$$

Orange. Sparingly sol. in water. Sol. in $NaHSO_3$ soln. Oxidised by CrO_3 or by $KMnO_4$ to diphenic acid M.P. 229°. On heating with zinc dust yields phenanthrene M.P. 100°; with soda-lime yields diphenyl M.P. 70°. Reduced by SO_2 in warm alc. to hydrophenanthrenequinone M.P. 147°. With NH_3 (gas) in warm alc. yields imide M.P. 158°. Di-p-nitro-phenylhydrazone M.P. 245°.

273° Anthraquinone

$$C_6H_4 \left\langle \begin{array}{c} CO \\ \\ CO \end{array} \right\rangle C_6H_4$$

Pale yellow. Sparingly sol. in cold benzene and ether; almost insol. in alc. Insol. in $NaHSO_3$ soln. Sol. unchanged in conc. H_2SO_4 and in warm conc. HNO_3. On boiling for 2 hours with 10 parts conc. HNO_3 yields 1-nitro deriv. M.P. 220°. On heating with zinc dust yields anthracene M.P. 216°. With Na hydrosulphite in boiling alc. yields oxanthranol M.P. 205°d. On warming with Zn dust + NH_4OH yields dihydroanthranol M.P. 76°. On boiling with acetic anhydride + Na acetate + $ZnCl_2$ yields anthrahydro-quinone diacetate M.P. 260°d. On heating with KOH at 250° yields benzoic acid M.P. 121°.

289° Alizarin

$$C_6H_4 \left\langle \begin{array}{c} CO \\ \\ CO \end{array} \right\rangle C_6H_2(OH)_2 \ (1{:}2)$$

Orange. Insol. in water, sol. in alkali giving purple

soln. $Ca(OH)_2$ and $Ba(OH)_2$ precipitate blue salts from soln in alkali ; salts of Al and Sn give red solns. Sol. in conc. H_2SO_4 with purple colour. On adding NaOH (or KOH) in alc. to boiling soln. in alc. the mono-Na (or K) salt separates (red crysts.). With acetic anhydride + Na acetate yields mono-acetyl deriv. M.P. 205°. On long treatment with excess of acetic anhydride yields diacetate M.P. 180°. On heating dry mono-K salt with methyl sulphate to 150–160° yields monomethyl ether M.P. 230°. Dimethyl ether M.P. 215°. Dibenzenesulphonate M.P. 183°.

SATURATED CARBOXYLIC ACIDS

LIQUID

B.P.

100° Formic   H.COOH

M.P. 8°. D. 1·245 (0°). Miscible with water. Sharp odour like that of SO_2. On heating with conc. H_2SO_4 yields CO. Decolorises acid $KMnO_4$. Gives yellow colour with conc. $NaHSO_3$ soln. Reduces $HgCl_2$ to Hg_2Cl_2. Ethyl ester B.P. 54°. p-Nitrobenzyl ester M.P. 31°. Anilide M.P. 47°. p-Toluidide M.P. 53°. Diphenylamide M.P. 73°. Ammonium salt M.P. 114°.

118° Acetic $CH_3 \cdot COOH$

M.P. 16°. D. 1·054 (16°). Miscible with water. Stable towards most oxidising agents. Ethyl ester B.P. 77°. p-Nitrobenzyl ester M.P. 78°. Phenacyl ester M.P. 40°. p-Bromophenacyl ester M.P. 85°. p-Iodophenacyl ester M.P. 114°. Chloride B.P. 55°. Amide M.P. 82°. Anilide M.P. 115°. p-Toluidide M.P. 147°. Ammonium salt M.P. 66°.

140° Propionic $CH_3 \cdot CH_2 \cdot COOH$

D. 0·996 (19°). Miscible with water. Ethyl ester B.P. 98°. p-Nitrobenzyl ester M.P. 31°. p-Bromophenacyl ester M.P. 59°. p-Iodophenacyl ester M.P. 95°. Chloride B.P. 80°. Amide M.P. 79°. Anilide M.P. 103°. p-Toluidide M.P. 124°. Acid ammonium salt M.P. 54°.

155° isoButyric $(CH_3)_2CH \cdot COOH$

D. 0·948 (20°). Sol. in 5 vols of cold water. Yields CO and SO_2 with conc. H_2SO_4 at 140–155°. Ethyl ester B.P. 110°. p-Nitrobenzyl ester is an oil. p-Bromophenacyl ester M.P. 77°. p-Iodophenacyl ester M.P. 109°. Chloride B.P. 92°. Amide M.P. 129°. Anilide M.P. 105°. *p*-Toluidide M.P. 104°.

163° *n*-Butyric $CH_3 \cdot [CH_2]_2 \cdot COOH$
D. 0·960 (19°). Miscible with water. Unpleasant odour. Soln. of Ca salt gives white ppte on warming. Ethyl ester B.P. 120°. *p*-Nitrobenzyl ester M.P. 35°. Phenacyl ester is an oil. *p*-Bromophenacyl ester M.P. 63°. *p*-Iodophenacyl ester M.P. 81°. Chloride B.P. 100°. Amide M.P. 115°. Anilide M.P. 90°. *p*-Toluidide M.P. 72°.

176° *iso*Valeric $(CH_3)_2CH \cdot CH_2 \cdot COOH$
D. 0·931 (20°). Sol. in 22 vols of cold water. Unpleasant odour. Ag and Zn salts insol. in water. Ethyl ester B.P. 134°. *p*-Bromophenacyl ester M.P. 68°. *p*-Nitrobenzyl ester is an oil. Chloride B.P. 115°. Amide M.P. 135°. Anilide M.P. 115°. *p*-Toluidide M.P. 98°.

186° *n*-Valeric $CH_3 \cdot [CH_2]_3 \cdot COOH$
D. 0·940 (19°). Sol. in 27 vols of cold water. Unpleasant odour. Methyl ester B.P. 127°. Ethyl ester B.P. 144°. *p*-Bromophenacyl ester M.P. 63°. Chloride B.P. 127°. Amide M.P. 104°. Anilide M.P. 60°. *p*-Toluidide M.P. 70°.

205° *n*-Caproic $CH_3 \cdot [CH_2]_4 \cdot COOH$
M.P. − 2° D. 0·929 (20°). Slightly sol. in cold water. Methyl ester B.P. 150°. Ethyl ester B.P. 166°. *p*-Bromophenacyl ester M.P. 71°. Chloride B.P. 152°. Amide M.P. 98°. Anilide M.P. 95°.

223° *n*-Heptylic (Oenanthic) $CH_3 \cdot [CH_2]_5 \cdot COOH$
D. 0·922 (15°). Sol. in about 400 vols of cold water. Methyl ester B.P. 173°. Ethyl ester B.P. 187°. Chloride B.P. 175°. Amide M.P. 94°. Anilide M.P. 71°. Zn salt M.P. 91°. Pb salt M.P. 78°.

237° *n*-Caprylic $CH_3 \cdot [CH_2]_6 \cdot COOH$
M.P. 16°. D. 0·917 (15°). Very slightly sol. in cold water. Methyl ester B.P. 193°. Ethyl ester B.P. 206°. Chloride B.P. 195°. Amide M.P. 105°. Anilide M.P. 57°. Zn salt M.P. 135°. Pb salt M.P. 84°.

253° Pelargonic $CH_3 \cdot [CH_2]_7 \cdot COOH$
M.P. 12°. D. 0·909 (15°). Almost insol. in water. Methyl ester B.P. 213°. Ethyl ester B.P. 227°. Chloride B.P. 98°/15 mm. Amide M.P. 99°. Anilide M.P. 57°. Zn salt M.P. 131°.

SOLID

16° Acetic B.P. 118°. See Saturated Acids (Liquid).

16° Caprylic B.P. 237°. See Saturated Acids (Liquid).

31° Capric $CH_3 \cdot [CH_2]_8 \cdot COOH$
B.P. 269°. Almost insol. in water. Volatile with steam. Methyl ester B.P. 223°. Ethyl ester B.P. 244°. p-Bromophenacyl ester M.P. 66°. Chloride B.P. 114°/15 mm. Amide M.P. 108°. Anilide M.P. 61°.

44° Lauric $CH_3 \cdot [CH_2]_{10} \cdot COOH$
B.P. 180°/16 mm. Volatile with steam. Insol. in water. Methyl ester M.P. 5°, B.P. 141°/15 mm. Ethyl ester B.P. 269°. Chloride B.P. 142°/15 mm. Amide M.P. 98°. Anilide M.P. 76°. Zn salt M.P. 127°. Pb salt M.P. 101°.

48° Hydrocinnamic $C_6H_5 \cdot [CH_2]_2 \cdot COOH$
B.P. 280°. Insol. in water. Oxidised by chromic acid to benzoic acid M.P. 121°. Methyl ester B.P. 236°. Ethyl ester B.P. 247°. p-Nitrobenzyl ester M.P. 36°. p-Bromophenacyl ester M.P. 104°. Chloride B.P. 117°/13 mm. Amide M.P. 82°. Anilide M.P. 92°.

53° Myristic $CH_3 \cdot [CH_2]_{12} \cdot COOH$
B.P. 199°/16 mm. Insol. in water. Methyl ester M.P. 18°, B.P. 167°/15 mm. Ethyl ester M.P. 10°, B.P. 295°. Chloride B.P. 168°/15 mm. Amide M.P. 102°. Anilide M.P. 84°.

62° Palmitic $CH_3 \cdot [CH_2]_{14} \cdot COOH$
Insol. in water. Though neutral to litmus in water, reacts acid in alc. soln. Methyl ester M.P. 30°. Ethyl ester M.P. 24°. p-Nitrobenzyl ester M.P. 42°. Phenacyl ester M.P. 52°. p-Bromophenacyl ester M.P. 81°. p-Iodophenacyl ester M.P. 90°. Chloride M.P. 12°, B.P. 192°/15 mm. Amide M.P. 106°. Anilide M.P. 90°. Pb salt M.P. 112°.

69° Stearic $CH_3 \cdot [CH_2]_{16} \cdot COOH$
Resembles palmitic acid M.P. 62°, though less sol. in alc. Methyl ester M.P. 38°. Ethyl ester M.P. 33°. No result with p-nitrobenzyl bromide. Phenacyl ester M.P. 64°. p-Bromophenacyl ester M.P. 78°. p-Iodophenacyl ester M.P. 90°. Chloride M.P. 23°, B.P. 215°/15 mm. Amide M.P. 108°. Anilide M.P. 93°. Pb salt M.P. 125°.

M.P.

76° Phenylacetic $C_6H_5 \cdot CH_2 \cdot COOH$
B.P. 262°. Sol. in hot water, sparingly in cold. Intense and characteristic odour. Oxidised to benz-aldehyde B.P. 179° with acid $KMnO_4$; with alkaline $KMnO_4$ yields benzoic acid M.P. 121°. Methyl ester B.P. 220°. Ethyl ester B.P. 227°. p-Nitrobenzyl ester M.P. 65°. p-Bromophenacyl ester M.P. 89°. Chloride B.P. 180°d. Amide M.P. 154°. Anilide M.P. 117°.

97° Glutaric $COOH \cdot [CH_2]_3 \cdot COOH$
B.P. 303°. Sol. in equal weight of cold water; slightly sol. in benzene. Methyl ester B.P. 214°. Ethyl ester B.P. 236°. Phenacyl ester M.P. 104°. Chloride B.P. 217°. Amide M.P. 174°, yields imide M.P. 154° on heating above 175°. On heating with aniline yields anil M.P. 144°.

101° Oxalic (Hydrated) $C(OH)_3 \cdot C(OH)_3$
Sol. in about 8 parts of water at 20°. Loses water on fusion, then subl. above 150°. M.P. 189° in closed tube. On heating with conc. H_2SO_4 yields CO and CO_2. Oxidised to CO_2 on warming to 60° with acid $KMnO_4$. Not attacked by dil. alk. $KMnO_4$. Ca salt insol. in water or dil. acetic acid. On distillation with excess n-butyl alcohol yields butyl ester B.P. 243°. p-Nitrobenzyl ester M.P. 204°. No result with phenacyl bromide. Anilide M.P. 245°. p-Toluidide M.P. 267°.

101° Methylsalicylic. See Alkyl Hydroxy Acids.

102° o-Toluic $CH_3 \cdot C_6H_4 \cdot COOH$ (1:2)
B.P. 259°. Sparingly sol. in water. Oxidised by alkaline $KMnO_4$ to phthalic acid M.P. 195°. Yields toluene B.P. 110° on heating with soda-lime. Methyl ester B.P. 207°. Ethyl ester B.P. 221°. p-Nitro-benzyl ester M.P. 90°. p-Bromophenacyl ester M.P. 57°. Chloride B.P. 211°. Amide M.P. 142°. Anilide M.P. 125°.

106° Azelaic $COOH \cdot [CH_2]_7 \cdot COOH$
B.P. 237°/15 mm. Sol. in about 500 parts cold water; miscible in all proportions with boiling water. Sol. in about 40 pts. of cold ether. Ethyl ester B.P. 291°. Chloride B.P. 165°/13 mm. Amide M.P. 175°. Anilide M.P. 185°.

109° m-Toluic $CH_3 \cdot C_6H_4 \cdot COOH$ (1:3)
B.P. 263°. Sparingly sol. in water. Oxidised by

M.P.

alkaline $KMnO_4$ to *iso*-phthalic acid (*q.v.*). Yields toluene B.P. 110° on heating with soda-lime. Methyl ester B.P. 214°. Ethyl ester B.P. 220°. *p*-Nitrobenzyl ester M.P. 86°. *p*-Bromophenacyl ester M.P. 108°. Chloride B.P. 218°. Amide M.P. 94°.

111° Ethylmalonic $C_2H_5 \cdot CH(COOH)_2$

Sol. in water. Heated above M.P. yields *n*-butyric acid B.P. 163° and CO_2. Ethyl ester B.P. 200°. *p*-Nitrobenzyl ester M.P. 75°.

117°d. Benzylmalonic $C_6H_5 \cdot CH_2 \cdot CH(COOH)_2$

Sol. in water. On heating yields hydrocinnamic acid M.P. 48° and CO_2. *p*-Nitrobenzyl ester M.P. 119°.

121° Benzoic $C_6H_5 \cdot COOH$

B.P. 249°. Sol. in hot water, sparingly so in cold. On nitration yields *m*-nitrobenzoic acid M.P. 140° with a little *o*-nitrobenzoic acid. Yields benzene B.P. 80° on heating with soda-lime. Methyl ester B.P. 198°. Ethyl ester B.P. 213°. *p*-Nitrobenzyl ester M.P. 89°. Phenacyl ester M.P. 118°. *p*-Iodophenacyl ester M.P. 126°. Chloride M.P. 0°. B.P. 197°. Amide M.P. 128°. Anilide M.P. 160°.

133° Malonic $CH_2(COOH)_2$

Very sol. in water. Ca, Ba, Ag salts insol. On heating above M.P. yields acetic acid B.P. 118° and CO_2. On warming with acetic anhydride gives orange colour with green fluorescence. With bromine water yields tribromoacetic acid M.P. 135° and CO_2. Ethyl ester B.P. 198°. *p*-Nitrobenzyl ester M.P. 85°. On warming with phenyl *iso*cyanate yields malondianilide M.P. 224°.

133° Sebacic $COOH \cdot [CH_2]_8 \cdot COOH$

Slightly sol. in hot water. Ca salt insol. On heating with soda-lime yields *n*-octane B.P. 125°. Methyl ester M.P. 38°, B.P. 288°d. Ethyl ester M.P. 4°, B.P. 307°. *p*-Nitrobenzyl ester M.P. 72°. *p*-Bromophenacyl ester M.P. 147°. Amide M.P. 210°. Anilide M.P. 198°.

133° Furoic (Pyromucic)   CH·O·C·COOH
                              ‖   ‖
                              CH —CH

Readily sol. in hot water, moderately (4 %) in cold. Sol. in benzene and in ether. Pyrrole is formed on heating the NH_4 salt (a pine splinter moistened with conc. HCl turns red in vapour). Methyl ester B.P.

M.P.

181°. Ethyl ester M.P. 34°, B.P. 209°. *p*-Nitro-benzyl ester M.P. 133°. *p*-Bromophenacyl ester M.P. 138°. Amide M.P. 141°. Anilide M.P. 123°.

135°d. Methylmalonic (*iso*Succinic) $CH_3 \cdot CH(COOH)_2$
Sol. in water. Ca, Ba, Pb, Ag salts insol. On heating yields propionic acid B.P. 140°. Methyl ester B.P. 178°. Ethyl ester B.P. 196°.

151°   Adipic $COOH \cdot [CH_2]_4 \cdot COOH$
B.P. 216°/15 mm. Sol. in 70 pts. cold water, in 170 pts. cold ether. Readily sol. in alc. Not attacked by hot HNO_3. Methyl ester M.P. 8°, B.P. 115°/13 mm. Ethyl ester B.P. 245°. Chloride B.P. 126°/11 mm. Amide M.P. 220°. Anilide M.P. 235°.

160°   α-Naphthoic $C_{10}H_7 \cdot COOH$ (1)
Sparingly sol. in water. Yields naphthalene M.P. 80° on heating with soda-lime. Ethyl ester B.P. 309°. Chloride B.P. 297°. Amide M.P. 202°. Anilide M.P. 160°.

177°   *p*-Toluic $CH_3 \cdot C_6H_4 \cdot COOH$ (1:4)
B.P. 275°. Sol. in hot water. On oxidation by alkaline $KMnO_4$ yields terephthalic acid (*q.v.*). Yields toluene B.P. 110° on heating with soda-lime. Methyl ester M.P. 32°, B.P. 217°. Ethyl ester B.P. 228°. *p*-Nitrobenzyl ester M.P. 104°. *p*-Bromophenacyl ester M.P. 153°. Chloride B.P. 224°. Amide M.P. 158°. Anilide M.P. 140°.

182°   β-Naphthoic $C_{10}H_7 \cdot COOH$ (2)
Insol. in water. Yields naphthalene M.P. 80° on heating with soda-lime. Methyl ester M.P. 77°, B.P. 290°. Ethyl ester B.P. 308°. Chloride M.P. 43°, B.P. 304°. Amide M.P. 192°. Anilide M.P 170°.

184°   Anisic. See Alkyloxy Acids.

185°   Succinic $COOH \cdot CH_2 \cdot CH_2 \cdot COOH$
B.P. 235°d. (giving anhydride M.P. 119°). Sol. in water. Fe salt insol. in dil. acetic acid. Ammonium salt yields pyrrole on ignition with Zn dust (pine splinter soaked in conc. HCl turns red in vapour). Methyl ester M.P. 18°, B.P. 195°. Ethyl ester B.P. 216°. *p*-Nitrobenzyl ester M.P. 88°. Phenacyl ester M.P. 148°. *p*-Chlorophenacyl ester M.P. 197°. *p*-Bromophenacyl ester M.P. 211°. Amide M.P. 242°. Imide M.P. 125°. Anilide M.P. 226°. Anil M.P. 156°.

187°   *d*-Camphoric $C_8H_{14}(COOH)_2$
Optically active, $[\alpha]_D = +47°$ in alc. Moderately

sol. in water. Pb salt insol. Heated with conc. H_2SO_4 yields CO. On warming with acetyl chloride yields anhydride M.P. 221°. Methyl ester B.P. 264°. Ethyl ester B.P. 285°. *p*-Nitrobenzyl ester M.P. 66°. Amide M.P. 192°. Imide M.P. 244°. Anil M.P. 117°.

189° Oxalic (Anhydrous) COOH·COOH
See Hydrated Oxalic Acid M.P. 101°

195°d. Phthalic $C_6H_4(COOH)_2$ (1:2)
Complete crystals melt at 213°. Loses water above M.P. forming anhydride M.P. 130°. Sol. in hot water and in $CHCl_3$. Yields benzene B.P. 80° on heating with soda-lime. Fused with resorcinol and a little conc. H_2SO_4 yields fluorescein (orange soln. with green fluorescence in alkali). Methyl ester B.P. 282°. Ethyl ester B.P. 298°. *p*-Nitrobenzyl ester M.P. 155°. Ammonium salt on prolonged fusion yields phthalimide M.P. 238°. Anil M.P. 205°. Chloride B.P. 275°.

Above
300° Isophthalic $C_6H_4(COOH)_2$ (1:3)
Insol. in water. Yields benzene B.P. 80° on heating with soda-lime. Ba salt sol. in water. Methyl ester M.P. 67°. Ethyl ester B.P. 302°. *p*-Nitrobenzyl ester M.P. 202°, B.P. 276°. Chloride M.P. 41°, B.P. 276°. Amide M.P. 265°. Anilide M.P. 250°.

Subl. Terephthalic $C_6H_4(COOH)_2$ (1:4)
Insol. in water and in $CHCl_3$. Yields benzene B.P. 80° on heating with soda-lime. Ca, Ba salts almost insol. in water. Methyl ester M.P. 140°. Ethyl ester M.P. 44°, B.P. 302°. *p*-Nitrobenzyl ester M.P. 263°. Chloride M.P. 77°, B.P. 259°. Amide insol. in all organic liquids.

UNSATURATED ACIDS

LIQUID

B.P.
140° Acrylic CH_2:CH·COOH
M.P. 8°. D. 1·062 (16°). Miscible with water. With bromine yields *αβ*-dibromopropionic acid M.P. 64°. With HCl yields *β*-chloropropionic acid M.P. 41°. Methyl ester B.P. 85°. Ethyl ester B.P. 101°. Amide M.P. 84°. Anilide M.P. 104°.

144°d. Propiolic CH:C·COOH
M.P. 6°. Miscible with water. With bromine yields *αβ*-dibromoacrylic acid M.P. 85°. With HCl yields

β-chloroacrylic acid M.P. 84°. Gives an explosive brown ppte. with ammon. CuCl. Ethyl ester B.P. 119°.

169°   *iso*Crotonic $CH_3 \cdot CH:CH \cdot COOH$
D. 1·031 (15°). Miscible with water. On heating to 150° with a trace of iodine is converted to α-crotonic acid. With bromine yields *iso*-αβ-dibromobutyric acid (liquid). Ethyl ester B.P. 136°.

223°/   Oleic $CH_3 \cdot [CH_2]_7 \cdot CH:CH \cdot [CH_2]_7 \cdot COOH$
10 mm.   M.P. 14°. D. 0·898 (14°). Insol. in water ; gives no acid reaction to litmus in water, but distinctly in alc. Oxidised by $KMnO_4$ to dihydroxystearic acid M.P. 134°, pelargonic acid B.P. 253° and azelaic acid M.P. 106°. With bromine yields an oily dibromostearic acid. *p*-Nitrobenzyl ester is an oil. Phenacyl ester is an oil. *p*-Bromophenacyl ester M.P. 62°. Chloride B.P. 213°/13 mm. Amide M.P. 78°.

SOLID

M.P.
51°   Elaidic $CH_3 \cdot [CH_2]_7 \cdot CH:CH \cdot [CH_2]_7 \cdot COOH$
(*Trans* isomer of oleic acid.) B.P. 225°/10 mm. Insol. in water. Acid reaction to litmus in alc. only (Cf. oleic acid). Forms with bromine a solid dibromostearic acid M.P. 27°. Yields pelargonic acid B.P. 253° and azelaic acid M.P. 106° on oxidation by $KMnO_4$. Chloride B.P. 216°d./13 mm. Amide M.P. 92°.

72°   α-Crotonic $CH_3 \cdot CH:CH \cdot COOH$
B.P. 180°. Sol. in water. Reduces ammoniacal $AgNO_3$ on warming. Yields *n*-butyric acid with Zn and dil. H_2SO_4. Bromine yields αβ-dibromobutyric acid M.P. 87°. Yields β-iodobutyric acid M.P. 110° with HI. Amide M.P. 150°.

80°   Citraconic $COOH \cdot CH:C(CH_3) \cdot COOH$
Sol. in water. On heating yields anhydride B.P. 213°. Warmed with bromine water yields dibromomethylsuccinic acid M.P. 150°. Methyl ester B.P. 210°. Ethyl ester B.P. 231°. Phenacyl ester M.P. 108°. Imide M.P. 109°.

133°   Cinnamic $C_6H_5 \cdot CH:CH \cdot COOH$
B.P. 299°. Sparingly sol. in water. On oxidation with acid $KMnO_4$ yields benzaldehyde B.P. 179° ; with alkaline $KMnO_4$ yields benzoic acid M.P. 121°. On warming with bromine water yields αβ-dibromophenylpropionic acid M.P. 195°. With fuming HNO_3

in the cold yields chiefly *p*-nitrocinnamic acid M.P. 285°. Methyl ester M.P. 36°, B.P. 263°. Ethyl ester B.P. 271°. *p*-Nitrobenzyl ester M.P. 116°. Phenacyl ester M.P. 140°. *p*-Bromophenacyl ester M.P. 145°. Chloride M.P. 35°, B.P. 252°. Amide M.P. 141°. Anilide M.P. 153°.

136° **Phenylpropiolic** $C_6H_5 \cdot C:C \cdot COOH$
Insol. in water. Heated with Zn dust and glacial acetic acid yields cinnamic acid. With conc. HBr yields *β*-bromoallocinnamic acid M.P. 159°. Ethyl ester B.P. 260°–270°. *p*-Nitrobenzyl ester M.P. 83°. Amide M.P. 102°.

139° **Maleic** $COOH \cdot CH:CH \cdot COOH$
Sol. in water. On heating in vac. above 150° yields anhydride M.P. 56°, B.P. 202°. On heating to 200° yields fumaric acid (*q.v.*). With bromine yields *iso*-dibromosuccinic acid M.P. 160°. Boiled with aniline yields phenylaspartic anil M.P. 211°. Methyl ester B.P. 205°. Ethyl ester B.P. 225°. *p*-Nitrobenzyl ester M.P. 89°. Phenacyl ester M.P. 119°. *p*-Bromophenacyl ester M.P. 168°d.

161° **Itaconic** $COOH \cdot C(:CH_2)CH_2 \cdot COOH$
Sol. in water. With bromine yields *ita*-dibromo-pyrotartaric acid (amorphous) ; with HCl yields *ita*-chloropyrotartaric acid M.P. 140°. Warmed with acetyl chloride yields anhydride M.P. 68°. Heated with aniline yields pseudoitaconanilic acid M.P. 190°. Methyl ester B.P. 210°. Ethyl ester B.P. 227°. Phenacyl ester M.P. 79°. Amide M.P. 192°.

191° **Aconitic** $COOH \cdot CH:C(COOH) \cdot CH_2 \cdot COOH$
Sol. in water. Heated at 200° yields itaconic anhydride M.P. 68° and CO_2. Decolorises bromine water only on warming. Methyl ester B.P. 270°. Ethyl ester B.P. 275°. *p*-Nitrobenzyl ester M.P. 76° (very poor yield). Phenacyl ester M.P. 90°. *p*-Chloro-phenacyl ester M.P. 169°. *p*-Bromophenacyl ester M.P. 186°.

Subl. **Fumaric** $COOH \cdot CH:CH \cdot COOH$
200° M.P. 286° in closed tube. Sparingly sol. in water. Warmed with bromine water yields a dibromosuccinic acid d. 200–235°. On heating with aniline yields phenylaspartic anil M.P. 211°. Methyl ester M.P. 102°, B.P. 192°. Ethyl ester B.P. 218°. *p*-Nitro-benzyl ester M.P. 150°. Phenacyl ester M.P. 197°.

M.P.
207°   Coumaric.   See Aromatic Hydroxy Acids.

216°   Piperic $(CH_2O_2):C_6H_3 [CH:CH]_2 \cdot COOH$ (1:2:4)
        Pale yellow.   Insol. in water.   Gently oxidised by
        acid $KMnO_4$ yields piperonal M.P. 37°.   Yields proto-
        catechuic acid M.P. 194°d. on fusion with potash.
        Ethyl ester M.P. 77°. p-Nitrobenzyl ester M.P. 145°.

ALIPHATIC HYDROXY ACIDS

SOLID

M.P.
18° dl-Lactic $CH_3 \cdot CH(OH) \cdot COOH$
        Generally a liquid, B.P. 119°/12 mm.   Miscible with
        water.   Decolorises acid $KMnO_4$ on warming.   Red
        colour formed on warming 0·2 c.c. of a 0·1 % soln
        with 2 c.c. of conc. H_2SO_4 for 2 mins. at 100°, cooling,
        and adding 2 drops of 5 % alc. guaiacol.   Oxidation by
        chromic acid yields acetaldehyde and acetic acid.
        Methyl ester B.P. 144°.   Ethyl ester B.P. 154°.
        p-Nitrobenzyl ester is an oil.   Phenacyl ester M.P. 96°.
        p-Bromophenacyl ester M.P. 112°. p-Iodophenacyl
        ester M.P. 139°.   Amide M.P. 74°.   Acetyl deriv.
        M.P. 57°, B.P. 127°/11 mm.

79°   Glycollic $CH_2OH \cdot COOH$
        Sol. in water ; tends to deliquesce.   On heating yields
        formaldehyde.   Guaiacol test (cf. lactic acid) gives
        violet colour in presence of 1 cc. glacial acetic acid.   Ag,
        Ca, Cu salts sp. sol. in cold water.   Oxidised by HNO_3
        to oxalic acid ($q.v.$).   Methyl ester B.P. 151°.   Ethyl
        ester B.P. 160°. p-Bromophenacyl ester M.P. 138°.
        Amide M.P. 120°.   Acetyl deriv. M.P. 66° (sol. in
        water, sparingly sol. in benzene).

100° l-Malic $COOH \cdot CH_2 \cdot CH(OH) \cdot COOH$
        Optically active, conc. solns rotate to right, dil.
        solns to left.   Hygroscopic.   Ba salt very sol.   Ca
        salt insol.   Neutral soln containing NH_4Cl gives no
        ppte. with $CaCl_2$ on boiling, but does on addition of 1–2
        vols. of alc.   With cobalt nitrate and excess NaOH
        gives blue colour.   With β-naphthol in conc. H_2SO_4
        green-yellow colour, clear yellow on warming, pale
        orange on dilution.   On heating to 180° yields
        fumaric acid and maleic anhydride ($q.v.$).   With
        PCl_5 in the cold yields α-chlorosuccinic acid M.P.
        176°d. after treatment with water.   Methyl ester B.P.
        122°/12 mm.   Ethyl ester B.P. 129°/12 mm. p-
        Nitrobenzyl ester M.P. 124°.   Phenacyl ester M.P. 106°.

M.P.

100°   Citric $COOH \cdot C(OH)(CH_2 \cdot COOH)_2 + H_2O$
Sol. in water. Loses water of crystallisation at 130°
forming anhydrous acid M.P. 153°. Soln of Ca salt
gives ppte on boiling or on addition of NaOH. With
warm conc. H_2SO_4 does not char, but gives a yellow
soln containing acetone dicarboxylic acid ; on neutralising and adding nitroprusside gives red colour
changed to violet with acetic acid. Insol. Ba salt
separates slowly. With β-naphthol in conc.H_2SO_4
blue colour, not changed to green on warming. With
$KMnO_4$ in water or glacial acetic acid yields acetone
(CHI_3 test). Ethyl ester B.P. 294°. p-Nitrobenzyl
ester M.P. 102°. Phenacyl ester M.P. 104°. p-
Bromophenacyl ester M.P. 148°. With acetyl chloride
yields acetylcitric anhydride M.P. 115°.

118° dl-Mandelic $C_6H_5 \cdot CH(OH) \cdot COOH$
Sol. in water. On warming with acid $KMnO_4$ yields
benzaldehyde B.P. 179°. Methyl ester M.P. 52°.
Ethyl ester M.P. 34°, B.P. 253°. Phenacyl ester
M.P. 84°. Acetyl deriv. M.P. 73°.

133° d- or l-Mandelic $C_6H_5 \cdot CH(OH) \cdot COOH$
Cf. Mandelic acid M.P. 118°.

150°   Benzilic $(C_6H_5)_2C(OH) \cdot COOH$
Sol. in hot water. Dissolves in conc. H_2SO_4 with
red colour. Oxidised by chromic acid to benzophe-
none M.P. 48°. Methyl ester M.P. 74°. Ethyl ester
M.P. 34°. p-Nitrobenzyl ester M.P. 99°. Amide
M.P. 154°. Acetyl deriv. M.P. 98°.

153°   Citric (anhydrous). See Citric M.P. 100°.

169° d-Tartaric $COOH \cdot [CH(OH)]_2 \cdot COOH$
Optically active. $[a]_D = + 12°$ (20% in water). Sol.
in water. Ca salt insol. in water but sol. in a cold
conc. soln of NaOH. No ppte. on adding $CaCl_2$ to soln
of free acid. Salts char on heating. Acid chars
and effervesces with hot conc. H_2SO_4. With cobalt
nitrate and excess NaOH colourless solution in cold,
blue on warming, colourless again on cooling. With
β-naphthol in conc. H_2SO_4 green colour, unchanged
on warming, orange on dilution. On adding successively $FeSO_4$, H_2O_2 and NaOH gives violet colour.
Conc. soln. gives ppte. of KH salt on adding K acetate.
With acetyl chloride yields diacetyltartaric anhydride
M.P. 126°. p-Nitrobenzyl ester M.P. 163°. Phenacyl
ester M.P. 130°. p-Bromophenacyl ester d. 216

M.P.

On distilling with excess *n*-butyl alc. yields ester M.P. 22°, B.P. 197°/15 mm. (diacetyl deriv. M.P. 58°).

13°d.   Mucic   COOH·[CH(OH)]$_4$·COOH

Sparingly sol. in water, insol. in alcohol.   Pyrrole is evolved on heating the sparingly sol. NH$_4$ salt (a pine shaving moistened with conc. HCl turns red when held in the vapours).   On heating yields furoic acid M.P. 133°.   Ethyl ester M.P. 158°d.   Tetra-acetyl deriv. M.P. 266°.   *p*-Nitrobenzyl ester M.P. above 310°.   Phenacyl ester M.P. 310°.   *p*-Bromo-phenacyl ester d. 225° (poor yield).

AROMATIC HYDROXY ACIDS

SOLID

M.P.

55°   Salicylic   HO·C$_6$H$_4$·COOH (1:2)

Sol. with difficulty in water.   Gives purple colour with FeCl$_3$ in water.   With 15 % HNO$_3$ yields 5-nitrosalicylic acid M.P. 226°.   Heated with soda-lime yields phenol.   Methyl ester (odour of winter-green) B.P. 224°.   Ethyl ester B.P. 231°.   *p*-Nitro-benzyl ester M.P. 96°.   Phenacyl ester M.P. 110°. *p*-Bromophenacyl ester M.P. 140°.   Amide M.P. 139°. Acetyl deriv. M.P. 135°.   Anilide M.P. 134° on heat-ing yields acridone M.P. 354°.   With methyl sulphate and alkali yields methylsalicylic acid M.P. 101°.

94°d.   Protocatechuic   (HO)$_2$C$_6$H$_3$·COOH (1:2:4)

Sol. in water.   Blue-green colour with FeCl$_3$ in water. On heating yields catechol M.P. 104° and CO$_2$. Reduces ammon. AgNO$_3$.   Methyl ester M.P. 134°. Ethyl ester M.P. 134°.   Diacetyl deriv. M.P. 151°. With methyl sulphate and alkali yields veratric acid M.P. 179.°

00°d.   Coumaric   HO·C$_6$H$_4$·CH:CH·COOH (1:2)

Sparingly sol. in water.   Unsaturated.   Gives a ppte. with FeCl$_3$.   On fusion with KOH yields salicylic acid M.P. 155°.   With conc. HBr yields coumarin M.P. 67° on standing.   *p*-Nitrobenzyl ester M.P. 152°. Acetyl deriv. M.P. 146°.

00°   *m*-Hydroxybenzoic   HO·C$_6$H$_4$·COOH (1:3)

Slightly sol. in water.   Gives no colour with FeCl$_3$. On heating with soda-lime yields phenol.   Methyl ester M.P. 70°.   Ethyl ester M.P. 72°.   Acetyl deriv. M.P. 127°.   With methyl sulphate and alkali yields

M.P.

m-methoxybenzoic acid M.P. 106°.   *p*-Nitrobenz
ester M.P. 106°.

207°   Vanillic $HO \cdot C_6H_3(OCH_3) \cdot COOH$ (1:2:4)
Sparingly sol. in water.   Gives no colour with FeCl
On boiling with 48% HBr yields protocatechuic ac
M.P. 194°.   Heated with soda-lime yields guaiac
M.P. 28°, B.P. 205°.   Methyl ester M.P. 62°, B.
285°.   Ethyl ester M.P. 44°, B.P. 292°.   *p*-Nitr
benzyl ester M.P. 140°d.   Acetyl deriv. M.P. 142
On methylation yields veratric acid M.P. 179°.

213°   *p*-Hydroxybenzoic $HO \cdot C_6H_4 \cdot COOH$ (1:4)
Sparingly sol. in water.   Gives red colour with FeCl
Heated with soda-lime yields phenol.   Methyl est
M.P. 131°.   Ethyl ester M.P. 116°.   *p*-Nitrobenz
ester M.P. 198°.   Acetyl deriv. M.P. 185°.   C
methylation yields anisic acid M.P. 184°.

d.200   Tannic (digallic) $C_{14}H_{10}O_9 + 2H_2O$
−220°   Sol. in water.   Deep blue colour with $FeCl_3$.   Easi
oxidised ;   soln. in NaOH turns brown in a
On heating yields pyrogallol M.P. 133° and CC
Astringent (coagulates soln. of gelatine).

222°   2-Hydroxy-3-naphthoic $HO \cdot C_{10}H_6 \cdot COOH$ (2:3)
Slightly sol. in cold water ;   soln. gives blue colo
with $FeCl_3$.   Methyl ester M.P. 75°.   Acetyl deri
M.P. 185°.   Benzoyl deriv. M.P. 208°.

263°   Gallic $(HO)_3C_6H_2 \cdot COOH$ (1:2:3:5)
Readily sol. in hot water.   Blue-black ppte. with FeC
Easily oxidised (*cf.* Tannic Acid).   Does not coagula
gelatine soln.   On heating yields pyrogallol M.
133° and CO_2.   Ethyl ester M.P. 141°.   Triacet
deriv. M.P. 170°d.   With methyl sulphate and alk
yields trimethylgallic acid M.P. 167°.

ALKYL- and ACYL-HYDROXY ACIDS

SOLID

M.P.
96°   Phenoxyacetic $C_6H_5O \cdot CH_2 \cdot COOH$
B.P. 285°.   Sol. in water.   Gives yellow ppte. wi
$FeCl_3$ in water.   Yields phenol and bromoacetic ac
(*q.v.*) on boiling with 48 % HBr.   Yields 2:4-dinitr
phenol M.P. 114° on warming with dil. HNO_3.   Meth
ester B.P. 245°.   Ethyl ester B.P. 251°.   Amide M
101°.   Anilide M.P. 99°.

M.P.

01° Methylsalicylic $CH_3O \cdot C_6H_4 \cdot COOH$ (1:2)
Sparingly sol. in water. Gives no colour with $FeCl_3$.
On heating with soda-lime yields anisole B.P. 154°.
On boiling with 48 % HBr yields salicylic acid M.P.
155°. Methyl ester B.P. 228°. Ethyl ester B.P.
235°. Chloride B.P. 254°. Amide M.P. 128°. Anilide
M.P. 62°.

35° Acetylsalicylic (' Aspirin ') $CH_3 \cdot COO \cdot C_6H_4 \cdot COOH$ (1:2)
Sparingly sol. in water. Gives no colour with $FeCl_3$.
Yields acetic acid and salicylic acid M.P. 155° on
boiling with alkali. Ethyl ester B.P. 272°. p-
Nitrobenzyl ester M.P. 140°. Chloride M.P. 43°,
B.P. 135°/12 mm.

84° Anisic $CH_3O \cdot C_6H_4 \cdot COOH$ (1:4)
B.P. 280°. Sparingly sol. in water. On heating with
soda-lime yields anisole B.P. 154°. On boiling with
48 % HBr or on fusion with KOH yields p-hydroxy-
benzoic acid M.P. 213°. Methyl ester M.P. 45°,
B.P. 255°. Ethyl ester M.P. 7°, B.P. 269°. p-
Nitrobenzyl ester M.P. 132°. p-Bromophenacyl ester
M.P. 152°. Chloride M.P. 22°, B.P. 145°/14 mm.
Amide M.P. 162°. Anilide M.P. 168°.

07° Vanillic. See Aromatic Hydroxy Acids.

16° Piperic. See Unsaturated Acids (Solid).

KETONIC ACIDS

SOLID

M.P.

13° Pyruvic $CH_3 \cdot CO \cdot COOH$
B.P. 165°. D. 1·288 (18°). Miscible with water.
Readily decolorises bromine water and $KMnO_4$.
Reduces ammon. $AgNO_3$. Ammoniacal soln gives
violet colour with nitroprusside, changed to red with
KOH and to blue with acetic acid. With β-naphthol
in conc. H_2SO_4 gives red colour, changing to blue
on warming. Yields iodoform M.P. 119° with iodine
and alkali. On warming with aniline and benzaldehyde in alc. yields phenylcinchoninic acid M.P. 208°.
With phenylhydrazine in ether yields unstable phenylhydrazone M.P. 192°. p-Nitrophenylhydrazone M.P.
219°. Methyl ester B.P. 135°. Ethyl ester B.P. 155°.

§° Levulinic $CH_3 \cdot CO \cdot [CH_2]_2 \cdot COOH$
B.P. 245°d. D. 1·137 (25°). Sol. in water. Readily
oxidised by chromic acid with formation of acetic,

malonic, and succinic acids (q.v.). With acetic anhy
dride forms an acetoxyl lactone M.P. 78°. Yield
iodoform M.P. 119° in the cold with NaOH and iodine
Phenylhydrazone M.P. 108°, on heating yields a
pyridazolone deriv. M.P. 81°. *p*-Nitrophenylhydra
zone M.P. 174°. Oxime M.P. 90°. Semicarbazone
M.P. 187°d. Methyl ester B.P. 191°. Ethyl este
B.P. 202°. *p*-Nitrobenzyl ester M.P. 61°. *p*-Bromo
phenacyl ester M.P. 84°.

ACID ANHYDRIDES

LIQUID

B.P.

138°	Acetic	D. 1·097 (0°). Irritating odour. Slightl sol. in cold water.
162°	Propionic	D. 1·034 (0°).
191°	*n*-Butyric	D. 0·978 (18°).
213°	Citraconic	M.P. 7°. D. 1·262 (4°).

SOLID

B.P.

42°	Benzoic	B.P. 360°. Very slowly decomposed b boiling water.
56°	Maleic	B.P. 202°. Readily decomposed by warr water.
119°	Succinic	B.P. 250°. Readily decomposed by warr water.
130°	Phthalic	B.P. 284°. Insol. in cold water, readil (with decomp.) in hot. On warming with CH_3OH yields monomethyl ester M.P. 85°. With Zn dust + acetic acid yields phthalide M.P. 73°. On fusio with resorcinol and trace of conc. H_2SO_4 yield fluorescein (*cf.* Phthalic Acid M.P. 195°).
221°	*d*-Camphoric	B.P. 270°. Readily yields *d*-camphoric aci M.P. 187° on boiling with water. With Na amalgan + alc. yields campholide M.P. 210°. With conc NH_4OH yields camphoraminic acid M.P. 174°.

ALKYL ESTERS OF SIMPLE CARBOXYLIC ACIDS

LIQUID

B.P.

32° Methyl Formate   D. 0·999 (0°)
Miscible with water.

P.		
54°	Ethyl Formate	D. 0·938 (0°)
	Sol. in 8 vols of cold water.	
57°	Methyl Acetate	D. 0·958 (0°)
	Sol. in 3 vols of cold water.	
68°	isoPropyl Formate	D. 0·883 (0°)
77°	Ethyl Acetate	D. 0·924 (0°)
	Sol. in 12 vols of cold water.	
79°	Methyl Propionate	D. 0·937 (0°)
81°	n-Propyl Formate	D. 0·918 (0°)
	Sol. in 42 vols of cold water.	
83°	Allyl Formate	D. 0·948 (18°)
	Pungent odour.	
89°	Methyl Carbonate	D. 1·065 (17°)
91°	IsoPropyl Acetate	D. 0·917 (0°)
92°	Methyl isoButyrate	D. 0·911 (0°)
98°	isoButyl Formate	D. 0·885 (0°)
	Sol. in 88 vols of cold water.	
98°	Ethyl Propionate	D. 0·912 (0°)
101°	n-Propyl Acetate	D. 0·910 (0°)
102°	Methyl n-Butyrate	D. 0·919 (0°)
104°	Allyl Acetate	D. 0·938 (0°)
	Sharp odour. Dibromide B.P. 227°.	
107°	n-Butyl Formate	D. 0·911 (0°)
110°	Ethyl isoButyrate	D. 0·890 (0°)
116°	Methyl isoValerate	D. 0·900 (0°)
116°	isoButyl Acetate	D. 0·892 (0°)
120°	Ethyl n-Butyrate	D. 0·900 (0°)
122°	n-Propyl Propionate	D. 0·902 (0°)
124°	isoAmyl Formate	D. 0·894 (0°)
	Sol. in 280 vols of cold water.	
126°	Ethyl Carbonate	D. 0·976 (20°)
126°	n-Butyl Acetate	D. 0·901 (0°)
127°	Methyl n-Valerate	D. 0·910 (0°)
128°	isoPropyl n-Butyrate	D. 0·879 (0°)
134°	Ethyl isoValerate	D. 0·885 (0°)
137°	isoButyl Propionate	D. 0·888 (0°)
139°	isoAmyl Acetate	D. 0·884 (0°)
	Odour of banana. Sol. in 400 vols of cold water.	
143°	n-Propyl n-Butyrate	D. 0·893 (0°)

B.P.		
145°	Ethyl *n*-Valerate	D. 0·894 (0°)
146°	*n*-Butyl Propionate	D. 0·895 (0°)
147°	*iso*Butyl *iso*Butyrate	D. 0·875 (0°)
150°	Methyl Caproate	D. 0·904 (0°)
157°	*iso*Butyl *n*-Butyrate	D. 0·880 (0°)
160°	*iso*Amyl Propionate	D. 0·888 (0°)
162°	Cyclohexyl Formate	D. 1·010 (0°)
165°	*n*-Butyl *n*-Butyrate	D. 0·888 (0°)
166°	Ethyl *n*-Caproate	D. 0·889 (0°)
168°	*n*-Propyl Carbonate	D. 0·949 (17°)
173°	Methyl Heptylate	D. 0·898 (0°)
175°	Cyclohexyl Acetate	D. 0·972 (19°)
178°	*iso*Amyl *n*-Butyrate	D. 0·882 (0°)
181°	Methyl Malonate	D. 1·175 (0°)

181°   Decolorises bromine in the cold. *Cf.* Ethyl Malonate B.P. 198°.

182°   Ethylene Glycol Monoacetate
     Miscible with water.

186°   Ethyl Oxalate   D. 1·103 (0°)
     Slightly sol. in water. With alc. NH_3 in cold yields ethyl oxamate M.P. 114°. With NH_4OH in excess yields oxamide (subl. without melting). On warming with aniline yields oxanilide M.P. 247°.

187°   Ethylene Glycol Diacetate D. 1·128 (0°).
     Sol. in 7 vols of cold water. On boiling with 48 % HBr yields ethylene bromide B.P. 129°. With HBr gas yields β-bromoethyl acetate B.P. 162°.

189°   Ethyl *n*-Heptylate   D. 0·888 (0°)

190°   *iso*Propyl Oxalate   D. 1·010 (18°)
     With NH_4OH in excess yields oxamide M.P. 418°.
     Cf. Ethyl Oxalate B.P. 186°.

190°   *iso*Butyl Carbonate   D. 0·919 (15°)

190°   *iso*Amyl *iso*Valerate   D. 0·870 (0°)

193°   Methyl Caprylate   D. 0·894 (0°)

195°   Methyl Succinate   M.P. 18°. D. 1·120 (18°)
     Sol. in cold water.

196°   Ethyl Methylmalonate   D. 1·019 (15°)
     Decolorises bromine in the cold. On treating Na deriv. with benzyl chloride yields ethyl methyl-benzylmalonate B.P. 300°; this on hydrolysis yields

B.P.

methyl benzylmalonic acid M.P. 135°d., which on heating yields methylbenzylacetic acid M.P. 37°, B.P. 272°.

198°   Ethyl Malonate   D. 1·076 (0°)
Forms a Na deriv. with C_2H_5ONa in alc., but displays no acidic properties in water. Decolorises bromine in the cold. With conc. NH_4OH yields malonamide M.P. 170°. On treating Na deriv. in absolute alc. with (1 mol.) benzyl chloride yields ethyl benzylmalonate B.P. 300°, which on hydrolysis yields benzylmalonic acid M.P. 117°; this on heating loses CO_2 to form hydrocinnamic acid M.P. 48°.

198°   Methyl Benzoate   D. 1·103 (0°).
On treating cold soln. in conc. H_2SO_4 with (1 mol.) conc. HNO_3 yields methyl m-nitrobenzoate M.P. 78°.

203°   Benzyl Formate   D. 1·081 (23°)

206°   Ethyl Caprylate   D. 0·884 (0°)

207°   n-Butyl Carbonate   D. 0·941 (0°)

209°   Trimethylene Glycol
                Diacetate   D. 1·070 (19°)
Sol. in 9 vols of cold water. With HBr gas yields γ-bromopropyl acetate B.P. 185°.

213°   n-Propyl Oxalate   D. 1·038 (0°)
Cf. Ethyl Oxalate B.P. 186°.

213°   Methyl Pelargonate   D. 0·892 (0°)

213°   Ethyl Benzoate   D. 1·066 (0°)
On adding (1 mol.) conc. HNO_3 to cold soln. in conc. H_2SO_4 yields ethyl m-nitrobenzoate M.P. 47°.

216°   Benzyl Acetate   D. 1·062 (15°)
On adding to cold fuming HNO_3 yields p-nitrobenzyl acetate M.P. 78°.

216°   Ethyl Succinate   D. 1·049 (15°)

218°   isoPropyl Benzoate   D. 1·023 (0°)

218°   Methyl Phenylacetate   D. 1·044 (16°)

227°   Ethyl Pelargonate   D. 0·866 (17°)

228°   isoAmyl Carbonate   D. 0·912 (15°)

229°   isoButyl Oxalate   D. 1·002 (14°)

229°   Ethyl Phenylacetate   D. 1·056 (4°)

230°   n-Propyl Benzoate   D. 1·025 (15°)

230°   Allyl Benzoate   D. 1·067 (4°)

232°   Methyl Caprate   D. 0·876 (18°)

B.P.

238°	Benzyl *n*-Butyrate	D. 1·033 (16°)
241°	*iso*Butyl Benzoate	D. 1·012 (4°)
243°	*n*-Butyl Oxalate	D. 1·001 (0°)

With alc. NH_3 yields *n*-butyl oxamate M.P. 88°.

245°	Ethyl Caprate	D. 0·868 (18°)
246°	*n*-Propyl Succinate	D. 1·016 (4°)
247°	*iso*Butyl Phenylacetate	D. 0·999 (18°)
249°	*n*-Butyl Benzoate	D. 1·020 (4°)
254°	*n*-Butyl Phenylacetate	D. 0·996 (18°)
258°	Glycerol Triacetate	
	(Triacetin)	D. 1·161 (15°)

Sol. in 16 vols cold water, miscible with ether and with benzene. With HBr gas yields dibromo-*iso*-propyl acetate B.P. 227°.

260°	Glycerol Diacetate	
	(Diacetin)	D. 1·176 (15°)

Sol. in water, sparingly sol. in ether and in benzene.

d.	Glycerol Monoacetate	

(Monacetin) D. 1·218 (15°). B.P. 158°/ 15 mm. Miscible with water, slightly sol. in ether, insol. in benzene.

262°	*iso*Amyl Oxalate	D. 0·968 (11°)
262°	*iso*Amyl Benzoate	D. 1·004 (0°)
265°	*iso*Butyl Succinate	D. 0·974 (15°)
268°	Methyl Laurate	D. 0·869 (19°) M.P. 5°.
269°	Ethyl Anisate	D. 1·119 (4°) M.P. 7°.
269°	Ethyl Laurate	D. 0·867 (13°)
271°	Ethyl Cinnamate	D. 1·050 (20°)
	Dibromide M.P. 74°.	
282°	Methyl Phthalate	D. 1·196 (19°)
289°	Glycerol Tripropionate	
	(Tripropionin)	D. 1·083 (19°)
296°	Methyl Myristate	D. 0·873 (19°) M.P. 18°.
297°	*iso*Amyl Succinate	D. 0·961 (13°)
298°	Ethyl Phthalate	D. 1·117 (20°)
300°	Ethyl Benzylmalonate	D. 1·077 (15°)
	Decolorises bromine in the cold.	
302°	*iso*Propyl Phthalate	D. 1·065 (19°)
306°	Ethyl Myristate	D. 0·865 (19°) M.P. 11°.
307°	Ethyl Sebacate	D. 0·965 (16°)

B.P.
318° Glycerol Tributyrate
                (Tributyrin)   D. 1·033 (17°)
323° Benzyl Benzoate   D. 1·114 (18°)   M.P. 18°.
338° n-Butyl Phthalate   D. 1·050 (19°)
349° isoAmyl Phthalate   D. 1·024 (19°)

SOLID

M.P.
18°   Benzyl Benzoate   B.P. 323° (see above)
19°   Methyl Succinate   B.P. 195° (see above)
24°   Ethyl Palmitate   B.P. 185°/10 mm.
29°   Bornyl Acetate   B.P. 221°
30°   Methyl Palmitate   B.P. 182°/12 mm.
33°   Ethyl Stearate   B.P. 200°/10 mm.
36°   Methyl Cinnamate   B.P. 263°
          Dibromide M.P. 117°.
38°   Methyl Sebacate   B.P. 288°d.
38°   Methyl Stearate   B.P. 199°/12 mm.
39°   Benzyl Cinnamate
42°   Benzyl Phthalate
42°   Benzyl Succinate   B.P. 238°/14 mm.
44°   Cinnamyl Cinnamate   Dibromide M.P. 151°.
45°   Methyl Anisate   B.P. 255°.
51°   Methyl Oxalate   B.P. 163°.
65°   Glycerol Tripalmitate (Tripalmitin)
          Sol. in 20,000 parts cold absolute alc. ; readily sol.
          in ether.
71°   Glycerol Tristearate (Tristearin)
          Almost insol. in cold alc., sparingly sol. in ether,
          readily sol. in CHCl₃ and in benzene.
73°   Ethylene Glycol Dibenzoate
80°   Benzyl Oxalate   B.P. 235°/14 mm.

ARYL ESTERS OF CARBOXYLIC ACIDS

LIQUID

B.P.
196° Phenyl Acetate   D. 1·081 (15°)
208° o-Cresyl Acetate   D. 1·048 (19°)
211° Phenyl Propionate   D. 1·054 (15°)   M.P. 20°.

B.P.

212°	*m*-Cresyl Acetate	
212°	*p*-Cresyl Acetate	D. 1·050 (23°)
227°	Phenyl *n*-Butyrate	D. 1·027 (15°)
244°	Thymyl Acetate	D. 1·009 (0°)
278°	Resorcinol Diacetate	D. 1·180 (19°)
283°	Resorcinol Monoacetate	See Phenols (Liquid)
307°	*o*-Cresyl Benzoate	D. 1·114 (19°)

SOLID

M.P.

20°   Phenyl Propionate   B.P. 211° (see above)

33°   Thymyl Benzoate

54°   *m*-Cresyl Benzoate

60°   *o*-Cresyl Carbonate
       On heating with soda-lime to 150° yields a brown
       substance which forms a red soln in alkalies.

68°   Phenyl Benzoate   B.P. 299°

70°   Phenyl Phthalate

71°   *p*-Cresyl Benzoate

72°   Phenyl Cinnamate

78°   Phenyl Carbonate   B.P. 306°

107°   β-Naphthyl Benzoate

111°   *m*-Cresyl Carbonate

115°   *p*-Cresyl Carbonate

117°   Resorcinol Dibenzoate

123°   Hydroquinone Diacetate

161°   Pyrogallol Triacetate

ESTERS OF ALIPHATIC HYDROXY ACIDS

LIQUID

B.P.

145°   Methyl Lactate   D. 1·090 (19°)
       Miscible with water. On adding 2 drops of a 1–2 %
       soln. of anisaldehyde in alc. to 2 c.c. of aqueous soln.
       and then 2 c.c. of conc. H_2SO_4 below the surface,
       upper layer has green colour. Benzoyl deriv. B.P.
       155°/15 mm.

154°   Ethyl Lactate   D. 1·031 (19°)
       Miscible with water. Colour test: see Methyl
       Lactate B.P. 145°. With acetyl chloride yields ethyl
       acetyl-lactate B.P. 177°. Benzoyl deriv. B.P. 288°.

B.P.
280°   Ethyl *d*-Tartrate   D. 1·199 (20°). M.P. 17°
        Optically active, $[a]_D = + 9·3°$. Miscible with water.
        On boiling with excess of acetic anhydride yields
        diacetyl deriv. M.P. 67°. Dibenzoyl deriv. M.P. 57°.
        Dicarbanilate M.P. 164°.

294°   Ethyl Citrate   D. 1·137 (20°)
        Acetyl deriv. B.P. 197°/15 mm. (d. 250–280° yielding
        acetic acid and ethyl aconitate B.P. 275°). Car-
        banilate M.P. 67°.

d.   *n*-Butyl *d*-Tartrate   B.P. 197°/15 mm. D. 1·098 (15°).
        M.P. 22°. Optically active, $[a]_D = + 11·3°$. Diacetyl
        deriv. B.P. 214°/20 mm.

d.   *n*-Butyl Citrate   B.P. 233°/17 mm. D. 1·050 (18°)

SOLID

M.P.
37°   Ethyl Mandelate   B.P. 254°.
        With NH_4OH yields amide M.P. 131°. Benzoyl deriv.
        M.P. 73°.

48°   Methyl *d*-Tartrate   B.P. 280°
        Exists in a second modification M.P. 61°, which is
        less sol. in water and in benzene. Optically active,
        rotation varies widely with solvent. Diacetyl deriv.
        M.P. 103°. Dibenzoyl deriv. M.P. 132°. Dicarbanil-
        ate M.P. 144°.

58°   Methyl Mandelate   B.P. 144°/20 mm.
        With NH_4OH yields amide M.P. 131°.

61°   Methyl *d*-Tartrate   *Cf.* Methyl *d*-Tartrate M.P. 48°.

79°   Methyl Citrate   B.P. 285°d., 176°/16 mm.
        Acetyl deriv. B.P. 281°d. (yielding acetic acid and
        methyl aconitate B.P. 270°), 171°/15 mm.

ESTERS OF AROMATIC HYDROXY ACIDS

LIQUID

B.P.
224°   Methyl Salicylate   D. 1·199 (4°)
        Odour of wintergreen. Violet colour with $FeCl_3$ in
        water. Sol. in 2 % (or more dil.) NaOH ; with 3 %
        (or stronger) NaOH, Na deriv. separates in cryst.
        form. Acetyl deriv. M.P. 48°. Benzoyl deriv. M.P. 82°.
        Carbanilate M.P. 96°. Methyl ether B.P. 228°.
        p-Nitrobenzyl ether M.P. 128°.

234°   Ethyl Salicylate   D. 1·147 (4°). M.P. 1°
        Violet colour with $FeCl_3$ in water. Sol. in 6 % (or

more dil.) NaOH ; Na deriv. separates on shaking with 8 % (or more conc.) NaOH. Acetyl deriv. B.P. 272°. Benzoyl deriv. M.P. 79°. Carbanilate M.P. 98°. Methyl ether B.P. 235°. *p*-Nitrobenzyl ether M.P. 125°.

237° *iso*Propyl Salicylate   D. 1·095 (19°)
Violet colour with FeCl$_3$ in water. Sol. in 5 % (or more dil.) NaOH ; Na deriv. separates as an oil with 10 % NaOH.

239° *n*-Propyl Salicylate   D. 1·098 (15°)
Faint violet colour with FeCl$_3$ in water.

268° *n*-Butyl Salicylate   D. 1·074 (19°)
Faint violet colour with FeCl$_3$ in water. Sol. in 1 % (or more dil.) NaOH ; with 2 % (or more conc.) NaOH, Na deriv. separates as a gel (mixture solidifies). Methyl ether B.P. 287°. *p*-Nitrobenzyl ether M.P. 92°.

277° *iso*Amyl Salicylate   D. 1·065 (15°).
Faint violet colour with FeCl$_3$ in water. Sol. in 1 % (or more dil.) NaOH ; with 1·5 % NaOH Na deriv. separates as a curd, while with 2 % (and more conc.) NaOH mixture sets to a gel.

320° Benzyl Salicylate   B.P. 208°/26 mm.

SOLID

42° Phenyl Salicylate (Salol).   B.P. 172°/12 mm.
No colour with FeCl$_3$. On heating under atm. press. yields phenol and xanthone M.P. 173°. Acetyl deriv. M.P. 97°. Benzoyl deriv. M.P. 80°. Carbanilate M.P. 241°. Methyl ether M.P. 59°.

70° Methyl *m*-Hydroxybenzoate
Violet colour with FeCl$_3$ in water. Methyl ether B.P. 237°.

72° Ethyl *m*-Hydroxybenzoate.   B.P. 282°.
Violet colour with FeCl$_3$ in water. Benzoyl deriv. M.P. 58°. Carbanilate M.P. 115°. Methyl ether B.P. 260°.

95° β-Naphthyl Salicylate.
Violet colour with FeCl$_3$ in water. Acetyl deriv. M.P. 136°. Carbanilate M.P. 268°.

116° Ethyl *p*-Hydroxybenzoate.
Violet colour with FeCl$_3$ in water. Benzoyl deriv. M.P. 89°. Carbanilate M.P. 134°. Methyl ether M.P. 7°, B.P. 269°.

M.P.
131° Methyl *p*-Hydroxybenzoate.
          Violet colour with $FeCl_3$ in water.   Acetyl deriv. M.P.
          85°.   Benzoyl deriv. M.P. 135°.   Methyl ether M.P.
          45°, B.P. 255°.

ESTERS OF KETONIC ACIDS

LIQUID

B.P.
135° Methyl Pyruvate $CH_3 \cdot CO \cdot COOCH_3$
          D. 1·154 (0°).   Oxime M.P. 68°.   Semicarbazone
          M.P. 208°.

155° Ethyl Pyruvate $CH_3 \cdot CO \cdot COOC_2H_5$
          D. 1·080 (14°).   Oxime M.P. 94°.   Semicarbazone
          M.P. 206°d.   Phenylhydrazone M.P. 116°.   On warm-
          ing with urea in alc. yields an insol. deriv. M.P. 200°d.

169° Methyl Acetoacetate $CH_3 \cdot CO \cdot CH_2 \cdot COOCH_3$
          D. 1·081 (15°).   Red colour with $FeCl_3$ in water.
          With NH_3 in ether yields methyl β-aminocrotonate
          M.P. 85°.   *Cf.* Ethyl Acetoacetate B.P. 181°.

181° Ethyl Acetoacetate $CH_3 \cdot CO \cdot CH_2 \cdot COOC_2H_5$
          D. 1·031 (16°).   Slightly sol. in water, sol. in dil.
          NaOH.   Red colour with $FeCl_3$ in water.   Combines
          readily with $NaHSO_3$.   With dil. alc. KOH in cold
          or with mineral acids, yields acetone, ethyl alc., and
          CO_2;   with conc. alc. KOH in cold yields K acetate.
          Forms a Na deriv. with C_2H_5ONa in abs. alc.;   this
          on treatment with benzyl chloride yields ethyl benzyl-
          acetoacetate B.P. 283°, which with dil. alc. KOH
          yields methyl β-phenylethyl ketone B.P. 235°.   With
          NH_3 in ether yields ethyl β-aminocrotonate M.P.
          33°, B.P. 154°.   Semicarbazone M.P. 129°d.   With
          hydroxylamine HCl in water yields a compd. d.140°
          (insol. in alc. and in water, sol. in dil. NaOH);   with
          hydroxylamine base in water at 40–50° yields methyl
          isoxazolone M.P. 169°d.   On warming with phenyl-
          hydrazine yields methylphenylpyrazolone M.P. 127°.

187° Ethyl Methylacetoacetate $CH_3 \cdot CO \cdot CH(CH_3)COOC_2H_5$
          D. 1·024 (15°).   Sol. in dil. NaOH.   Violet colour
          with $FeCl_3$ in water.   With dil. KOH yields methyl
          ethyl ketone B.P. 80°.   On adding $NaNO_2$ to soln in
          dil. NaOH and acidifying in cold yields diacetyl-
          monoxime M.P. 74°;   this with hydroxylamine yields
          dimethylglyoxime M.P. 240°.

198° Ethyl Ethylacetoacetate $CH_3 \cdot CO \cdot CH(C_2H_5)COOC_2H_5$
          D. 0·983 (10°).   Sol. in dil. NaOH.   Blue colour with

B.P.

FeCl$_3$ in water. With dil. KOH yields methyl *n*-propyl ketone B.P. 102°. On boiling with C$_2$H$_5$ONa in alc. yields ethyl acetate and ethyl *n*-butyrate B.P. 120°. On adding NaNO$_2$ to soln in dil. NaOH and acidifying in cold yields methyl *iso*nitrosopropyl ketone M.P. 53°.

205°   Ethyl Levulinate   CH$_3$:CO·CH$_2$·CH$_2$·COOC$_2$H$_5$

D. 1·016 (20°). Appreciably sol. in water, not more so in NaOH. Combines slowly with NaHSO$_3$. On boiling with dil. NaOH yields Na levulinate (free acid M.P. 33°, B.P. 245°). Oxime M.P. 38°. Semicarbazone M.P. 135°. Phenylhydrazone M.P. 110°.

250°   Ethyl Acetonedicarboxylate.   CO(CH$_2$·COOC$_2$H$_5$)$_2$

D. 1·113 (20°). Sparingly sol. in water, sol. in dil. Na$_2$CO$_3$ or NaOH soln. Red colour with FeCl$_3$ in water. With Na acetate and CuSO$_4$ soln. yields sparingly sol. Cu salt (v. sol. in CHCl$_3$) M.P. 142°. With conc. alc. KOH yields K acetate and malonate. With conc. NH$_4$OH below 0° yields a deriv. M.P. 86°. With aniline in cold yields ethyl β-anilinoglutaconate M.P. 97°. With phenylhydrazine yields ethyl methyl-phenylpyrazolonecarboxylate M.P. 85° (free acid M.P. 134°). Semicarbazone M.P. 94°.

LACTONES

SOLID

M.P.

67°   Coumarin C_6H_4 $\begin{cases} CH:CH \ (1) \\ | \\ O—CO \ (2) \end{cases}$

B.P. 290°. Fairly sol. in hot water. Characteristic odour. Unsaturated. Dibromide M.P. 105°. On boiling with Ba(OH)$_2$ soln. yields a sol. salt from which coumarin is regenerated by CO$_2$ or acids ; this soln. on shaking with methyl sulphate and then acidifying yields *cis-o*-methoxycinnamic acid M.P. 88°. On long boiling with conc. KOH yields a soln. with green fluorescence, from which HCl pptes. coumaric acid M.P. 208°d., and on methylation yields *trans-o*-methoxycinnamic acid M.P. 185°. Readily sol. in conc. HCl ; soln. yields an insol. platinichloride M.P. 95–100°. On standing with conc. soln. of HgCl$_2$ in ether or in 25 % alc. yields addition product M.P. 164°.

M.P.

73°   Phthalide $C_6H_4\!\!\begin{array}{c}CH_2\\ \\CO\end{array}\!\!\!>\!O$

B.P. 290°. On boiling with alkali yields o-hydroxy-methylbenzoic acid M.P. 120°. Readily oxidised by $KMnO_4$ to phthalic acid M.P. 195°. On warming with PCl_5 yields o-chloromethylbenzoyl chloride B.P. 135°/12 mm. which with water yields o-chloromethyl-benzoic acid M.P. 131°. On long heating with $(NH_4)_2CO_3$ yields phthalimidine M.P. 150°.

128°   Lactide $CH_3 \cdot HC \cdot CO \cdot O$
$\qquad\qquad\qquad | \qquad\qquad |$
$\qquad\qquad\quad O \cdot CO \cdot CH \cdot CH_3$

B.P. 255°. On boiling with water or alkali yields lactic acid (q.v.).

250°   Phenolphthalein   See Phenols (Solid).

CARBOHYDRATES

SOLID

M.P.

95–
105°   **Levulose (Fructose, Fruit Sugar)**

$\qquad\qquad\qquad\qquad\qquad CH_2OH \cdot [CH(OH)]_3 \cdot CO \cdot CH_2OH$

$[a]_D$ in water : $-106°$ (immediately after dissolving) falling to constant value $-92°$ after 35 minutes or on addition of a trace of Na_2CO_3. Extremely sol. in cold water ; sol. in 12 parts of cold abs. alc. Reduces Fehling's soln in cold, and Cu acetate in dil. acetic acid on warming. Gives red colour on heating with resorcinol + conc. HCl. On boiling with 10% HCl yields furfural (vapours redden aniline acetate paper). Yields no saccharic acid with HNO_3. Gives no ppte with ammon. $CuSO_4$. Gives blue colour on warming with NH_4 molybdate (specific for levulose). Not oxidised by bromine water in cold. Phenyl-osazone M.P. 205° separates after 5 minutes. Methyl-phenylhydrazone M.P. 159°. Methylphenylosazone M.P. 152°. β-Naphthylhydrazone M.P. 161° is readily sol. in water. Oxime M.P. 118°.

100°   Maltose $C_{12}H_{22}O_{11} + H_2O$

Loses water with difficulty ; decomposes on heating to 110°. $[a]_D$ in water : $+96°$ (immediately after dissolving) rising to constant value $+137°$ (calc. on anhydrous sugar) after 5 hours or on adding trace of NH_3. Readily sol. in cold water, sparingly sol. in abs. alc., sol. in hot CH_3OH. Reduces Fehling's soln. but not Cu acetate in dil. acetic acid. On warming with very dil. HCl yields dextrose (q.v.) ; resulting soln has $[a]_D = + 52·8°$ (calc. on hydrated maltose), reduces about 50% more Fehling's soln than before hydrolysis, and yields phenylglucosazone M.P. 205° with phenylhydrazine. Phenylosazone M.P. 206° (formed on warming for 1 hour) is sol. in hot water, slightly in cold. Phenylhydrazone M.P. 130° d. On boiling with acetic anhydride + Na acetate yields octa-acetate M.P. 158°.

118°   Raffinose $C_{18}H_{32}O_{16} + 5H_2O$
Loses water at 80–105°. $[a]_D$ in water = + 104°. Sol. in 6 parts of water at 16°, sol. in 10 parts of CH_3OH, insol. in abs. alc. On hydrolysis by warming with dil. HCl yields dextrose, levulose and galactose. Does not reduce Fehling's soln nor react with phenylhydrazine. On oxidation by HNO_3 yields oxalic, saccharic and mucic acids. Gives ppte with Pb acetate, also on shaking with sat. $Ca(OH)_2$ soln. On heating with acetic anhydride + Na acetate yields hendeka-acetate M.P. 99°.

119°   *d*-Galactose (Hydrated)   See *d*-Galactose M.P. 166°.

132°   *d*-Mannose $CH_2OH·[CH(OH)]_4·CHO$
$[a]_D$ in water : − 13° (3 minutes after dissolving) rising to constant value + 14·2° after 6 hours or on adding trace of NH_3. Extremely sol. in cold water, sol. in 250 parts of abs. alc. Reduces Fehling's soln and Cu acetate in dil. acetic acid. With phenylhydrazine forms (almost immediately) a colourless insol. phenylhydrazone M.P. 195° (186° on slow heating). Diphenylhydrazone M.P. 155°. Benzylphenylhydrazone M.P. 165°. Oxime M.P. 176–184° d.

144°   *l*-Xylose $CH_2OH·[CH(OH)]_3·CHO$
$[a]_D$ in water : + 85° (immediately after dissolving) falling to constant value + 19° after 2 hours or on adding trace of NH_3. Sol. in equal weight of cold water ; readily sol. in hot alc. Reduces Fehling's soln and Cu acetate in dil. acetic acid. On boiling with 10% HCl yields furfural (vapours redden aniline acetate paper). Gives red colour on warming with phloroglucinol + dil. HCl. On boiling conc. aqueous soln with paraformaldehyde, diformal deriv. M.P. 56° separates. Phenylosazone M.P. 160° separates after 13 minutes. Diphenylhydrazone M.P. 107°. Benzylphenylhydrazone M.P. 99°. β-Naphthylhydrazone M.P. 124°.

M.P.
146° Dextrose (d-Glucose, Grape Sugar)

$$CH_2OH \cdot [CH(OH)]_4 \cdot CHO$$

$[\alpha]_D$ in water : $+ 109°$ (immediately after dissolving)
falling to constant value $+ 52 \cdot 8°$ after 4·5 hours or
on adding trace of NH_3. Sol. in equal weight of
cold water ; readily sol. in hot alc. Insol. in hot
ethyl acetate. Reduces Fehling's soln. and Cu acetate
in dil. acetic acid. On oxidation by HNO_3 yields
saccharic acid. Phenylosazone M.P. 205° separates
after 8 minutes. Methylphenylosazone M.P. 152°.
Diphenylhydrazone M.P. 161°. Benzylphenylhydrazone M.P. 165°. β-Naphthylhydrazone M.P. 178°.
Oxime M.P. 137°. On boiling with acetic anhydride
+ Na acetate yields penta-acetate M.P. 111°.

159° l-Arabinose $CH_2OH \cdot [CH(OH)]_3 \cdot CHO$

$[\alpha]_D$ in water : $+ 170–190°$ (immediately after
dissolving) falling to constant value $+ 105°$ after
90 minutes or on adding trace of NH_3. Sol. in about
1·5 part of cold water, insol. in abs. alc. Reduces
Fehling's soln. and Cu acetate in dil. acetic acid.
On boiling with 10% HCl yields furfural (vapours
redden aniline acetate paper). Gives red colour on
warming with phloroglucinol + dil. HCl. Phenylosazone M.P. 157° appears as a turbidity after 30
minutes. Methylphenylosazone M.P. 168° d. Diphenylhydrazone M.P. 204°. Benzylphenylhydrazone M.P. 174°. β-Naphthylhydrazone M.P. 176°.

160° Sucrose (Cane Sugar) $C_{12}H_{22}O_{11}$

$[\alpha]_D$ in water $= + 66 \cdot 5°$. Sol. in half its weight of
cold water ; sol. in 80 parts of boiling abs. alc. ; sol.
in ethyl acetate. No reaction with Fehling's soln.
nor with phenylhydrazine. Forms blue soln. with
$CuSO_4$ + NaOH. Gives violet colour on warming
with $Co(NO_3)_2$ + NaOH. Gives red colour on
boiling with sat. ammon. $NiSO_4$ soln and adding
mineral acid. On warming with very dil. HCl
yields dextrose + levulose ; resulting soln. has $[\alpha]_D =$
$- 37 \cdot 4°$, reduces Fehling's soln., and yields phenylglucosazone M.P. 205° with phenylhydrazine. On
oxidation with HNO_3 yields saccharic acid. On
boiling with acetic anhydride + Na acetate yields
octa-acetate M.P. 67°.

166° d-Galactose $CH_2OH \cdot [CH(OH)]_4 \cdot CHO$

$[\alpha]_D$ in water : $+ 140°$ (immediately after dissolving)
falling to constant value $+ 81°$ after 4·5 hours or on

adding trace of NH_3. Readily sol. in hot water, on cooling separates as monohydrate M.P. 119°. Insol. in abs. alc. Reduces Fehling's soln. and Cu acetate in dil. acetic acid. On oxidation by HNO_3 yields mucic acid. Phenylosazone M.P. 196° separates after 30 minutes. Phenylhydrazone M.P. 160° is sparingly sol. in cold water. Methylphenylhydrazone M.P. 187°. Diphenylhydrazone M.P. 157°. Benzylphenyl-hydrazone M.P. 189°. β-Naphthylhydrazone M.P. 189°. Oxime M.P. 175° d. On boiling with acetic anhydride + Na acetate yields penta-acetate M.P. 142°.

203°d. **Lactose (Milk Sugar)** $C_{12}H_{22}O_{11} + H_2O$

Loses water at about 130°, turns yellow at about 160°. $[a]_D$ in water : + 87° (immediately after dissolving) falling to constant value + 52·5° after about 24 hours or on adding 0·1% of NH_4OH. Sol. in 6 parts of cold water ; insol. in abs. alc. Reduces Fehling's soln. but not Cu acetate in dil. acetic acid. On warming with very dil. HCl yields dextrose + d-galactose ; soln. reduces about 50% more Fehling's soln. than before hydrolysis. On oxidation by HNO_3 yields saccharic and mucic acids. Phenylosazone M.P. 200°d. (formed on warming for 1·5 hour) is sol. in hot water, sparingly in cold. On boiling with acetic anhydride + Na acetate yields octa-acetate M.P. 95–100°.

225° **Inositol** See Alcohols (Solid).

d. **Inulin** $(C_6H_{10}O_5)_n + H_2O$

Insol. in cold water, sol. on warming ; on cooling separates very slowly, more readily on addition of alc. $[a]_D = - 33$ to 40°. Does not reduce Fehling's soln. Gives no colour with iodine. On boiling with dil. HCl or (better) oxalic acid yields only levulose ($q.v.$). On oxidation by HNO_3 yields neither sac-charic nor mucic acids.

d. **Glycogen** $(C_6H_{10}O_5)_n + H_2O$

Sol. in cold water, forming opalescent soln. ; separates on adding alc. $[a]_D$ in water = about + 196°. Does not reduce Fehling's soln. With a trace of iodine gives red-brown colour which vanishes on warming to 60° and returns on cooling. On hydrolysis by boiling with very dil. HCl yields only dextrose ($q.v.$) Soln. in water gives ppte. with basic Pb acetate soln.

d.   " Dextrin "

A mixture of hydrolysis products of starch. **Pale yellowish, nearly white** powder. Sol. in **warm water**, forming a viscous, opalescent soln. Reduces Fehling's soln. On boiling with dil. HCl yields dextrose (*q.v.*) ; resulting soln. reduces much more Fehling's soln than before hydrolysis. Gives brown colour with trace of iodine. Gives no ppte with basic Pb acetate soln.

d.   Starch $(C_6H_{10}O_5)_n + H_2O$

White powder ; microscopic appearance of grains differs characteristically in starches from different sources. Insol. in cold water, sol. in boiling water ; does not separate on cooling. On boiling with dil. HCl yields dextrose (*q.v.*). Gives ppte. with tannin and basic Pb acetate solns. Gives blue colour with trace of iodine.

GLUCOSIDES

M.P.
165°   *a*-Methylglucoside

$$CH_3O \cdot CH \cdot [CH(OH)]_2 \cdot CH \cdot CH(OH) \cdot CH_2OH$$
$$|\underline{\hspace{2em}O\hspace{2em}}|$$

$[a]_D$ in water $= + 157 \cdot 6°$. Sol. in half its weight of water at 17°, in 200 parts of cold abs. alc. ; insol. in ether. Does not react with Fehling's soln. nor phenyl-hydrazine. On boiling with dil. mineral acids yields CH_3OH and dextrose (*q.v.*). Tetra-acetate M.P. 101°. On heating at 145–165° with benzaldehyde+anhydrous Na_2SO_4 yields benzylidene deriv. M.P. 160°.

165°   Arbutin

$$HO \cdot C_6H_4 \cdot O \cdot CH \cdot [CH(OH)]_2 \cdot CH \cdot CH(OH) \cdot CH_2OH \qquad (1:4)$$
$$|\underline{\hspace{2em}O\hspace{2em}}|$$

Sol. in hot water or alc., insol. in ether. More sol. in cold dil. NaOH than in cold water. Gives transient violet colour with $FeCl_3$. On boiling with dil. H_2SO_4 yields dextrose (*q.v.*) and hydroquinone M.P. 169°. Yields benzoquinone M.P. 115° on boiling with HCl and $FeCl_3$. Pentabenzoyl deriv. M.P. 159–165°.

175°   Helicin

$$CHO \cdot C_6H_4 \cdot O \cdot CH \cdot [CH(OH)]_2 \cdot CH \cdot CH(OH) \cdot CH_2OH \ (1:2)$$
$$|\underline{\hspace{2em}O\hspace{2em}}|$$

$[a]_D$ in water $= - 60 \cdot 4°$. Fairly sol. in water, readily

M.P.

in alc. ; insol. in ether. Restores pink colour to Schiff's soln. No colour with $FeCl_3$. On hydrolysis yields dextrose (*q.v.*) and salicylaldehyde B.P. 196°. With Na amalgam yields salicin M.P. 201°.

180°　Populin　$C_6H_5 \cdot COO \cdot CH_2 \cdot C_6H_4 \cdot O \cdot C_6H_{11}O_5$　(1 : 2)
(Benzoylsalicin.) Levorotatory. Almost insol. in cold water, fairly sol. in hot water ; soluble in conc. acids and alkalies. Gives red colour with conc. H_2SO_4. On boiling with baryta water yields salicin M.P. 201° and benzoic acid M.P. 121°.

185°　Coniferin

$$\overline{|\overline{O}|}$$
$$CH_2OH \cdot CH(OH) \cdot CH \cdot [CH_2(OH)]_2 \cdot CHO \cdot C_6H_3(OCH_3) \cdot CH : CH \cdot$$
$$CH_2OH \quad (1 : 3 : 4)$$

$[a]_D$ in water = − 66·9°. Slightly sol. in cold water or alc., readily in hot water ; insol. in ether. On warming with phenol and conc. HCl gives blue colour. On hydrolysis yields dextrose (*q.v.*) and coniferyl alcohol M.P. 73°. On oxidation by acid $KMnO_4$ or CrO_3 yields glucovanillin M.P. 192° ; on oxidation after hydrolysis yields vanillin M.P. 80°. Tetra-acetyl deriv. M.P. 125°. Tribenzoyl deriv. M.P. 80°.

201°　Salicin
$$CH_2OH \cdot C_6H_4 \cdot O \cdot CH_2 \cdot [CH(OH)]_2 \cdot CH \cdot CH(OH) \cdot CH_2OH \ (1: 2)$$
$$|\overline{O}|$$

$[a]_D$ in water = − 62·5°. Sol. in hot water or hot alc., insol. in ether. Sol. in NaOH and in acetic acid. On hydrolysis yields dextrose (*q.v.*) and saligenin M.P. 86°. Gives crimson colour with conc. H_2SO_4. Oxidation after hydrolysis by acid $KMnO_4$ or chromic acid yields salicylaldehyde B.P. 196°. Reduces ammon. $AgNO_3$. With bromine water yields bromo deriv. M.P. 170°. Tetra-acetyl deriv. M.P. 130°.

214°　Amygdalin　$C_6H_5 \cdot CH(CN) \cdot OC_{12}H_{21}O_{10}$
Contains nitrogen. $[a]_D$ in water = − 41°. On hydrolysis with dil. H_2SO_4 yields dextrose (*q.v.*), benzaldehyde B.P. 179° and HCN. On hydrolysis with NaOH yields NH_3 and amygdalinic acid, which on hydrolysis with dil. H_2SO_4 yields dextrose and mandelic acid M.P. 133°.

217°d.　Digitalin　$C_{29}H_{46}O_{12}$
Slightly sol. in cold water, readily in alc. ; almost

insol. in ether or $CHCl_3$. On hydrolysis yields dextrose, a heptose, and digitalenin M.P. 210°. Soln. in conc. HCl or conc. H_2SO_4 yellow; in H_2SO_4 containing $Fe_2(SO_4)_3$ red, then red-violet. Soln. in conc. H_2SO_4 gives deep brown colour with a drop of bromine water. Reduces ammon. $AgNO_3$.

ALIPHATIC CHLORO-HYDROCARBONS

LIQUID

B.P.

37° *iso*Propyl Chloride $CH_3 \cdot CHCl \cdot CH_3$
D. 0·859 (20°). *p*-Naphthyl ether M.P. 41° (forms a picrate M.P. 92°).

42° Methylene Chloride CH_2Cl_2
D. 1·378 (0°). With sodium ethylate yields ethylal B.P. 88°. *β*-Naphthyl ether M.P. 133°.

46° *n*-Propyl Chloride $CH_3 \cdot CH_2 \cdot CH_2Cl$
D. 0·802 (20°). *β*-Naphthyl ether M.P. 39° (forms a picrate M.P. 75°).

46° Allyl Chloride $CH_2 : CH \cdot CH_2Cl$
D. 0·955 (0°). Unsaturated. With chlorine yields glycerol trichlorohydrin B.P. 155°. Dibromide B.P. 195°.

51° *tert.*-Butyl Chloride $(CH_3)_3CCl$
D. 0·847 (15°). Rapidly hydrolysed by cold water, yielding *tert*-butyl alc. M.P. 25°, B.P. 83°.

55° Dichloroethylene   CHCl:CHCl
D. 1·25. Insol. in conc. H_2SO_4 but sol. in fuming sulphuric acid. Forms a dibromide M.P. 190–195°.

60° Ethylidene Chloride $CH_3 \cdot CHCl_2$
D. 1·180 (22°). With sodium ethoxide yields acetal B.P. 104°. Di-*β*-naphthyl ether M.P. 200°.

61° Chloroform $CHCl_3$
D. 1·504 (12°). On warming with aniline and alcoholic KOH yields phenyl *iso*cyanide (odour). On warming with resorcinol and dil. NaOH gives red colour. Colour test with pyridine, see p. 67.

68° *iso*Butyl Chloride $(CH_3)_2CH \cdot CH_2Cl$
D. 0·880 (15°). *β*-Naphthyl ether M.P. 33° (forms a picrate M.P. 80°).

77° *n*-Butyl Chloride $CH_3 \cdot [CH_2]_2 \cdot CH_2Cl$
D. 0·887 (20°). Phenyl ether B.P. 210°.

B.P.

78° Carbon Tetrachloride   CCl$_4$.
D. 1·608 (10°). On warming with aniline and alc. KOH yields phenyl *iso*cyanide, but more slowly than chloroform.

83° Ethylene Chloride   CH$_2$Cl·CH$_2$Cl.
D. 1·252 (20°). On prolonged heating with aniline yields diphenylpiperazine M.P. 163°. Di-β-naphthyl ether M.P. 217°. Diphenyl ether M.P. 97°.

86° *tert.*-Amyl Chloride   (CH$_3$)$_2$CCl·C$_2$H$_5$
D. 0·870 (19°). Rapidly hydrolysed by cold water, yielding *tert*-amyl alc. B.P. 102°.

88° Trichloroethylene   CHCl : CCl$_2$
With sodium ethoxide yields dichlorovinyl ethyl ether B.P. 128°.

98° Propylene Chloride   CH$_3$·CHCl·CH$_2$Cl
D 1·166 (14°). On heating with anhydrous Na acetate in acetic acid yields propylene glycol diacetate B.P. 186°.

100° *iso*Amyl Chloride   (CH$_3$)$_2$CH·CH$_2$·CH$_2$Cl
D. 0·886 (0°). β-Naphthyl ether M.P. 26°, B.P. 323°d. (forms a picrate M.P. 90°).

114° ααβ-Trichloroethane   CH$_2$Cl·CHCl$_2$
D. 1·457 (10°). With KOH yields αα-dichloroethylene B.P. 35°.

116° Epichlorohydrin. See Halogen Ethers.

120° Trimethylene Chloride   CH$_2$Cl·CH$_2$·CH$_2$Cl
D. 1·180 (18°). Di-β-naphthyl ether M.P. 148°. Diphenyl ether M.P. 61°.

121° Tetrachloroethylene   CCl$_2$:CCl$_2$
D. 1·631 (9°·4). Forms a dibromide d.200°.

142° Chloro*cyclo*hexane   CH$_2$·CH$_2$·CHCl
                             | |
                             CH$_2$·CH$_2$·CH$_2$

D. 1·326 (15°). On boiling with alc. KOH yields *cyclo*hexene B.P. 82°.

147° *s*-Tetrachloroethane (Acetylene Tetrachloride)
                                    CHCl$_2$·CHCl$_2$
D. 1·614 (0°). With zinc dust in alcohol yields acetylene. With alc. KOH yields trichloroethylene B.P. 88°.

155° Glycerol Trichlorohydrin   CH$_2$Cl·CHCl·CH$_2$Cl
D. 1·417 (15°). On boiling with alc. KOH yields

B.P.

ethyl propargyl ether B.P. 80° (gives ppte. with ammon. AgNO₃).

161°   Pentachloroethane $CHCl_2 \cdot CCl_3$
D. 1·963 (10°). On boiling with alc. KOH yields tetrachloroethylene B.P. 121°.

179°   Benzyl Chloride $C_6H_5 \cdot CH_2Cl$
D. 1·114 (4°). Warmed with alc. KOH yields ethyl benzyl ether B.P. 185°. With fuming HNO₃ in cold yields *p*-nitro deriv. M.P. 71°. On boiling with Pb(NO₃)₂ soln yields benzaldehyde B.P. 179°. On oxidation with $K_2Cr_2O_7 + H_2SO_4$ yields benzoic acid M.P. 121°. With quinoline yields addition product M.P. 170° (forms hydrates M.P. 65° and 129°). β-Naphthyl ether M.P. 99°.

212°   Benzal Chloride $C_6H_5 \cdot CHCl_2$
D. 1·295 (16°). On boiling with Na_2CO_3 soln. yields benzaldehyde B.P. 179°.

213°   Benzotrichloride $C_6H_5 \cdot CCl_3$
D. 1·380 (14°). On boiling with alc. yields HCl and ethyl benzoate B.P. 213°; with Na_2CO_3 soln. yields benzoic acid M.P. 121°.

SOLID

M.P.
157°   α-Benzene Hexachloride   CHCl·CHCl·CHCl
| |
CHCl·CHCl·CHCl

Sol. in 15 parts of cold benzene. Volatile with steam. On heating yields HCl and 1 : 2 : 4-trichlorobenzene M.P. 16°, B.P. 213°. Yields benzene B.P. 80° on boiling in alc. soln. with zinc.

182°   Naphthalene Tetrachloride.   See Aromatic Chloro-Hydro-carbons.

187°   Hexachloroethane $CCl_3 \cdot CCl_3$
Subl. 185°. Camphor-like odour. With Zn and dil. H_2SO_4 yields tetrachloroethylene B.P. 121°.

310°   β-Benzene Hexachloride   CHCl·CHCl·CHCl
| |
CHCl·CHCl·CHCl

Sol. in 200 parts cold benzene. Not volatile with steam. More stable than α-compd ; yields 1 : 2 : 4-trichlorobenzene (M.P. 16°, B.P. 213°) only on boiling with alc. KOH.

ALIPHATIC BROMO-HYDROCARBONS

LIQUID

B.P.

38° Ethyl Bromide C_2H_5Br
 D. 1·450 (15°). β-Naphthyl ether M.P. 37°, B.P. 282°.

60° isoPropyl Bromide $CH_3 \cdot CHBr \cdot CH_3$
 D. 1·310 (20°). Cf. isoPropyl Chloride B.P. 37°.

70° Allyl Bromide $CH_2 \colon CH \cdot CH_2Br$
 D. 1·436 (15°). Unsaturated. With bromine yields glycerol tribromohydrin B.P. 219°.

71° n-Propyl Bromide $CH_3 \cdot CH_2 \cdot CH_2Br$
 D. 1·352 (20°). Cf. n-Propyl Chloride B.P. 46°.

72° tert.-Butyl Bromide $(CH_3)_3CBr$
 D. 1·202 (15°). Readily hydrolysed by cold water.

90° sec.-Butyl Bromide $CH_3 \cdot CHBr \cdot CH_2 \cdot CH_3$
 D. 1·250 (25°). With Na acetate in acetic acid yields sec.-butyl acetate B.P. 112°.

91° isoButyl Bromide $(CH_3)_2CH \cdot CH_2Br$
 D. 1·273 (15°). Cf. isoButyl Chloride B.P. 68°.

97° Methylene Bromide CH_2Br_2
 D. 2·498 (15°). Cf. Methylene Chloride B.P. 42°.

100° n-Butyl Bromide $CH_3 \cdot [CH_2]_2 \cdot CH_2Br$
 D. 1·279 (20°). Cf. n-Butyl Chloride B.P. 77°.

108° tert.-Amyl Bromide $(CH_3)_2CBr \cdot C_2H_5$
 Readily hydrolysed by cold water. Cf. tert.-Amyl Chloride B.P. 86°.

118° isoAmyl Bromide $(CH_3)_2CH \cdot CH_2 \cdot CH_2Br$
 D. 1·206 (22°). Cf. isoAmyl Chloride B.P. 100°.

129° Ethylene Bromide $CH_2Br \cdot CH_2Br$
 M.P. 9°. D. 2·178 (20°). Addition product with pyridine M.P. 295°d. Cf. Ethylene Chloride B.P. 83°.

142° Propylene Bromide $CH_3 \cdot CHBr \cdot CH_2Br$
 D. 1·933 (20°). Cf. Propylene Chloride B.P. 98°.

149° isoButylene Bromide $(CH_3)_2CBr \cdot CH_2Br$
 D. 1·759 (20°). On boiling with alc. KOH yields isocrotyl bromide B.P. 98°.

151° Bromoform $CHBr_3$
 M.P. 9°. D. 2·904 (15°). Cf. Chloroform B.P. 61°.

158° β-Butylene Bromide $CH_3 \cdot CHBr \cdot CHBr \cdot CH_3$
 D. 1·83. On boiling with alc. KOH yields mixture of stereoisomeric β-bromobutylenes B.P. 84° and 93°.

B.P.

165°   α-Butylene Bromide $CH_3 \cdot CH_2 \cdot CHBr \cdot CH_2Br$
         D. 1·820 (20°).

165°   Bromo*cyclo*hexane $CH_2 \cdot CH_2 \cdot CHBr$
         $\qquad\qquad\qquad\qquad CH_2 \cdot CH_2 \cdot CH_2$
         D. 1·326 (15°).   *Cf.* Chloro*cyclo*hexane B.P. 142°.

165°   Trimethylene Bromide $CH_2Br \cdot CH_2Br$
         D. 1·923 (17°).   Addition product with pyridine
         M.P. 225°.   *Cf.* Trimethylene Chloride B.P. 125°.

189°d.   Carbon Tetrabromide CBr_4
         M.P. 92°.   *Cf.* Carbon Tetrachloride B.P. 78°.

198°   Benzyl Bromide $C_6H_5 \cdot CH_2Br$
         D. 1·438 (22°).   Very irritating odour.   *Cf.* Benzyl
         Chloride B.P. 179°.

200°d.   s-Tetrabromoethane $CHBr_2 \cdot CHBr_2$
         D. 2·971 (17°).   *Cf.* s-Tetrachloroethane B.P. 147°.

219°   Glycerol Tribromohydrin $CH_2Br \cdot CHBr \cdot CH_2Br$
         M.P. 16°.   *Cf.* Glycerol Trichlorohydrin B.P. 155°.

220°d.   β-Bromostyrene $C_6H_5 \cdot CH:CHBr$
         M.P. 7°.   D. 1·429 (19°).   B.P. 108°/20 mm.   Not
         attacked by boiling alc. KOH or Zn dust.   With
         bromine yields tribromoethylbenzene M.P. 37°.
         With fuming HNO_3 at 0° yields dinitro deriv. M.P.
         135° (sp. sol. in alc.).

ALIPHATIC IODO-HYDROCARBONS

LIQUID

B.P.

43°   Methyl Iodide CH_3I
         D. 2·285 (15°).   Gives a ppte. with alc. $AgNO_3$ in
         cold.   β-Naphthyl ether M.P. 70°, B.P. 274°.   With
         dimethylaniline rapidly forms trimethylphenylam-
         monium iodide which volatilises at 220° and dissolves
         in 90 parts of cold alc.   Addition product with pyri-
         dine M.P. 117°; with quinoline M.P. 72°.

72°   Ethyl Iodide C_2H_5I
         D. 1·943 (15°).   Gives a ppte. with alc. $AgNO_3$ in
         cold.   With dimethylaniline rapidly forms dimethyl-
         ethylphenylammonium iodide M.P. 136° (sol. in
         2·2 pts. cold alc.).   Addition product with pyridine
         M.P. 90°; with quinoline M.P. 159°.   *Cf.* Ethyl
         Bromide B.P. 38°.

B.P.

89°   *iso*Propyl Iodide $CH_3 \cdot CHI \cdot CH_3$
D. 1·703 (20°). With dimethylaniline slowly forms addition-product M.P. 163° (sol. in 9 parts cold alc.). Addition product with pyridine M.P. 114°. *Cf.* *iso*Propyl Chloride B.P. 37°.

98°   *tert.*-Butyl Iodide $(CH_3)_3CI$
D. 1·571 (0°). Readily hydrolysed by cold water. Usually contains free iodine. On boiling with K_2CO_3 soln. yields *iso*butylene and KI.

101°   Allyl Iodide $CH_2{:}CH \cdot CH_2I$
Gives a ppte. with alc. $AgNO_3$ in the cold. With dimethylaniline rapidly forms addition product M.P. 86°; with quinoline M.P. 177°. With bromine yields glycerol tribromohydrin B.P. 219° and iodine.

102°   *n*-Propyl Iodide $CH_3 \cdot CH_2 \cdot CH_2I$
D. 1·743 (20°). With dimethylaniline slowly forms addition product M.P. 68°; with pyridine M.P. 52°; with quinoline M.P. 145°. *Cf.* *n*-Propyl Chloride B.P. 46°.

119°   *sec.*-Butyl Iodide $CH_3 \cdot CH_2 \cdot CHI \cdot CH_3$
D. 1·595 (20°). *Cf.* *sec.*-Butyl Bromide B.P. 90°.

120°   *iso*Butyl Iodide $(CH_3)_2CH \cdot CH_2I$
D. 1·608 (19°). With dimethylaniline very slowly forms addition-product M.P. 155° (sol. in 4 parts cold alc.). *Cf.* *iso*Butyl Chloride B.P. 68°.

128°   *tert.*-Amyl Iodide $(CH_3)_2CI \cdot C_2H_5$
D. 1·479 (19°). With K_2CO_3 soln. in the cold yields *tert.*-amyl alc. B.P. 102°. On warming with alc. KOH yields trimethylethylene B.P. 38°.

130°   *n*-Butyl Iodide $CH_3 \cdot [CH_2]_2 \cdot CH_2I$
D. 1·613 (20°). Addition-product with quinoline M.P. 174°. *Cf.* *n*-Butyl Chloride B.P. 77°.

148°   *iso*Amyl Iodide $(CH_3)_2CH \cdot CH_2 \cdot CH_2I$
D. 1·473 (20°). With dimethylaniline very slowly forms addition-product M.P. 138° (sol. in 5·4 parts cold alc.); with quinoline M.P. 184°. *Cf.* *iso*Amyl Chloride B.P. 100°.

180°d.   Methylene Iodide CH_2I_2
D. 3·285 (15°). Addition-product with pyridine d.220°; with quinoline M.P. 132°. Yields methylene bromide B.P. 97° with bromine. *Cf.* Methylene Chloride B.P. 42°.

SOLID

M.P.

24°   Benzyl Iodide $C_6H_5 \cdot CH_2I$
      Decomp. on heating. Highly irritating odour. With
      dimethylaniline rapidly forms addition-product M.P.
      165° (sol. in 37 parts cold alc.).   Cf. Benzyl Chloride
      B.P. 179°.

81°   Ethylene Iodide $CH_2I \cdot CH_2I$
      Yields ethylene bromide B.P. 129° with bromine.
      Cf. Ethylene Chloride B.P. 83°.

119°   Iodoform CHI_3
      Yellow leaflets. Characteristic odour. Almost insol.
      in water. A small quantity warmed with a little
      phenol in dil. alcoholic NaOH gives red colour.
      With quinoline (in dry ether) forms addition product
      M.P. 65°d.   Cf. Chloroform B.P. 61°.

AROMATIC CHLORO-HYDROCARBONS

LIQUID

B.P.

132°   Chlorobenzene C_6H_5Cl
      D. 1·107 (20°). On warming to 80–90° with (2 mols.)
      HNO_3 in conc. H_2SO_4 yields 2:4-dinitro deriv. M.P.
      52°. On adding to large excess of chlorosulphonic
      acid in cold yields p-sulphochloride M.P. 53° which
      with NH_4OH yields the sulphonamide M.P. 143°.

159°   o-Chlorotoluene $CH_3 \cdot C_6H_4Cl$ (1 : 2)
      D. 1·081 (20°). Oxidised to o-chlorobenzoic acid
      M.P. 137° by alkaline $KMnO_4$. On warming to
      80–90° with (2 mols.) HNO_3 in conc. H_2SO_4 yields
      3:5-dinitro deriv. M.P. 45°.

162°   m-Chlorotoluene $CH_3 \cdot C_6H_4Cl$ (1 : 3)
      D. 1·072 (20°). Oxidised to m-chlorobenzoic acid
      M.P. 153°. With conc. $HNO_3 + H_2SO_4$ yields 4:6-
      dinitro deriv. M.P. 91°.

162°   p-Chlorotoluene $CH_3 \cdot C_6H_4Cl$ (1 : 4)
      M.P. 7°. D. 1·070 (20°). Sulphonated very slowly
      by conc. H_2SO_4. Oxidised to p-chlorobenzoic acid
      M.P. 236°. With cold conc. $HNO_3 + H_2SO_4$ yields
      2-nitro deriv. M.P. 38°.

172°   m-Dichlorobenzene $C_6H_4Cl_2$ (1 : 3)
      D. 1·307 (0°). Nitration with fuming HNO_3 yields
      2:4-dichloronitrobenzene M.P. 33° and a dinitro
      deriv. M.P. 103°.

B.P.

179°   Benzyl Chloride. ·   See Aliphatic Chloro-Hydrocarbons.

179°   o-Dichlorobenzene $C_6H_4Cl_2$ (1:2)
          D. 1·327 (0°). On nitration yields 3:4-dichloronitro-
          benzene M.P. 43° and a dinitro deriv. M.P. 110°.

212°   Benzal Chloride. See Aliphatic Chloro-Hydrocarbons.

213°   Benzotrichloride. See Aliphatic Chloro-Hydrocarbons.

259°   α-Chloronaphthalene $C_{10}H_7Cl$ (1)
          D. 1·194 (20°). With fuming HNO_3 yields a dinitro
          deriv. M.P. 180° (sp. sol. in alc.). On heating to
          140° with conc. H_2SO_4 yields 1:4-chloronaphthalene-
          sulphonic acid M.P. 130°. Forms a picrate M.P. 137°.

                            SOLID

M.P.

53°   p-Dichlorobenzene $C_6H_4Cl_2$ (1:4)
          B.P. 172°. Nitration with conc. HNO_3 yields 2:5-
          dichloronitrobenzene M.P. 54°. Not sulphonated
          by conc. H_2SO_4 at 100°.

56°   β-Chloronaphthalene $C_{10}H_7Cl$ (2)
          B.P. 265°. On adding (2 mols.) HNO_3 to suspension
          in conc. H_2SO_4 and warming for 8–10 hours, yields
          1:8-dinitro deriv. M.P. 175°.

182°   Naphthalene Tetrachloride
          $$C_6H_4 \begin{cases} CHCl \cdot CHCl \\ | \\ CHCl \cdot CHCl \end{cases}$$
          Sparingly sol. in hot alc. On boiling with HNO_3
          yields phthalic and oxalic acids (q.v.). On rapid
          heating yields HCl and 1:4-dichloronaphthalene
          M.P. 67°. On boiling with alc. KOH yields 1:3-
          dichloronaphthalene M.P. 61°. On boiling with dil.
          $AgNO_3$ yields a compd M.P. 195°.

226°   Hexachlorobenzene C_6Cl_6
          B.P. 326°. Sparingly sol. in alc. On boiling with
          fuming HNO_3 yields chloranil M.P. 290°.

          AROMATIC BROMO-HYDROCARBONS

                           LIQUID

B.P.

157°   Bromobenzene C_6H_5Br
          D. 1·49 (20°). On nitration in cold yields o- and
          p-nitrobromobenzenes, the o-deriv. M.P. 42° being
          far more sol. in alc. than the p-deriv. M.P. 126°.
          With conc. $HNO_3 + H_2SO_4$ at 80–90° yields 2:4-

B.P.

dinitrobromobenzene M.P. 75°. On adding to large excess of cold $ClSO_3H$ yields *p*-bromobenzene-sulphochloride M.P. 75°, which with NH_4OH yields the amide M.P. 160°. On bromination yields mainly *p*-dibromobenzene M.P. 87°.

81° *o*-Bromotoluene $CH_3 \cdot C_6H_4Br$ (1:2)
D. 1·422 (20°). Oxidised by dil. HNO_3 or alkaline $KMnO_4$ to *o*-bromobenzoic acid M.P. 147°. With (2 mols.) bromine yields 2:4:5-tribromotoluene M.P. 113°. With warm conc. $HNO_3 + H_2SO_4$ yields dinitro deriv. M.P. 82°.

83° *m*-Bromotoluene $CH_3 \cdot C_6H_4Br$ (1:3)
D. 1·410 (20°). Oxidised to *m*-bromobenzoic acid M.P. 155°. With cold conc. HNO_3 yields a nitro deriv. M.P. 55°; in warm a dinitro deriv. M.P. 103°.

98° Benzyl Bromide. See Aliphatic Bromo-Hydrocarbons.

19° *m*-Dibromobenzene $C_6H_4Br_2$ (1:3)
D. 1·955 (18°·6). On nitration yields 2:4-dibromo-nitrobenzene M.P. 61°. With excess $ClSO_3H$ yields sulphochloride M.P. 79°, which with NH_4OH yields the sulphonamide M.P. 190°.

24° *o*-Dibromobenzene $C_6H_4Br_2$ (1:2)
D. 1·977 (17°·6). With warm conc. $HNO_3 + H_2SO_4$ yields a dinitro deriv. M.P. 114°. With excess $ClSO_3H$ yields a sulphochloride M.P. 34°, which with NH_4OH yields the sulphonamide M.P. 175°.

34° 2-Bromocymene $(CH_3)_2CH \cdot C_6H_3(CH_3)Br$ (4:1:2)
D. 1·269 (17°). With cold fuming HNO_3 yields a dinitro deriv. M.P. 97°.

81° *a*-Bromonaphthalene $C_{10}H_7Br$ (1)
M.P. 4°. D. 1·488 (17°). Oxidation by chromic acid in glacial acetic acid yields phthalic acid M.P. 195°. With conc. HNO_3 yields 4-nitro deriv. M.P. 85°. Forms a picrate M.P. 134°.

SOLID

M.P.
28° *p*-Bromotoluene $CH_3 \cdot C_6H_4Br$ (1:4)
B.P. 185°. Oxidised to *p*-bromobenzoic acid M.P. 251°. Sulphonated very slowly by conc. H_2SO_4 at 100°. On nitration yields the 2-nitro deriv. M.P. 47°; the oily filtrate from cryst. product contains

the 3-nitro deriv. which solidifies (M.P. 32°) on
standing. On bromination at 120° in sunlight
(without catalyst) yields p-bromobenzyl bromide
M.P. 61°.

59° β-Bromonaphthalene $C_{10}H_7Br$ (2)
       B.P. 281°. Forms a picrate M.P. 79°.

89° p-Dibromobenzene $C_6H_4Br_2$ (1:4)
       B.P. 219°. On nitration yields 2:5-dibromonitro-
       benzene M.P. 84°. Not sulphonated by conc.
       H_2SO_4 at 100°; with fuming H_2SO_4 yields 2:5-
       dibromobenzenesulphonic acid (chloride M.P. 71°,
       amide M.P. 193°).

AROMATIC IODO-HYDROCARBONS

LIQUID

B.P.
188°   Iodobenzene C_6H_5I
       D. 1·832 (20°). Readily reduced to benzene by Na
       amalgam in moist ether. With chlorine in $CHCl_3$
       yields dichloride $C_6H_5ICl_2$ (yellow needles d.80°).
       On nitration yields p-nitro deriv. M.P. 171° and the
       much more sol. o-nitro deriv. M.P. 49°. On bromina-
       tion yields p-bromoiodobenzene M.P. 91°.

207° o-Iodotoluene $CH_3 \cdot C_6H_4I$ (1:2)
       D. 1·697 (20°). Oxidised by dil. HNO_3 to o-iodo-
       benzoic acid M.P. 162°. With chlorine in $CHCl_3$
       yields dichloride d.85°. With cold fuming HNO_3
       yields 6-nitro deriv. M.P. 103°.

204   m-Iodotoluene $CH_3 \cdot C_6H_4I$ (1:3)
       D. 1·698 (20°). Oxidised to m-iodobenzoic acid M.P.
       186°. With chlorine in $CHCl_3$ yields dichloride d.88°.
       Yields a nitro deriv. M.P. 108°. On heating to
       205–240° with copper powder yields di-m-tolyl
       M.P. 5°, B.P. 286°.

SOLID

M.P.
35° p-Iodotoluene $CH_3 \cdot C_6H_4I$ (1:4)
       B.P. 211°. Oxidised by chromic acid to p-iodoben-
       zoic acid M.P. 265°. With chlorine in $CHCl_3$ yields
       dichloride (2 forms; d. 85° and d. 110°). On heating
       to 210–260° with copper powder yields di-p-tolyl
       M.P. 121°.

ALIPHATIC a-HALOGEN-SUBSTITUTED ETHERS

LIQUID

B.P.

59° Chloromethyl Ether $CH_3 \cdot O \cdot CH_2Cl$
D. 1·062 (10°). With cold water yields methyl alc.
and formaldehyde. With CH_3OH yields methylal
B.P. 42°. With NH_4OH yields hexamethylenetetramine (q.v.). With K acetate yields methoxymethyl acetate B.P. 117°. With C_6H_5ONa yields
methoxymethyl phenyl ether B.P. 184°; analogous
deriv. of p-cresol B.P. 207°.

80° Chloromethyl Ethyl Ether $C_2H_5 \cdot O \cdot CH_2Cl$
With cold water yields ethyl alcohol and formaldehyde. With C_2H_5OH yields ethylal B.P. 88°. With
NH_4OH yields hexamethylenetetramine (q.v.). With
Na acetate yields ethoxymethyl acetate B.P. 130°.
With p-cresol Na salt yields ethoxymethyl p-cresyl
ether B.P. 219°.

98° a-Chloroethyl Ether $CH_3 \cdot CHCl \cdot O \cdot C_2H_5$
With cold water yields ethyl alcohol and acetalde-
hyde. With C_2H_5ONa yields acetal B.P. 104°.
With Na acetate yields a-ethoxyethyl acetate
B.P. 127°.

105° aa'-Dichloromethyl Ether $CH_2Cl \cdot O \cdot CH_2Cl$
D. 1·328 (15°). With cold water yields formaldehyde.
With NH_4OH yields hexamethylenetetramine (q.v.).
With alc. KOH yields ethylal (B.P. 88°) and aa'-
diethoxymethyl ether B.P. 140°. With anhydrous
Na acetate yields a diacetate B.P. 208°.

111° Chloromethyl Acetate. See Halogen-substituted Esters.

116° aa'-Dichloroethyl Ether $CH_3 \cdot CHCl \cdot O \cdot CHCl \cdot CH_3$
D. 1·137 (12°). With cold water yields acetaldehyde.
With alc. KOH yields acetal (B.P. 104°) and diethoxy-
ethyl ether B.P. 153°. With anhydrous Na acetate
yields a diacetate B.P. 192°.

130° Bromomethyl Acetate. See Halogen-substituted Esters.

143° aβ-Dichloroethyl Ether. $CH_2Cl \cdot CHCl \cdot O \cdot C_2H_5$
D. 1·174 (23°). With cold water yields ethyl alc.
and chloroacetaldehyde hydrate (M.P. 43–50°, B.P.
85°). With C_2H_5OH yields chloroacetal B.P. 157°.

150° Dibromomethyl Ether $CH_2Br \cdot O \cdot CH_2Br$
D. 2·201 (20°). Reactions as with dichloromethyl
ether B.P. 105°.

O.A.   N

ALIPHATIC HALOGEN-SUBSTITUTED ETHERS
(other than a)

LIQUID

B.P.

107° β-Chloroethyl Ether $C_2H_5O \cdot CH_2 \cdot CH_2Cl$
  D. 1·057 (0°).

117 Epichlorhydrin $CH_2Cl \cdot CH\!-\!\!-\!CH_2$

$\diagdown\!\!O\!\!\diagup$

  D. 1·204 (0°). With KOH in methyl alc. yields glycerol αγ-dimethyl ether B.P. 169°. On boiling with phenol + NaOH in alc. yields glycerol diphenyl ether M.P. 81°. With conc. HCl yields glycerol a-dichlorohydrin B.P. 176°. With PCl_5 yields glycerol trichlorohydrin B.P. 155°.

127° β-Bromo-ethyl Ether $C_2H_5 \cdot O \cdot CH_2 \cdot CH_2Br$
  D. 1·370 (0°).

157° Chloroacetal. See Halogen-substituted Aldehydes.

170°d. Bromoacetal. See Halogen-substituted Aldehydes.

177° ββ'-Dichloroethyl Æther $(CH_2Cl \cdot CH_2)_2O$
  D. 1·213 (20°). On heating with aniline and NaOH yields phenylmorpholine M.P. 57°.

215° γγ'-Dichloropropyl Ether $(CH_2Cl \cdot CH_2 \cdot CH_2)_2O$
  D. 1·140 (20°).

AROMATIC HALOGEN-SUBSTITUTED ETHERS

LIQUID

B.P.

195° o-Chloroanisole $CH_3O \cdot C_6H_4Cl$ (1:2)
  With fuming HNO_3 yields 4-nitro deriv. M.P. 95°.

198° p-Chloroanisole $CH_3O \cdot C_6H_4Cl$ (1:4)
  With fuming HNO_3 yields 2-nitro deriv. M.P. 98°.

208° o-Chlorophenetole $C_2H_5O \cdot C_6H_4Cl$ (1:2)
  With fuming HNO_3 yields 4-nitro deriv. M.P. 82°.

212° p-Chlorophenetole $C_2H_5O \cdot C_6H_4Cl$ (1:4)
  M.P. 20°. With conc. HNO_3 yields 2-nitro deriv. M.P. 61°.

218° o-Bromoanisole. $CH_3O \cdot C_6H_4Br$ (1:2)
  With a mixture of equal parts fuming HNO_3 and glacial acetic acid in the cold yields 4-nitro deriv. M.P. 106°. On boiling with 48% HBr yields methyl bromide B.P. 4° and a mixture of o- and p-bromophenol.

B.P.

223°   *p*-Bromoanisole $CH_3O \cdot C_6H_4Br$ (1:4)
         M.P. 9°. With fuming HNO_3 and glacial acetic acid
         in the cold yields 2-nitro deriv. M.P. 88°.

224°   *o*-Bromophenetole $C_2H_5O \cdot C_6H_4Br$ (1:2)
         On nitration yields 4-nitro deriv. M.P. 98°.

229°   *p*-Bromophenetole $C_2H_5O \cdot C_6H_4Br$ (1:4)
         M.P. 4°. With fuming HNO_3 at – 10° yields 2-
         nitro deriv. M.P. 47° and some 4-nitro-2-bromophene-
         tole M.P., 98°.

SOLID

M.P.

43°   *s*-Trichlorophenetole $Cl_3C_6H_2 \cdot OC_2H_5$ (2:4:6:1)
         B.P. 246°. On boiling with 48% HBr yields ethyl
         bromide B.P. 38° and trichlorophenol M.P. 67°.
         On long warming with conc. $HNO_3 + H_2SO_4$ yields
         dinitro deriv. M.P. 100°.

60°   *s*-Trichloroanisole $Cl_3C_6H_2 \cdot OCH_3$ (2:4:6:1)
         B.P. 240°. On boiling with 48% NBr yields methyl
         bromide B.P. 40° and trichlorophenol M.P. 67°. On
         long warming with conc. $HNO_3 + H_2SO_4$ yields.
         dinitro deriv. M.P. 95°.

72°   *s*-Tribromophenetole⁻ $Br_3C_6H_2 \cdot OC_2H_5$ (2:4:6:1)
         On boiling with 48% HBr yields ethyl bromide B.P.
         38° and tribromophenol M.P. 95°.

87°   *s*-Tribromoanisole $Br_3C_6H_2 \cdot OCH_3$ (2:4:6:1)
         On boiling with 48% HBr yields methyl bromide
         B.P. 4° and tribromophenol M.P. 95°.

HALOGEN-SUBSTITUTED ALCOHOLS

LIQUID

B.P.

127°   Ethylene Chlorohydrin $CH_2Cl \cdot CH_2OH$
         D. 1·233 (0°). Miscible with water. Reduced by
         Na amalgam and water to ethyl alcohol. Oxidised
         by $K_2Cr_2O_7$ in conc. H_2SO_4 to chloroacetic acid
         (*q.v.*). With solid NaOH yields ethylene oxide
         B.P. 13°; with boiling dil. NaOH yields ethylene
         glycol B.P. 197°. Acetate B.P. 145°. Benzoate B.P.
         255°. Carbanilate M.P. 51°. α-Naphthylcarbamate
         M.P. 101°. On boiling with phenol + NaOH in alc.
         yields ethylene glycol monophenyl ether B.P. 237°.

149°   Ethylene Bromohydrin $CH_2Br \cdot CH_2OH$
         D. 1·685 (17°). Miscible with water. Acetate B.P.

162°. Benzoate B.P. 280°d. α-Naphthylcarbamate M.P. 86°. *Cf.* Ethylene Chlorohydrin B.P. 127°.

161°d. **Trimethylene Chlorohydrin.** $CH_2Cl \cdot CH_2 \cdot CH_2OH$
D. 1·132 (17°). Sol. in 2–3 vols of cold water. With solid NaOH yields trimethylene oxide B.P. 49° On oxidation with HNO_3 yields β-chloropropionic acid M.P. 44°, B.P. 204°. Acetate B.P. 164°. α-Naphthylcarbamate M.P. 76°. On boiling with phenol + NaOH in alc. yields trimethylene glycol monophenyl ether B.P. 249°.

176° **Glycerol α-Dichlorohydrin** $CH_2Cl \cdot CH(OH) \cdot CH_2Cl$
D. 1·383 (0°). Miscible with water. Oxidised by $K_2Cr_2O_7$ in conc. H_2SO_4 to chloroacetic acid ; by $K_2Cr_2O_7$ in dil. H_2SO_4 to s-dichloroacetone M.P. 45° B.P. 172°. With solid NaOH yields epichlorohydrin B.P. 117°. On boiling with phenol + NaOH in alc. yields glycerol diphenyl ether M.P. 81°. Acetate B.P. 205°. Benzoate B.P. 230°/150 mm. Carbanilate M.P. 73°.

176°d. **Trimethylene Bromohydrin** $CH_2Br \cdot CH_2 \cdot CH_2OH$
B.P. 83°/23 mm. D. 1·537 (20°). Sol. in 9 vols o. cold water. With solid NaOH yields trimethylene oxide B.P. 49°. On oxidation with HNO_3 yields β-bromopropionic acid M.P. 62°. Acetate B.P. 185° Benzoate B.P. 148°/6 mm. α-Naphthylcarbamate M.P. 73°.

182° **Glycerol β-Dichlorohydrin** $CH_2Cl \cdot CHCl \cdot CH_2OH$
D. 1·380 (0°). Oxidised by HNO_3 to αβ-dichloropropionic acid M.P. 50°. With solid NaOH yields epichlorohydrin B.P. 117°. Carbanilate M.P. 73°.

213°d. **Glycerol α-Monochlorohydrin** $CH_2Cl \cdot CH(OH) \cdot CH_2OH$
D. 1·338 (0°). Miscible with water, alcohol, and ether Reduced by Na amalgam and water to propylene glycol B.P. 188°. Diacetate B.P. 245°.

219°d. **Glycerol α-Dibromohydrin** $CH_2Br \cdot CH(OH) \cdot CH_2Br$
D. 2·02 (18°·5). On distillation yields epibromohydrin B.P. 138° and acrolein. Oxidised by dil. chromic acid to s-dibromoacetone M.P. 24°. Acetate B.P. 227°. *Cf.* Glycerol α-dichlorohydrin B.P. 176°.

219° **Glycerol β-Dibromohydrin** $CH_2Br \cdot CHBr \cdot CH_2OH$
D. 2·168 (0°). Oxidised by HNO_3 to αβ-dibromopropionic acid M.P. 64°. Acetate B.P. 227°.

HALOGEN-SUBSTITUTED PHENOLS

LIQUID

B.P.
75° o-Chlorophenol   Cl·C₆H₄·OH (1:2)
Methyl ether B.P. 195°. Ethyl ether B.P. 208°.
With PCl₅ yields o-dichlorobenzene B.P. 179°. Benzoyl deriv. B.P. 213°. Carbanilate M.P. 120°.
p-Nitrobenzyl ether M.P. 100°. With ethylene
bromide + NaOH in alc. yields ethylene glycol
di-o-chlorophenyl ether M.P. 103°. With HNO₃
in acetic acid yields dinitro deriv. M.P. 111°. Picrate
M.P. 81°.

94° o-Bromophenol   Br·C₆H₄·OH (1:2)
With HNO₃ in acetic acid yields dinitro deriv. M.P.
118°. With bromine water yields tribromophenol
M.P. 95°. Methyl ether B.P. 210°. Ethyl ether
B.P. 218°.

SOLID

M.P.
28° m-Chlorophenol   Cl·C₆H₄·OH (1:3)
B.P. 214°. On adding to 47% HNO₃ in cold yields
4-nitro deriv. M.P. 133°. Methyl ether B.P. 193°.
With PCl₅ yields m-dichlorobenzene B.P. 172°.

35° 2:4-Dibromophenol   Br₂C₆H₃·OH (2:4:1)
B.P. 238°. With bromine water yields tribromophenol
M.P. 95°. With conc. HNO₃ in cold yields nitro
deriv. M.P. 117°. Methyl ether M.P. 59°. Ethyl
ether M.P. 50°. Benzoyl deriv. M.P. 97°.

37° p-Chlorophenol   Cl·C₆H₄·OH (1:4)
B.P. 217°. On adding to conc. HNO₃ yields dinitro
deriv. M.P. 81°. With PCl₅ yields p-dichlorobenzene
M.P. 53°. Methyl ether B.P. 197°. Ethyl ether
M.P. 20°, B.P. 211°. p-Nitrobenzyl ether M.P. 101°.
Benzoyl deriv. M.P. 93°. Carbanilate M.P. 138°.

43° 2:4-Dichlorophenol   Cl₂C₆H₃·OH (2:4:1)
B.P. 209°. With bromine yields dichlorobromo-
phenol M.P. 68°. With conc. HNO₃ yields nitro
deriv. M.P. 122°. Methyl ether M.P. 27°, B.P.
238°. Ethyl ether B.P. 236°. Acetyl deriv. B.P.
244°. Benzoyl deriv. M.P. 97°.

63° p-Bromophenol   Br·C₆H₄·OH (1:4)
B.P. 235°. With bromine water yields tribromophenol M.P. 95°. Methyl ether B.P. 223°. Ethyl
ether B.P. 233°. Benzoyl deriv. M.P. 102°. Carbanilate M.P. 144°.

M.P.
67°   s-Trichlorophenol $Cl_3C_6H_2 \cdot OH$ (2:4:6:1)
       B.P. 244°. Almost insol. in water. Gives a strong
       acid reaction. Methyl ether M.P. 60°. Ethyl ether
       M.P. 43°. With NO_2 in alc. yields dichloroquinone
       M.P. 120°. Acetyl deriv. B.P. 261°. Benzoyl M.P.
       70°. Benzene sulphonyl deriv. M.P. 66°.

95°   s-Tribromophenol $Br_3C_6H_2 \cdot OH$ (2:4:6:1)
       Almost insol. in water. Gives a strong acid reaction.
       With NO_2 in acetic acid or ethyl nitrite in alc. yields
       2:4-dibromo-6-nitrophenol M.P. 117°. Methyl ether
       M.P. 87°. Ethyl ether M.P. 72°. Benzyl ether M.P.
       86°. p-Nitrobenzyl ether M.P. 163°. Acetyl deriv.
       M.P. 82°. Benzoyl deriv. M.P. 81°. Benzenesulph-
       onyl deriv. M.P. 85°. Carbanilate M.P. 168°.

106°   Chlorohydroquinone $Cl \cdot C_6H_3(OH)_2$ (2:1:4)
       B.P. 263°. Very sol. in cold water and alc. slightly
       sol. in C_6H_6 and $CHCl_3$. With dil. $K_2Cr_2O_7$ +
       H_2SO_4 in cold yields chloroquinone M.P. 57°. Di-
       acetate M.P. 72°. Dibenzoate M.P. 130°.

110°   Bromohydroquinone $Br \cdot C_6H_3(OH)_2$ (2:1:4)
       Very sol. in water; sparingly in $CHCl_3$. With
       $FeCl_3$ in water yields bromoquinone M.P. 55°. Di-
       methyl ether B.P. 262°. Diacetate M.P. 72°.

HALOGEN-SUBSTITUTED ALDEHYDES, ACETALS, etc.

LIQUID

B.P.
98°   Chloral $CCl_3 \cdot CHO$
       D. 1·512 (20°). With water yields chloral hydrate
       M.P. 57°. With C_2H_5OH yields chloral alcoholate
       M.P. 56°. Insol. in conc. H_2SO_4. With conc.
       NaOH in cold yields chloroform B.P. 61° and sodium
       formate. Colour test with pyridine see p. 67. With
       KI soln yields free iodine and chloroform. With
       KCN in alc. yields ethyl dichloroacetate B.P. 158°.
       Oxidised by fuming HNO_3 to trichloroacetic acid
       M.P. 57°. Reduces ammon. $AgNO_3$ on warming.
       Forms a bisulphite compd. With NH_3 in $CHCl_3$
       yields chloral-ammonia M.P. 62°. Forms an addition-
       compd. with semicarbazide, M.P. 90°d. With acetic
       anhydride forms a diacetate B.P. 221°; with acetyl
       chloride yields tetrachloroethyl acetate B.P. 185°.

B.P.
157° Chloroacetal $CH_2Cl \cdot CH(OC_2H_5)_2$
D. 1·026 (15°). On heating with 30% H_2SO_4 or with anhydrous oxalic acid yields chloroacetaldehyde B.P. 85° (sharp odour), which forms a semicarbazone M.P. 134°d. With phenylhydrazine at 130° yields glyoxalosazone M.P. 155°.

170°d. Bromoacetal $CH_2Br \cdot CH(OC_2H_5)_2$
B.P. 66°/18 mm. On heating with anhydrous oxalic acid yields bromoacetaldehyde B.P. 104° (sharp odour), which forms a semicarbazone M.P. 130°. Cf. Chloroacetal B.P. 157°.

174° Bromal $CBr_3 \cdot CHO$
D. 3·34. With water yields bromal hydrate M.P. 53°. With C_2H_5OH yields bromal alcoholate M.P. 44°. With NaOH yields bromoform B.P. 151° and sodium formate. Colour test with pyridine see p. 67. Forms a bisulphite compd. With acetic anhydride yields a diacetate M.P. 76°.

208° o-Chlorobenzaldehyde $Cl \cdot C_6H_4 \cdot CHO$ (1:2)
M.P. 11°. D. 1·29 (8°). On oxidation by $KMnO_4$ yields o-chlorobenzoic acid M.P. 137°. With $NH_2OH \cdot HCl$ + excess Na_2CO_3 soln yields α-oxime M.P. 75°. Anil is an oil. With conc. HNO_3 + H_2SO_4 in cold yields nitro deriv. M.P. 80°.

SOLID

M.P.
44° Bromal Alcoholate $CBr_3 \cdot CH(OH) \cdot OC_2H_5$
Sparingly sol. in cold water. On distillation yields bromal and C_2H_5OH. Cf. Bromal B.P. 174°.

47° p-Chlorobenzaldehyde $Cl \cdot C_6H_4 \cdot CHO$ (1:4)
B.P. 213°. On oxidation by $KMnO_4$ yields p-chlorobenzoic acid M.P. 236°. On boiling with acetic anhydride yields diacetate M.P. 82°. On warming with $NH_2OH \cdot HCl$ + Na_2CO_3 soln. yields α-oxime M.P. 106°. Anil M.P. 66°. With conc. HNO_3 + H_2SO_4 at 80° yields nitro deriv. M.P. 62°.

53° Bromal Hydrate $CBr_3 \cdot CH(OH)_2$
Sol. in water. On distillation yields bromal and water. Cf. Bromal B.P. 174°.

56° Chloral Alcoholate $CCl_3 \cdot CH(OH) \cdot OC_2H_5$
B.P. 115°. Dissolves slowly, though very sol., in water. Yields chloral B.P. 98° with cold conc. H_2SO_4. Insol. in conc. $CaCl_2$ soln. With acetyl

M.P.

chloride yields acetyl deriv. B.P. 198°. *Cf.* Chloral B.P. 98°.

57°   Chloral Hydrate $CCl_3 \cdot CH(OH)_2$
B.P. 97°d., partially breaking up into chloral and water. Yields chloral B.P. 98° with cold conc. H_2SO_4. With acetyl chloride yields tetrachloroethyl acetate B.P. 185°. *Cf.* Chloral B.P. 98°.

HALOGEN-SUBSTITUTED KETONES

LIQUID

B.P.
118°   Chloroacetone $CH_2Cl \cdot CO \cdot CH_3$
D. 1·158 (13°). Extremely irritating odour. Appreciably sol. in water. Very readily hydrolysed by alkalies. Gives red colour with K_2CO_3 soln. Forms acetonesulphonic salts with sulphites, chlorine being eliminated. With β-naphthol Na salt yields β-naphthoxyacetone M.P. 78°. On heating with anhydrous Na acetate yields acetol acetate B.P. 174°. On adding slowly to excess NH_2OH soln. yields methylglyoxime M.P. 153°. With semicarbazide HCl yields semicarbazone M.P. 164°d.

120° aa-Dichloroacetone $CHCl_2 \cdot CO \cdot CH_3$
D. 1·234 (15°). Sparingly sol. in cold water. On boiling with 10% K_2CO_3 soln. yields K acrylate (*cf.* acrylic acid p. 142) ; with KOH yields K formate and acetate. With NH_2OH yields methylglyoxime M.P. 153°.

SOLID

M.P.
45° $a\gamma$-Dichloroacetone $CH_2Cl \cdot CO \cdot CH_2Cl$
B.P. 173°. Sparingly sol. in cold water. Irritating odour. Readily hydrolysed. Forms a bisulphite compd.

50° ω-Bromoacetophenone $C_6H_5 \cdot CO \cdot CH_2Br$
Very irritating odour. Forms no bisulphite compd. Yields benzoic acid M.P. 121° on oxidation by chromic acid. On boiling in alc. soln. with various sodium salts yields phenacyl derivs. : Phenyl ether M.P. 72°. β-Naphthyl ether M.P. 105°. Acetate M.P. 40°. Benzoate M.P. 118°. Sulphide M.P. 77°. With phenylhydrazine in alc. yields tetraphenyltetracarbazone M.P. 137°. With aniline in cold yields acetophenoneanilide M.P. 93°. With cold fuming HNO_3 yields *m*-nitro deriv. M.P. 96°.

M.P.
59°   ω-Chloroacetophenone $C_6H_5 \cdot CO \cdot CH_2Cl$
        B.P. 244°. Very irritating odour. Yields same
        phenacyl derivs. as ω-bromoacetophenone M.P. 50°.

76°   α-Bromocamphor

$$C_8H_{14} \begin{cases} CHBr \\ | \\ CO \end{cases}$$

        B.P. 274°d. Odour like camphor. Optically active,
        $[a]_D = +140°$ (10% in alc.). Oxidised by $KMnO_4$
        to camphoric acid M.P. 187°. With (1 mol.) bromine
        at 100° yields αα-dibromocamphor M.P. 60°. With
        (3 mols.) phenylhydrazine at 100° yields ' camphor-
        osazone ' M.P. 55°.

CARBOXYLIC ACID HALIDES

LIQUID

B.P.
55°	Acetyl Chloride	D. 1·105 (20°).
80°	Propionyl Chloride	D. 1·065 (20°).
80°	Acetyl Bromide	D. 1·640 (25°).
92°	isoButyryl Chloride	D. 1·017 (20°).
100°	n-Butyryl Chloride	D. 1·028 (20°).
103°	Chloroacetyl Chloride	D. 1·495 (0°).
115°	isoValeryl Chloride	D. 0·989 (20°).
127°	n-Valeryl Chloride	D. 1·015 (15°).
149°	Bromoacetyl Bromide	D. 2·317 (21°).
153°	α-Bromopropionyl Bromide	D. 2·061 (16°).
190°d	Succinyl Chloride	M.P. 16°. D. 1·407 (20°). B.P. 103°/25 mm.
197°	Benzoyl Chloride	M.P. −1°. D. 1·212 (20°).
210°	Phenylacetyl Chloride	B.P. 94°/12 mm. D. 1·168 (20°).
	Anisoyl Chloride	M.P. 22°. B.P. 145°/14 mm.
281°	Phthalyl Chloride	M.P. about 12°. D. 1·421 (15°).

ALKYL CHLOROFORMATES (CHLOROCARBONATES)

LIQUID

B.P.
71°   Methyl $Cl \cdot COOCH_3$
        D. 1·236 (15°). Sharp odour. With aniline yields
        methyl carbanilate M.P. 47°. With ammonia yields

B.P.

     methyl carbamate M.P. 57°. With CH_3OH yields methyl carbonate B.P. 89°; with C_2H_5OH yields methyl ethyl carbonate B.P. 109°. With phenol in dil. NaOH yields methyl phenyl carbonate B.P. 190–200°.

93°   Ethyl $Cl \cdot COOC_2H_5$

     D. 1·144 (15°). Sharp odour. Ethyl carbanilate M.P. 52°. Ethyl carbamate M.P. 49°. Methyl ethyl carbonate B.P. 109°. Ethyl carbonate B.P. 126°. Ethyl phenyl carbonate B.P. 228°. (*Cf.* Methyl chloroformate above).

105°   *iso*Propyl $Cl \cdot COOCH(CH_3)_2$

     Sharp odour. *iso*Propyl carbanilate M.P. 90°. *iso*Propyl carbamate M.P. 92°. Ethyl *iso*propyl carbonate B.P. 132°. (*Cf.* Methyl chloroformate, above).

115°   *n*-Propyl $Cl \cdot COOCH_2 \cdot CH_2 \cdot CH_3$

     D. 1·094 (15°). *n*-Propyl carbanilate M.P. 58°. *n*-Propyl carbamate M.P. 60°. Methyl propyl carbonate B.P. 131°. Ethyl propyl carbonate B.P. 145°. (*Cf.* Methyl chloroformate, above).

129°   *iso*Butyl $Cl \cdot COOCH_2 \cdot CH(CH_3)_2$

     D. 1·053 (15°). *iso*Butyl carbanilate M.P. 80°. *iso*Butyl carbamate M.P. 64°. Methyl *iso*butyl carbonate B.P. 143°. Ethyl *iso*butyl carbonate B.P. 160°. (*Cf.* Methyl chloroformate, above).

137°   *n*-Butyl $Cl \cdot COOCH_2 \cdot [CH_2]_2 \cdot CH_3$

     On warming with *n*-butyl alc. yields *n*-butyl carbonate B.P. 207°. With NH_3 yields *n*-butyl carbamate M.P. 54°. With phenol yields *n*-butyl phenyl carbonate B.P. 129°/25 mm.

154°   *iso*Amyl $Cl \cdot COOCH_2 \cdot CH_2 \cdot CH(CH_3)_2$

     D. 1·032 (15°). *iso*Amyl carbanilate M.P. 55°. *iso*Amyl carbamate M.P. 64°. Ethyl *iso*amyl carbonate B.P. 182° (*Cf.* Methyl chloroformate, above).

ALIPHATIC HALOGEN-SUBSTITUTED CARBOXYLIC ACIDS

LIQUID

B.P.

186°   a-Chloropropionic $CH_3 \cdot CHCl \cdot COOH$

     D. 1·306 (9°). Miscible with water. Reduced by Zn + HCl to propionic acid B.P. 141°. On alkaline hydrolysis yields lactic acid (*q.v.*). Methyl ester B.P. 132°. Ethyl ester B.P. 147°. Chloride B.P. 110°.

Amide M.P. 80°. Anilide M.P. 92°. With phenol + NaOH yields α-phenoxypropionic acid M.P. 112°.

190° Dichloroacetic   CHCl₂·COOH
M.P. 10°. D. 1·571 (15°). Miscible with water. Methyl ester B.P. 143°. Ethyl ester B.P. 158°. Chloride B.P. 107°. Amide M.P. 96°. Anilide M.P. 118°. Forms a cryst. aniline salt M.P. 122°.

SOLID

M.P.
24° α-Bromopropionic   CH₃·CHBr·COOH
B.P. 205°. Sol. in water. Ethyl ester B.P. 162° (sharp odour). Chloride B.P. 132°. Amide M.P. 123°. Anilide M.P. 99°. On boiling conc. soln of Na salt with NaNO₂ yields nitroethane B.P. 114°. Cf. α-chloropropionic acid B.P. 186°.

41° β-Chloropropionic acid   CH₂Cl·CH₂·COOH
B.P. 204°d. Readily sol. in water. On alkaline hydrolysis yields acrylic acid (q.v.). Methyl ester B.P. 156°. Ethyl ester B.P. 162°. Chloride B.P. 144°.

50° Bromoacetic   CH₂Br·COOH
B.P. 208°. Very sol. in water. Causes blisters on skin. Methyl ester B.P. 144° (sharp odour). Ethyl ester B.P. 159° (sharp odour). p-Nitrobenzyl ester M.P. 88°. Chloride B.P. 127°. Amide M.P. 91°. Anilide M.P. 130°. Cf. Chloroacetic acid M.P. 63°.

55° Trichloroacetic   CCl₃·COOH
B.P. 196°. Sol. in water. Soln of Na salt yields CHCl₃ on prolonged boiling. On heating with aniline yields CHCl₃ and CO₂. Methyl ester B.P. 152°. Ethyl ester B.P. 168°. p-Nitrobenzyl ester M.P. 80° (v. poor yield). Chloride B.P. 118°. Amide M.P. 141°. Anilide M.P. 94°.

62° β-Bromopropionic CH₂Br·CH₂·COOH
Sol. in water. Ethyl ester B.P. 179° (pleasant odour). Cf. β-Iodopropionic acid M.P. 82°.

63° Chloroacetic   CH₂Cl·COOH
B.P. 185°. Sol. in water. Causes blisters on skin. On alkaline hydrolysis yields glycollic acid (q.v.). Methyl ester B.P. 130°. Ethyl ester B.P. 144°. p-Nitrobenzyl ester is an oil. Chloride B.P. 103°. Amide M.P. 119°. Anilide M.P. 134°. With phenol + NaOH in water yields phenoxyacetic acid M.P. 96°; similarly with β-naphthol yields β-naphthoxy-acetic acid M.P. 156°. Na salt + Na₂S in water

yields thiodiglycollic acid M.P. 129°.   On boiling a
conc. soln. of Na salt with NaNO₂ nitromethane B.P.
101° is formed.   Addition product with pyridine M.P.
202°.

64°   αβ-Dibromopropionic   CH₂Br·CHBr·COOH
Sol. in water.   On reduction with Zn dust yields
acrylic acid (q.v.).   On boiling with KI soln yields
acrylic acid and iodine.   Methyl ester B.P. 205°.
Ethyl ester B.P. 214°.   Chloride B.P. 192°d.

82°   β-Iodopropionic   CH₂I·CH₂·COOH
Readily sol. in hot water, slightly in cold.   Methyl
ester B.P. 188° (pleasant odour).   Ethyl ester B.P.
200° (pleasant odour).   Amide M.P. 101°.   With
bromine water yields β-bromopropionic acid M.P. 62°
and iodine.   With conc. Na₂S soln, yields thiodihydra-
crylic acid M.P. 128°.

83°   Iodoacetic   CH₂I·COOH
Readily sol. in hot water, sparingly in cold.   Causes
severe blisters on skin.   Readily hydrolysed to hydriodic and glycollic acids (q.v.).   Methyl ester B.P.
170° (very sharp odour).   Ethyl ester B.P. 179° (very
sharp odour).   Cf. Chloroacetic acid M.P. 63°.

124°   Trichlorolactic   CCl₃·CH(OH)·COOH
Readily sol. in water.   With dil. KOH yields chloral
(q.v.) ; with conc. KOH yields CHCl₃.   Soln. of Na
salt yields dichloroacetaldehyde B.P. 88° on boiling.
Ethyl ester M.P. 66°, B.P. 235°.   On boiling with
acetic anhydride yields acetyl deriv. M.P. 65°.

AROMATIC HALOGEN-SUBSTITUTED CARBOXYLIC ACIDS

SOLID

M.P.

137°   o-Chlorobenzoic   Cl·C₆H₄·COOH (1:2)
Sol. in hot water.   Yields benzoic acid with Na
amalgam.   On fusion with KOH yields m-hydroxybenzoic acid M.P. 200° with only traces of salicylic
acid.   Methyl ester B.P. 234°.   Ethyl ester B.P. 243°.
p-Nitrobenzyl ester M.P. 106°.   Chloride B.P. 229°.
Amide M.P. 139°.   Anilide M.P. 114°.

150°   o-Bromobenzoic   Br·C₆H₄·COOH (1:2)
Sol. in hot water.   With conc. H₂SO₄ + HNO₃ at
130–140° yields dinitro deriv. M.P. 213°.   Methyl
ester B.P. 250°.   Ethyl ester B.P. 254°.   Chloride
B.P. 245°.   Amide M.P. 155°.   Anilide M.P. 141°.

M.P.

158°   m-Chlorobenzoic $Cl \cdot C_6H_4 \cdot COOH$ (1:3)
        Sparingly sol. in cold water. Yields benzoic acid
        M.P. 121° with Na amalgam. On fusion with KOH
        yields m-hydroxybenzoic acid M.P. 200°. Methyl
        ester B.P. 231°. Ethyl ester B.P. 245°. Chloride
        B.P. 222°. Amide M.P. 134°.

155°   m-Bromobenzoic $Br \cdot C_6H_4 \cdot COOH$ (1:3)
        Sparingly sol. in water. On fusion with KOH yields
        m-hydroxybenzoic acid M.P. 200°. Yields isophthalic
        acid (q.v.) on fusing K salt with Na formate. Methyl
        ester M.P. 31°, B.P. 122°/15 mm. Ethyl ester B.P.
        259°. p-Nitrobenzyl ester M.P. 105°. Chloride B.P.
        243°. Amide M.P. 155°. Anilide M.P. 137°.

(191°) 3:6-Dichlorophthalic $Cl_2C_6H_2(COOH)_2$ (1:4:2:3)
        Decomposes at 130–140° yielding the anhydride M.P.
        191°. Sol. in hot water. With C_2H_5OH and HCl gas
        yields the monoethyl ester M.P. 128°d. Diethyl
        ester M.P. 60°. Imide M.P. 242°. Anil M.P. 191°.

236°   p-Chlorobenzoic $Cl \cdot C_6H_4 \cdot COOH$ (1:4)
        Sparingly sol. in water. Methyl ester M.P. 43°.
        Ethyl ester B.P. 238°. p-Nitrobenzyl ester M.P.
        129°. Chloride B.P. 220°. Amide M.P. 179°. Anil-
        ide M.P. 194°.

250°d   Tetrachlorophthalic $Cl_4C_6(COOH)_2$ (1:2)
        Yields the anhydride M.P. 253° on melting. Sol. in
        hot water. Monomethyl ester M.P. 142°. Dimethyl
        ester M.P. 92°. Monoethyl ester M.P. 94°. Diethyl
        ester M.P. 60°. p-Nitrobenzyl ester M.P. 180°.
        Imide M.P. 360°. Anil M.P. 268°.

251°   p-Bromobenzoic $Br \cdot C_6H_4 \cdot COOH$ (1:4)
        Sparingly sol. in hot water. Methyl ester M.P. 81°.
        Ethyl ester B.P. 262°. p-Nitrobenzyl ester M.P. 139°.
        Phenacyl ester M.P. 87°. Chloride M.P. 41°, B.P.
        245°d. Amide M.P. 189°. Anilide M.P. 197°.

HALOGEN-SUBSTITUTED CARBOXYLIC ESTERS

LIQUID

B.P.

71°   Methyl Chloroformate.   See Alkyl Chloroformates.

93°   Ethyl Chloroformate.   See Alkyl Chloroformates.

111°   Chloromethyl Acetate $CH_3 \cdot COOCH_2Cl$
        D. 1·195 (14°). Sharp odour. Decomp. by water,
        yielding HCl, acetic acid, and formaldehyde. With
        C_2H_5OH yields ethylal B.P. 88° and ethyl acetate.

With anhydrous Na acetate yields methylene diacetate B.P. 170°.

130° Methyl Chloroacetate $CH_2Cl \cdot COOCH_3$
D. 1·238 (20°). With conc. NH_4OH in cold yields chloroacetamide M.P. 119°. With aniline yields methyl anilinoacetate M.P. 48°. With Na_2S in CH_3OH yields methyl thiodiglycollate B.P. 253°.

130° Bromomethyl Acetate $CH_3 \cdot COOCH_2Br$
D. 1·656 (12°). Cf. Chloromethyl Acetate B.P. 111°.

144° Methyl Bromoacetate $CH_2Br \cdot COOCH_3$
D. 1·657 (19°). Highly irritating odour. With conc. NH_4OH at 0° yields bromoacetamide M.P. 91°. Cf. Methyl Chloroacetate B.P. 130°.

144° Ethyl Chloroacetate $CH_2Cl \cdot COOC_2H_5$
D. 1·158 (20°). With conc. NH_4OH in cold yields chloroacetamide M.P. 119°. With aniline yields ethyl anilinoacetate M.P. 57°. With Na_2S in alc. yields ethyl thiodiglycollate B.P. 267°. With ethyl sodiomalonate in abs. alc. yields ethyl ethanetricarboxylate B.P. 278° (free acid M.P. 159° yields succinic acid M.P. 185° on heating). Addition product with pyridine M.P. 100°.

145° β-Chloroethyl Acetate $CH_3 \cdot COOCH_2 \cdot CH_2Cl$
D. 1·178 (0°). On boiling with dil. NaOH yields ethylene glycol B.P. 197°; with solid NaOH in cold yields ethylene oxide B.P. 13°. On boiling with CH_3OH containing 1% of HCl gas yields methyl acetate B.P. 57° and ethylene chlorohydrin B.P. 127°.

147° Ethyl α-Chloropropionate $CH_3 \cdot CHCl \cdot COOC_2H_5$
D. 1·087 (20°). With conc. NH_4OH in cold yields amide M.P. 80°. With C_2H_5ONa in alc. yields ethyl α-ethoxypropionate B.P. 155°. On heating with dry C_6H_5ONa yields ethyl α-phenoxypropionate B.P. 243°. With ethyl sodiomalonate in abs. alc. yields ethyl propane-ααβ-tricarboxylate B.P. 269° (free acid M.P. 146° yields methylsuccinic acid M.P. 112° on heating).

158° Ethyl Dichloroacetate $CHCl_2 \cdot COOC_2H_5$
D. 1·282 (20°). With NH_3 in alc. yields amide M.P. 98°. On boiling with C_6H_5ONa in alc. yields ethyl diphenoxyacetate B.P. 208°/28 mm. (free acid M.P. 91°).

159° Ethyl Bromoacetate $CH_2Br \cdot COOC_2H_5$
D. 1·506 (20°). Highly irritating odour. Addition product with quinoline M.P. 180°. Cf. Methyl bro-

B.P.

moacetete B.P. 144° and Ethyl chloroacetate B.P. 144°.

160°   Ethyl α-Bromopropionate $CH_3 \cdot CHBr \cdot COOC_2H_5$
D. 1·329 (20°). Irritating odour. *Cf.* Ethyl α-chloropropionate B.P. 147°.

163°   β-Bromoethyl Acetate $CH_3 \cdot COOCH_2 \cdot CH_2Br$
D. 1·524 (0°). Pleasant odour. On boiling with CH_3OH containing 1% of HCl gas yields methyl acetate B.P. 57° and ethylene bromohydrin B.P. 149°. *Cf.* β-Chloroethyl acetate B.P. 145°.

167°   Ethyl Trichloroacetate $CCl_3 \cdot COOC_2H_5$
D. 1·369 (15°). With conc. NH_4OH in cold yields amide M.P. 141°. Yields $CHCl_3$ on long boiling with (1 mol.) NaOH in water.

175°   *n*-Butyl Chloroacetate $CH_2Cl \cdot COOCH_2 \cdot CH_2 \cdot C_2H_5$
D. 1·081 (15°). With conc. NH_4OH yields chloroacetamide M.P. 119° and *n*-butyl alc. B.P. 116°.

179°   Ethyl β-Bromopropionate $CH_2Br \cdot CH_2 \cdot COOC_2H_5$
D. 1·425 (20°). On boiling with conc. NaOH yields acrylic acid (*q.v.*). With ethyl sodiomalonate in abs. alc. yields ethyl propane-ααγ-tricarboxylate B.P. 283°, which on alkaline hydrolysis with subsequent heating yields glutaric acid M.P. 97°.

SOLID

M.P.

66°   Ethyl Trichlorolactate $CCl_3 \cdot CH(OH) \cdot COOC_2H_5$
B.P. 162°. Sol. in cold dil. KOH, pptd by CO_2. On boiling with dil. NaOH yields dichloroacetic acid (*q.v.*) and tartronic acid (forms sparingly sol. Ba salt).

ALIPHATIC PRIMARY AMINES

LIQUID

B.P.

Gas   Methylamine $CH_3 \cdot NH_2$
Gives yellow ppte. with Nessler's soln., insol. in excess of reagent. Gives no ppte. with soln. of HgI_2 in KI. Not attacked by $KMnO_4$ in boiling acid soln. Hydrochloride M.P. 225° is sparingly sol. in alc., insol. in $CHCl_3$. Hydrobromide M.P. 250°. With benzaldehyde forms benzylidene deriv. B.P. 180°. With 2:4 dinitrochlorobenzene in cold alc. yields 2:4-dinitromethylaniline M.P. 175°. Acetyl deriv. M.P. 28°, B.P. 206°. Benzoyl deriv. M.P. 80°. *m*-Nitrobenzoyl deriv. M.P. 174°. *p*-Nitrobenzoyl deriv. M.P. 218°.

Benzenesulphonyl deriv. M.P. 30°. *p*-Toluenesulphonyl deriv. M.P. 75°. *p*-Bromobenzenesulphonyl deriv. M.P. 77°. *m*-Nitrobenzenesulphonyl deriv. M.P. 128°. Compound with phenyl *iso*cyanate M.P. 151°. Picrate M.P. 207°.

18°   Ethylamine $C_2H_5 \cdot NH_2$

Gives white ppte with Nessler's soln. Very slowly oxidised by $KMnO_4$ in boiling dil. H_2SO_4. Aqueous soln. readily dissolves $Al(OH)_3$. Hydrochloride (hygroscopic) is very sol. in alc., insol. in $CHCl_3$. Hydrobromide (not very hygroscopic) M.P. 159° is sol. in alc., insol. in $CHCl_3$. Platinichloride M.P. 218°d. With benzaldehyde forms benzylidene deriv. B.P. 195°. Acetyl deriv. B.P. 205°. Benzoyl deriv. M.P. 71°. *m*-Nitrobenzoyl deriv. M.P. 120°. Benzenesulphonyl deriv. M.P. 58°. *p*-Toluenesulphonyl deriv. M.P. 63°. *m*-Nitrobenzenesulphonyl deriv. M.P. 81°. *p*-Bromobenzenesulphonyl deriv. M.P. about 0°. Picrate M.P. 165°. With 2:4-dinitrochlorobenzene yields 2:4-dinitroethylaniline M.P. 113°. Compound with phenyl *iso*cyanate M.P. 99°.

33°   *iso*Propylamine $(CH_3)_2CH \cdot NH_2$

D. 0·694 (15°). Miscible with water. Hydrochloride (very hygroscopic) M.P. 139° is readily sol. in alc. Benzenesulphonyl deriv. M.P. 26°. *p*-Bromobenzenesulphonyl deriv. M.P. 99°. With 2:4-dinitrochlorobenzene yields 2:4-dinitro*iso*propylaniline M.P. 94°.

49°   *n*-Propylamine $CH_3 \cdot CH_2 \cdot CH_2 \cdot NH_2$

D. 0·722 (15°). Miscible with water. Gives brown ppte. with Nessler's soln. Hydrochloride M.P. 157°. Platinichloride M.P. 214°. With benzaldehyde yields benzylidene deriv. B.P. 209°. Acetyl deriv. B.P. 223°. Benzoyl deriv. M.P. 84°. Benzenesulphonyl deriv. M.P. 36°. *p*-Bromobenzenesulphonyl deriv. M.P. 65°. With ethyl oxalate yields dipropyloxamide M.P. 162°. Picrate M.P. 135°. With 2:4-dinitrochlorobenzene yields 2:4-dinitropropylaniline M.P. 95°.

53°   Allylamine $CH_2 : CH \cdot CH_2 \cdot NH_2$

D. 0·769 (15°). Miscible with water. Unsaturated (dibromide is an oil sparingly sol. in water, which forms a hydrobromide M.P. 164° sparingly sol. in cold water). Hydrochloride M.P. 105–110°. Acetyl deriv. B.P. 215°. Benzoyl deriv. B.P. 173°/14 mm. forms a dibromide M.P. 135°. Benzenesulphonyl deriv. M.P. 39°. *p*-Toluenesulphonyl deriv. M.P. 64°. With

B.P.

ethyl oxalate yields diallyloxamide M.P. 154°. Picrate M.P. 140°. With 2:4-dinitrochlorobenzene yields 2:4-dinitroallylaniline M.P. 75°.

68° *iso*Butylamine $(CH_3)_2CH \cdot CH_2 \cdot NH_2$
D. 0·736 (15°). Miscible with water. Hydrochloride (hygroscopic) M.P. 160°. Platinichloride M.P. 225°d. Acetyl deriv. B.P. 226°. Benzoyl deriv. M.P. 57°. Benzenesulphonyl deriv. M.P. 53°. *p*-Toluenesulphonyl deriv. M.P. 78°. With ethyl oxalate yields di-*iso*butyloxamide M.P. 167°. With 2:4-dinitrochlorobenzene yields 2:4-dinitro*iso*butylaniline M.P. 80°. On oxidation with chromic acid yields *iso*butyric acid B.P. 155°.

77° *n*-Butylamine $CH_3 \cdot [CH_2]_2 \cdot CH_2 \cdot NH_2$
D. 0·742 (15°). Miscible with water. Hydrochloride M.P. 195°. Benzenesulphonyl deriv. is an oil. *p*-Bromobenzenesulphonyl deriv. M.P. 58°. With ethyl oxalate yields dibutyloxamide M.P. 153°. With 2:4-dinitrochlorobenzene yields 2:4-dinitrobutylaniline M.P. 58°. On oxidation with chromic acid yields *n*-butyric acid B.P. 163°.

95° *iso*Amylamine $(CH_3)_2CH \cdot CH_2 \cdot CH_2 \cdot NH_2$
D. 0·750 (18°). Miscible with water. Acetyl deriv. B.P. 238°. Benzenesulphonyl deriv. is an oil. With ethyl oxalate yields di-*iso*amyloxamide M.P. 136°. On oxidation by chromic acid yields *iso*valeric acid B.P. 176°. Compound with phenyl *iso*cyanate M.P. 155°.

116° Ethylenediamine $CH_2(NH_2)CH_2(NH_2)$
M.P. 8°. D. 0·902 (15°). Miscible with water, almost insol. in ether, insol. in benzene. Forms a hydrate M.P. 10°, B.P. 118°, D. 0·970 (15°), from which the water can be removed by distillation with sodium. Hydrochloride is insol. in alc. Diacetyl deriv. M.P. 172°. Dibenzoyl deriv. M.P. 249°. Dibenzenesulphonyl deriv. M.P. 168°. Di-*p*-toluenesulphonyl deriv. M.P. 160°. Picrate M.P. 234°. With 2:4-dinitrochlorobenzene yields di-2:4-dinitrophenylethylenediamine M.P. 302°. Compound with phenyl *iso*cyanate M.P. 263°.

185° Benzylamine $C_6H_5 \cdot CH_2 \cdot NH_2$
D. 0·982 (19°). Miscible with less than 8 and more than about 40 vols. of water at 5°, and with less than 5 and more than about 40 vols. of water at 95°. Hydrochloride M.P. 248°. Oxalate M.P. 201°d.

O.A.   O

B.P.

Acetyl deriv. M.P. 60°. Benzoyl deriv. M.P. 105°.
Benzenesulphonyl deriv. M.P. 88°. *p*-Bromobenzene-
sulphonyl deriv. M.P. 117°. With ethyl oxalate yields
dibenzyloxamide M.P. 216°. With 2:4-dinitrochloro-
benzene yields 2:4-dinitrophenylbenzylamine M.P.
115°. Compound with phenyl *iso*cyanate M.P. 168°.

SOLID

M.P.
110°d. *d*-Glucosamine $CH_2OH \cdot [CH(OH)]_3 \cdot CH(NH_2) \cdot CHO$
Readily sol. in water, slightly sol. in alc., insol. in
ether and in $CHCl_3$. Optically active, $[a]_D = + 47°$
in water. Reduces Fehling's soln. Hydrochloride
d. 200° is readily sol. in water, almost insol. in alc.;
$[a]_D$ in water is $+ 100°$ immediately after dissolving,
falls to $+ 72 \cdot 5°$ on standing. With acetic anhydride
in cold abs. alc. yields monoacetyl deriv. d. 190°. On
boiling with acetic anhydride $+$ Na acetate yields two
penta-acetyl derivs. M.P. 183° and 133°. Pentabenzoyl deriv. M.P. 203°. Oxime M.P. 127°d. (forms a
hydrochloride M.P. 166°). Semicarbazone M.P.
165°d. With phenylhydrazine in dil. acetic acid
yields *d*-glucosazone M.P. 205°.

ALIPHATIC SECONDARY AMINES

LIQUID

B.P.
7°   Dimethylamine $(CH_3)_2NH$
Gives white ppte with Nessler's soln; sol. on dilution
with water. Hydrochloride M.P. 170° is hygroscopic,
very sol. in alc. and in $CHCl_3$. Hydrobromide M.P.
133° is hygroscopic, sol. in alc., sparingly sol. in $CHCl_3$.
Acetyl deriv. B.P. 165°. Benzoyl deriv. M.P. 41°,
B.P. 255°. Benzenesulphonyl deriv. M.P. 47°. *p*-
Toluenesulphonyl deriv. M.P. 79°. *p*-Bromobenzene-
sulphonyl deriv. M.P. 93°. Nitroso deriv. B.P. 153°.
2:4-Dinitrophenyl deriv. M.P. 87°. Picrate M.P. 156°.

55°   Diethylamine $(C_2H_5)_2NH$
D. 0·723 (4°). Miscible with water. Gives white
cryst. ppte. with Nessler's soln.; yellow ppte. with soln
of HgI_2 in KI. Hydrochloride M.P. 216° is hygroscopic, very sol. in $CHCl_3$, less sol. in abs. alc. Hydrobromide M.P. 213°. Acetyl deriv. B.P. 185°. Benzoyl deriv. B.P. 280°. Benzenesulphonyl deriv. M.P.
42°. *p*-Toluenesulphonyl deriv. M.P. 60°. *m*-Nitro-
benzenesulphonyl deriv. M.P. 66°. Nitroso deriv.

B.P.

B.P. 177°.   2:4-Dinitrophenyl deriv. M.P. 80°.   Compound with phenyl *iso*cyanate M.P. 85°.

105°   Piperidine.   See Heterocyclic Bases.

110°   Di-*n*-propylamine $(CH_3 \cdot CH_2 \cdot CH_2)_2NH$
D. 0·752 (4°).   Sol. in 18 vols. of cold water.   Acetyl
deriv. B.P. 209°.   Benzenesulphonyl deriv. M.P. 51°.
Nitroso deriv. B.P. 206°.   2:4-Dinitrophenyl deriv.
M.P. 40°.   Picrate M.P. 75°.

138°   Di-*iso*butylamine $[(CH_3)_2CH \cdot CH_2]_2NH$
D. 0·749 (15°).   Sol. in 220 vols. of cold water.
Hydrochloride M.P. 262°.   Platinichloride M.P. 212°d.
Aurichloride M.P. 220°.   Acid Oxalate M.P. 246°.
Acetate M.P. 86°.   Nitroso deriv. B.P. 214°d.   2:4-
Dinitrophenyl deriv. M.P. 112ᶜ.   Compound with
phenyl *iso*cyanate M.P. 105°.

158°   Di-*n*-butylamine $(CH_3 \cdot CH_2 \cdot CH_2 \cdot CH_2)_2NH_2$
D. 0·761 (18°).   Sol. in 280 vols. of cold water.
Nitroso deriv. B.P. 235°.   *m*-Nitrobenzenesulphonyl
deriv. M.P. 61°.   Compound with phenyl *iso*cyanate
M.P. 86°.   Picrate M.P. 59°.

167°   *d*-Coniine.   See Alkaloids.

186°   Di-*iso*amylamine $[(CH_3)_2CH \cdot CH_2 \cdot CH_2]_2NH$
D. 0·767 (21°).   Almost insol. in water.   Hydrochloride
M.P. 276°.   Benzoyl and benzenesulphonyl derivs. are
oils.   Nitroso deriv. B.P. 137°/20 mm.   Compound
with phenyl *iso*cyanate M.P. 107°.

247°   Nicotine.   See Alkaloids.

315°   Dibenzylamine $(C_6H_5 \cdot CH_2)_2NH$
D. 1·042 (14°).   Hydrochloride M.P. 256°.   Benzoyl
deriv. M.P. 112°.   Benzenesulphonyl deriv. M.P. 68°.
Nitroso deriv. M.P. 61°.   2:4-Dinitrophenyl deriv.
M.P. 106°.   Compound with phenyl *iso*cyanate M.P.
127°.

SOLID

M.P.

44°   Piperazine Hydrate.   See Heterocyclic Bases.

104°   Piperazine.   See Heterocyclic Bases.

ALIPHATIC TERTIARY AMINES

LIQUID

B.P.

3°   Trimethylamine $(CH_3)_3N$
Gives reddish-yellow ppte with Nessler's soln. ; yellow
ppte. with soln. of HgI_2 in KI.   Hydrochloride M.P.

B.P.

277°d. is readily sol. in alc. and in CHCl₃. Hydrobromide M.P. 243°. Forms a stable salt with (4 mols)
acetic acid B.P. 154°. Platinichloride d. 242° is
sparingly sol. in alc. With iodine in KI + HCl yields
a sparingly sol. addition product M.P. 65°. With
CH₃I yields tetramethylammonium iodide d. 230°
(sparingly sol. in cold water). With chloroacetic acid
yields betaine hydrochloride M.P. 227°d. (sparingly
sol. in cold abs. alc.). Picrate M.P. 216°

89° Triethylamine $(C_2H_5)_3N$

D. 0·733 (15°). Miscible in all proportions with water
below 18°. Hydrochloride M.P. 253° is sol. in alc.
and in CHCl₃. Hydrobromide M.P. 248°d. Forms a
salt with (4 mols) acetic acid B.P. 162°. Platinichloride is very sol. in water. With ethyl iodide
yields tetraethylammonium iodide (sparingly sol. in
abs. alc.). Picrate M.P. 173°.

115° Pyridine. See Heterocyclic Bases.

129° α-Picoline. See Heterocyclic Bases.

SOLID

M.P.

91° Tribenzylamine $(C_6H_5 \cdot CH_2)_3N$

B.P. 215°/15 mm. Very weak base. Hydrochloride
M.P. 227° is hydrolysed in water. Hydrobromide
M.P. 208°. Sulphate M.P. 106° is almost insol. in
water. On warming with bromine water yields
benzaldehyde B.P. 179° and dibenzylamine B.P. 315°.
Picrate M.P. 190°.

AROMATIC PRIMARY AMINES

LIQUID

B.P.

183° Aniline $C_6H_5 \cdot NH_2$

D. 1·027 (17°). Sol. in 29 vols of cold water. In
very dil. aqueous soln gives transient purple colour
with bleaching powder soln. On warming with alc.
KOH + CHCl₃ yields phenyl *iso*cyanide B.P. 165°d.
(evil odour). With bromine water yields ppte of
tribromo deriv. M.P. 118°. Hydrochloride M.P. 198°,
B.P. 258°. Acetyl deriv. M.P. 113°. Benzoyl deriv.
M.P. 160°. Benzenesulphonyl deriv. M.P. 112°.
p-Toluenesulphonyl deriv. M.P. 103°. *p*-Bromoben-
zenesulphonyl deriv. M.P. 119°. Thiourea M.P. 153°.
Benzal deriv. M.P. 54°. Azo-β-naphthol deriv. M.P.

131°. With phenyl *iso*cyanate yields carbanilide
M.P. 238°. 2:4-Dinitrophenyl deriv. M.P. 156°.

197°   *o*-Toluidine $CH_3 \cdot C_6H_4 \cdot NH_2$ (1:2)
D. 1·003 (20°). Sol. in 70 vols. of cold water. Gives
brown colour on shaking ethereal soln. with dil.
bleaching powder soln. Soln. in 50% H_2SO_4 gives
blue colour with $K_2Cr_2O_7$, changed to purple on
dilution. On warming with alc. KOH + $CHCl_3$ yields
o-tolyl *iso*cyanide (evil odour) B.P. 183°. With
bromine water yields dibromo deriv. M.P. 50°.
Hydrochloride M.P. 214°, B.P. 242°. Acetyl deriv.
M.P. 112°. Benzoyl deriv. M.P. 143°. Benzenesulphonyl deriv. M.P. 124°. *p*-Toluenesulphonyl deriv.
M.P. 108°. *p*-Bromobenzenesulphonyl deriv. M.P.
116°. Thiourea M.P. 161°. Azo-β-naphthol deriv.
M.P. 128°. Compound with phenyl *iso*cyanate M.P.
207°. 2:4-Dinitrophenyl deriv. M.P. 120°.

199°   *m*-Toluidine $CH_3 \cdot C_6H_4 \cdot NH_2$ (1:3)
D. 0·989 (20°). On shaking ethereal soln with dil.
bleaching powder soln, water layer becomes yellow-
brown, ether becomes red. Soln. in 50% H_2SO_4 gives
yellow-brown colour with $K_2Cr_2O_7$, red with HNO_3.
Hydrochloride M.P. 228°, B.P. 250°. Acetyl deriv.
M.P. 65°. Benzoyl deriv. M.P. 125°. Benzenesulphonyl deriv. M.P. 95°. *p*-Toluenesulphonyl deriv.
M.P. 114°. Thiourea M.P. 112°. Azo-β-naphthol
deriv. M.P. 140°. Compound with phenyl *iso*cyanate
M.P. 173°. 2:4-Dinitrophenyl deriv. M.P. 161°.

212°   4-*m*-Xylidine $(CH_3)_2C_6H_3 \cdot NH_2$ (1:3:4)
D. 0·981 (15°). Hydrochloride M.P. 235°, B.P. 255°.
Acetate M.P. 68°. Acetyl deriv. M.P. 133°. Benzoyl
deriv. M.P. 192°. Benzenesulphonyl deriv. M.P. 128°.
Thiourea M.P. 152°. Azo-β-naphthol deriv. M.P.
166°. Compound with phenyl *iso*cyanate M.P. 242°.

213°   *p*-Xylidine $(CH_3)_2C_6H_3 \cdot NH_2$ (1:4:5)
M.P. 15°. D. 0·968 (25°). Hydrochloride M.P. 228°,
B.P. 247°. Acetyl deriv. M.P. 139°. Benzoyl deriv.
M.P. 140°. Benzenesulphonyl deriv. M.P. 138°.
p-Toluenesulphonyl deriv. M.P. 119°. Benzal deriv.
M.P. 101°. Azo-β-naphthol deriv. M.P. 150°. Pi-
crate M.P. 171°d. Platinichloride M.P. 195°d.

218°   *o*-Anisidine $CH_3O \cdot C_6H_4 \cdot NH_2$ (1:2)
M.P. 5°. D. 1·095 (15°). On boiling with 48% HBr
yields *o*-aminophenol M.P. 174° and methyl bromide
B.P. 4°. Acetyl deriv. M.P. 84°. Benzenesulphonyl

    deriv. M.P. 89°. *p*-Toluenesulphonyl deriv. M.P. 127°. Thiourea M.P. 135°. Azo-β-naphthol deriv. M.P. 180°. Compound with phenyl *iso*cyanate M.P. 144°. 2;4-Dinitrophenyl deriv. M.P. 151°.

229°   *o*-Phenetidine $C_2H_5O\cdot C_6H_4\cdot NH_2$ (1:2)
    D. 1·049 (18°). Hydrochloride M.P. 214°. On boiling with 48% HBr yields *o*-aminophenol M.P. 174° and ethyl bromide B.P. 38°. Acetyl deriv. M.P. 79°. Compound with phenyl *iso*cyanate M.P. 169°. 2:4-Dinitrophenyl deriv. M.P. 164°.

254°   *p*-Phenetidine $C_2H_5O\cdot C_6H_4\cdot NH_2$ (1:4)
    M.P. 2°. D. 1·061 (15°). Hydrochloride M.P. 234° gives red colour with $FeCl_3$ or bleaching powder soln. On boiling with 48% HBr yields *p*-aminophenol M.P. 184°d. and ethyl bromide B.P. 38°. Acetyl deriv. M.P. 135°. Benzoyl deriv. M.P. 173°. Benzenesulphonyl deriv. M.P. 143°. Benzal deriv. M.P. 76°. Azo-β-naphthol deriv. M.P. 139°. Compound with phenyl *iso*cyanate M.P. 178°.

255°   Methyl Anthranilate.　See Amino Acids, etc.

260°   Ethyl Anthranilate.　See Amino Acids, etc.

15°   *p*-Xylidine B.P. 213°.　See Aromatic Primary Amines (Liquid).

25°   Methyl Anthranilate.　See Amino Acids, etc.

41°   *p*-Aminodimethylaniline $(CH_3)_2N\cdot C_6H_4\cdot NH_2$ (1:4)
    B.P. 262°. Darkens rapidly in air. Sol. in water. Soln. of dihydrochloride M.P. 220° gives purple colour with excess $AgNO_3$ in cold, odour of quinone on warming. On treating soln. successively with H_2S and $FeCl_3$ yields methylene blue. Acetyl deriv. M.P. 130°. Benzoyl deriv. M.P. 228°. Benzal deriv. M.P. 101°. 2:4-Dinitrophenyl deriv. M.P. 168°.

45°   *p*-Toluidine $CH_3\cdot C_6H_4\cdot NH_2$ (1:4)
    B.P. 200°. Sol. in 150 parts of cold water. Forms a hydrate M.P. 41°. Hydrochloride M.P. 240°, B.P. 257°. Gives no colour with bleaching powder soln. Soln. in 50% H_2SO_4 gives yellow colour with $K_2Cr_2O_7$; blue with HNO_3, changing gradually through violet and red to brown. With bromine water yields dibromo deriv. M.P. 73°. Acetyl deriv. M.P. 148°. Benzoyl deriv. M.P. 158°. Benzenesulphonyl deriv. M.P. 120°. *p*-Toluenesulphonyl deriv. M.P. 117°.

p-Bromobenzenesulphonyl deriv. M.P. 98°. Benzal deriv. M.P. 35°. Thiourea M.P. 176°. Azo-β-naphthol deriv. M.P. 130°. Compound with phenyl *iso*cyanate M.P. 213°. 2:4-Dinitrophenyl deriv. M.P. 137°.

50°   α-Naphthylamine $C_{10}H_7 \cdot NH_2$ (1)
B.P. 300°. Evil odour. Slightly sol. in hot water. Soln. of hydrochloride M.P. 286° gives a blue ppte. with $FeCl_3$. Acetyl deriv. M.P. 159°. Benzoyl deriv. M.P. 160°. Benzenesulphonyl deriv. M.P. 167°. *p*-Toluenesulphonyl deriv. M.P. 157°. *p*-Bromobenzenesulphonyl deriv. M.P. 183°. *m*-Nitrobenzenesulphonyl deriv. M.P. 166°. Benzal deriv. M.P. 73°. Thiourea M.P. 207°. Azo-β-naphthol deriv. M.P. 274°. Compound with phenyl *iso*cyanate M.P. 222°. 2:4-Dinitrophenyl deriv. M.P. 190°. Picrate M.P. 161°.

57°   *p*-Anisidine $CH_3O \cdot C_6H_4 \cdot NH_2$ (1:4)
B.P. 239°. Sparingly sol. in hot water. Soln. of hydrochloride M.P. 216° gives violet colour with $FeCl_3$. On boiling with 48% HBr yields *p*-aminophenol M.P. 184°d. and methyl bromide B.P. 4°. Acetyl deriv. M.P. 127°. Benzoyl deriv. M.P. 154°. Benzenesulphonyl deriv. M.P. 95°. *p*-Toluenesulphonyl deriv. M.P. 114°. *p*-Bromobenzenesulphonyl deriv. M.P. 142°. Benzal deriv. M.P. 62°. Thiourea M.P. 185°. Azo-β-naphthol deriv. M.P. 139°. 2:4-Dinitrophenyl deriv. M.P. 141°.

63°   *m*-Phenylenediamine $C_6H_4(NH_2)_2$ (1:3)
B.P. 283°. Darkens rapidly in air. Readily sol. in hot water. Soln of dihydrochloride M.P. 348° gives brown ppte. with $NaNO_2$. On warming soln of hydrochloride with 1% soln of acetaldehyde in 50% alc. gives yellow colour with green fluorescence. With bromine in dil. HCl yields tribromo deriv. M.P. 158°. Diacetyl deriv. M.P. 191°. Dibenzoyl deriv. M.P. 240°. Dibenzenesulphonyl deriv. M.P. 194°. Di-*p*-toluenesulphonyl deriv. M.P. 172°. Dibenzal deriv. M.P. 104°. 2:4-Dinitrophenyl deriv. M.P. 172°.

89°   Ethyl *p*-Aminobenzoate. See Amino Acids, etc.

99°   *m*-Toluylenediamine $CH_3 \cdot C_6H_3(NH_2)_2$ (1:2:4)
B.P. 280°. Darkens rapidly in air. Readily sol. in hot water. Closely resembles *m*-phenylenediamine M.P. 63°. Dihydrochloride M.P. 305°. Diacetyl deriv. M.P. 224°. Dibenzoyl deriv. M.P. 224°.

M.P.

    Dibenzenesulphonyl deriv. M.P. 178°. Di-p-toluene-sulphonyl deriv. M.P. 192°. Dibenzal deriv. M.P. 175°. 2:4-Dinitrophenyl deriv. M.P. 184°.

102° o-Phenylenediamine $C_6H_4(NH_2)_2$ (1:2)
    B.P. 257°. Readily sol. in hot water. Conc. soln. of dihydrochloride M.P. 260° gives red ppte. with $FeCl_3$, and with benzaldehyde yields phenylbenzylbenzimin-azole M.P. 133°; with Na acetate + benzaldehyde yields dibenzal deriv. M.P. 106°. On distilling with acetic acid yields methylbenziminazole M.P. 175°. With acetic anhydride in cold water yields diacetyl deriv. M.P. 185°. Dibenzoyl deriv. M.P. 301° on heating yields phenylbenziminazole M.P. 280°. Di-benzenesulphonyl deriv. M.P. 186°. Di-p-toluene-sulphonyl deriv. M.P. 201°.

111° β-Naphthylamine $C_{10}H_7 \cdot NH_2$ (2)
    B.P. 294°. Odourless. Sparingly sol. in hot water. Gives no colour with $FeCl_3$. Hydrochloride M.P. 260°. Acetyl deriv. M.P. 132°. Benzoyl deriv. M.P. 162°. Benzenesulphonyl deriv. M.P. 102°. p-Toluene-sulphonyl deriv. M.P. 133°. p-Bromobenzenesul-phonyl deriv. M.P. 129°. m-Nitrobenzenesulphonyl deriv. M.P. 165°. Benzal deriv. M.P. 102°. Thiourea M.P. 192°. Azo-β-naphthol deriv. M.P. 174°. Com-pound with pheny, isocyanate M.P. 220°. 2:4-Di-nitrophenyl deriv. M.P. 179°. Picrate M.P. 195°d.

127°   Benzidine $NH_2 \cdot C_6H_4 \cdot C_6H_4 \cdot NH_2$ (4:4')
    B.P. 400°. Slightly sol. in hot water. Sulphate is almost insol. in water and in alc. On boiling with dil. H_2SO_4 + MnO_2 yields benzoquinone M.P. 115°. On gradually adding bromine to soln. in CS_2 under water the aqueous layer becomes first blue, then green, finally colourless, the CS_2 layer becoming red. Dihy-drochloride M.P. 385°. Diacetyl deriv. M.P. 317°. Dibenzoyl deriv. M.P. 352°. Dibenzenesulphonyl deriv. M.P. 232°. Di-p-toluenesulphonyl deriv. M.P. 243°. Dibenzal deriv. M.P. 239°. Compound with phenyl isocyanate M.P. above 300°. Disazo-β-naph-thol deriv. M.P. 302°. On diazotising in dil. H_2SO_4 and boiling yields p-diphenol M.P. 272°.

129° o-Tolidine $CH_3 \cdot (NH_2)C_6H_3 \cdot C_6H_3(NH_2) \cdot CH_3$ (3:4:4':3')
    Closely resembles benzidine. On boiling with dil. H_2SO_4 + MnO_2 yields toluquinone M.P. 68°. Dihy-drochloride M.P. 355°. Diacetyl deriv. M.P. 314°. Dibenzoyl deriv. M.P. 265°. Disazo-β-naphthol deriv.

M.P.

M.P. 297°. On diazotising in dil. H_2SO_4 and boiling yields dicresol M.P. 160°.

131° Dianisidine $CH_3O \cdot (NH_2)C_6H_3 \cdot C_6H_3(NH_2) \cdot OCH_3$

$(3:4:4':3')$

Closely resembles benzidine. Dihydrochloride M.P. 312°. Diacetyl deriv. M.P. 242°. Dibenzoyl deriv. M.P. 236°. Disazo-β-naphthol deriv. M.P. 298°. On diazotising in alc. + H_2SO_4 yields m-dianisole M.P. 35°, B.P. 328°.

140° p-Phenylenediamine $C_6H_4(NH_2)_2$ (1:4)

B.P. 267°. Sol. in hot water. Soln of dihydrochloride (M.P. above 390°) gives with excess of $AgNO_3$ in cold green colour rapidly changing through red to brown ; no odour of quinone on warming. Yields benzoquinone M.P. 115° on boiling with dil. $FeCl_3$ or H_2SO_4 + MnO_2. Soln. of dihydrochloride yields ppte. of quinonedichloroimide d.124° with bleaching powder soln. Diacetyl deriv. M.P. 304°. Dibenzoyl deriv. M.P. above 300°. Dibenzenesulphonyl deriv. M.P. 247°. Di-p-toluenesulphonyl deriv. M.P. 266°. Dibenzal deriv. M.P. 138°. 2:4-Dinitrophenyl deriv. M.P. 190°.

162° p-Aminoacetanilide. See Substituted Amides.

AROMATIC SECONDARY AMINES

LIQUID

B.P.

193° Methylaniline $C_6H_5 \cdot NH \cdot CH_3$

D. 0·976 (15°). Gives no colour with bleaching powder soln. Hydrochloride M.P. 121°. Nitrosoamine M.P. 12°, B.P. 121°/13 mm. yields the p-nitroso deriv. M.P. 118° with HCl gas in ether. Acetyl deriv. M.P. 102°. Benzoyl deriv. M.P. 63°. Benzenesulphonyl deriv. M.P. 79°. p-Toluenesulphonyl deriv. M.P. 94°. p-Bromobenzenesulphonyl deriv. M.P. 92°. m-Nitrobenzenesulphonyl deriv. M.P. 100°.

206° Ethylaniline $C_6H_5 \cdot NH \cdot C_2H_5$

D. 0·963 (20°). Gives no colour with bleaching powder soln. Hydrochloride M.P. 176°. Nitrosoamine B.P. 134°/16 mm. yields the p-nitroso deriv. M.P. 78° with HCl gas in ether. Acetyl deriv. M.P. 54°. Benzoyl deriv. M.P. 60°. Benzenesulphonyl deriv. is an oil. p-Toluenesulphonyl deriv. M.P. 87°. p-Bromobenzenesulphonyl deriv. M.P. 91°. m-Nitrobenzenesulphonyl deriv. M.P. 100°.

222° n-Propylaniline $C_6H_5 \cdot NH \cdot CH_2 \cdot CH_2 \cdot CH_3$
         D. 0·900 (24°). Nitrosoamine (oil) yields p-nitroso
         deriv. M.P. 59° with HCl gas in ether. Acetyl deriv.
         M.P. 47°. Benzenesulphonyl deriv. M.P. 54°. p-
         Bromobenzenesulphonyl deriv. M.P. 109°. m-Nitro-
         benzenesulphonyl deriv. M.P. 111°.

235° n-Butylaniline $C_6H_5 \cdot NH \cdot CH_2 \cdot CH_2 \cdot CH_2 \cdot CH_3$
         D. 0·934 (20°). Nitrosoamine is an oil. Acetyl deriv.
         B.P. 274°. p-Bromobenzenesulphonyl deriv. M.P.
         87°. m-Nitrobenzenesulphonyl deriv. M.P. 78°.

251°   Tetrahydroquinoline.   See Heterocyclic Bases.

254° isoAmylaniline $C_6H_5 \cdot NH \cdot CH_2 \cdot CH_2 \cdot CH(CH_3)_2$
         D. 0·928 (15°). Nitrosoamine is an oil. Acetyl deriv.
         B.P. 278°.

                         SOLID

37°   Benzylaniline $C_6H_5 \cdot NH \cdot CH_2 \cdot C_6H_5$
         B.P. 299°. Hydrochloride M.P. 197°. Platini-
         chloride M.P. 155°. Nitrosoamine M.P. 58° is
         converted by HCl in alc. into benzalaniline HCl ($q.v.$)
         and benzylaniline HCl. With amyl nitrite + alc.
         HCl yields p-nitroso deriv. M.P. 129°. Acetyl deriv.
         M.P. 58°. Benzoyl deriv. M.P. 107°. Benzenesul-
         phonyl deriv. M.P. 119°.

54°   Diphenylamine $(C_6H_5)_2NH$
         B.P. 310.° Weak base; hydrochloride M.P. 180° and
         sulphate M.P. 124° are hydrolysed by water. Soln.
         in conc. HCl or H_2SO_4 gives blue colour with trace of
         HNO_2 or HNO_3. Nitrosoamine M.P. 67° yields
         p-nitroso deriv. M.P. 144° with HCl in alc. Acetyl
         deriv. M.P. 101°. Benzoyl deriv. M.P. 180°. Ben-
         zenesulphonyl deriv. M.P. 124°. p-Toluenesulphonyl
         deriv. M.P. 141°.

79°   Di-p-tolylamine $(CH_3 \cdot C_6H_4)_2NH$
         B.P. 330°. Resembles diphenylamine, but gives
         yellow (not blue) colour in conc. H_2SO_4 with trace of
         HNO_3. Nitrosoamine M.P. 101°. Acetyl deriv. M.P.
         85°. Benzoyl deriv. M.P. 125°.

238°   Carbazole. See Heterocyclic Bases.

AROMATIC TERTIARY AMINES

                        LIQUID

185°   Dimethyl-o-toluidine $CH_3 \cdot C_6H_4 \cdot N(CH_3)_2$ (1:2)
         D. 0·926 (20°). Hydrochloride M.P. 156°. With (1

mol.) bromine in acetic acid yields bromo deriv. B.P.
244°. With acetyl bromide in cold yields acetyl-
methyltoluidine M.P. 55° and trimethyl-*o*-tolyl-
ammonium bromide. On boiling with benzoyl
chloride yields benzoylmethyl-*o*-toluidine M.P. 65°
and CH_3Cl. On boiling with 90% HNO_3 yields
methyldinitrotoluidine M.P. 120°. With HNO_3 +
H_2SO_4 at 0° yields nitro deriv. B.P. 280° (hydrochloride M.P. 192°). Does not condense with CH_2O +
HCl. Benzeneazo deriv. M.P. 66°.

193° Dimethylaniline $C_6H_5 \cdot N(CH_3)_2$
M.P. 1°. D. 0·958 (20°). Hydrochloride (deliquescent) M.P. 85–95°. Hydrobromide M.P. 75°. Sulphate M.P. 80°. Acid oxalate M.P. 139°. Methiodide
subl. 220°. Ethiodide M.P. 136°. Nitroso deriv. M.P.
85° on boiling with conc. NaOH yields dimethylamine
(*q.v.*). With acetyl bromide in cold yields methylacetanilide M.P. 102° and trimethylphenylammonium
bromide M.P. 213°d. On boiling with benzoyl
chloride yields benzoylmethylaniline M.P. 65° and
CH_3Cl. With bromine in acetic acid yields *p*-bromo
deriv. M.P. 55°. With HNO_3 in acetic acid yields
dinitro deriv. M.P. 87°. Benzeneazo deriv. M.P. 115°.
Picrate M.P. 163°.

201° Methylethylaniline $C_6H_5 \cdot N(CH_3)C_2H_5$
D. 0·940 (15°). Hydrochloride M.P. 114°. Methiodide M.P. 125°. Ethiodide M.P. 102°. *p*-Nitroso
deriv. M.P. 66°. Picrate M.P. 134°.

209° Diethyl-*o*-toluidine $CH_3 \cdot C_6H_4 \cdot N(C_2H_5)_2$ (1:2)
D. 0·906 (15°). Hydriodide (+ H_2O) M.P. 72°.
Gives blue cryst. ppte. M.P. 100° on treating soln. in dil.
acid with iodine in KI.

211° Dimethyl-*p*-toluidine $CH_3 \cdot C_6H_4 \cdot N(CH_3)_2$ (1:4)
D. 0·938 (20°). With acetyl bromide in cold yields
acetylmethyl-*p*-toluidine M.P. 83° and trimethyl-*p*-
tolylammonium bromide M.P. 219°. On boiling with
benzoyl chloride yields benzoylmethyl-*p*-toluidine M.P.
47°. On treating soln. in conc. H_2SO_4 with HNO_3 and
pouring into ice-water yields nitro deriv. M.P. 37°;
on pouring into 4 vols of water (without cooling)
yields dinitro deriv. M.P. 103°. Forms a compound
with *m*-dinitrobenzene M.P. 43° (black crysts.).

216° Diethylaniline $C_6H_5 \cdot N(C_2H_5)_2$
D. 0·935 (20°). Methiodide M.P. 102°. *p*-Nitroso

deriv. M.P. 84° on distilling with conc. NaOH yields diethylamine B.P. 55°. Benzeneazo deriv. M.P. 97°. Picrate M.P. 142°.

229° Diethyl-p-toluidine $CH_3 \cdot C_6H_4 \cdot N(C_2H_5)_2$ (1:4)
D. 0·921 (18°). Hydrochloride M.P. 157°. On boiling with HNO_3 yields dinitrotolylethylnitramine M.P. 116°.

238° Quinoline. See Heterocyclic Bases.

240° iso-Quinoline. See Heterocyclic Bases.

245° Di-n-propylaniline $C_6H_5 \cdot N(CH_2 \cdot CH_2 \cdot CH_3)_2$
D. 0·910 (20°). Methiodide M.P. 156°. p-Nitroso deriv. M.P. 42° (forms a hydrochloride d. 160–165°) yields di-n-propylamine B.P. 110° on boiling with conc. NaOH.

247° Quinaldine. See Heterocyclic Basses.

261° Di-n-butylaniline $C_6H_5 \cdot N(CH_2 \cdot CH_2 \cdot CH_2 \cdot CH_3)_2$
D. 0·911 (18°). Hydrochloride M.P. 90–105°. p-Nitroso deriv. (green oil, forms a compound with $ZnCl_2$ M.P. 153°d.) yields di-n-butylamine B.P. 158° on boiling with conc. NaOH. Picrate M.P. 125°.

296° Methyldiphenylamine $(C_6H_5)_2N \cdot CH_3$
D. 1·052 (15°). Salts hydrolysed by water. Gives violet colour with HNO_3. p-Nitroso deriv. M.P. 44°.

299° Ethylbenzylaniline $C_6H_5 \cdot N(C_2H_5)(CH_2 \cdot C_6H_5)$
D. 1·030 (18°). p-Nitroso deriv. M.P. 62°. Picrate M.P. 111°.

M.P.   SOLID

24° isoQuinoline B.P. 240° See Heterocyclic Bases.

41° p-Aminodimethylaniline. See Aromatic Primary Amines.

70° Dibenzylaniline $C_6H_5 \cdot N(CH_2 \cdot C_6H_5)_2$
Salts hydrolysed by water. On oxidation by $K_2Cr_2O_7$ + dil. H_2SO_4 yields benzaldehyde B.P. 179° and benzalaniline M.P. 54°. With amyl nitrite + alc. HCl yields p-nitroso deriv. M.P. 91°. Picrate M.P. 131°d.

73° p-Dimethylaminobenzaldehyde $(CH_3)_2N \cdot C_6H_4 \cdot CHO$ (1:4)
With aniline acetate soln. yields yellow anil M.P. 100° ; with aniline HCl soln gives yellow colour ; with benzidine HCl soln gives red ppte. M.P. 318°. On adding dimethylaniline, passing HCl into mixture, and then adding $FeCl_3$ yields violet dye. Oxime M.P. 148°. Phenylhydrazone M.P. 148°.

90° Tetramethyldiaminodiphenylmethane (Michler's Hydride)
$(CH_3)_2N·C_6H_4·CH_2·C_6H_4·N(CH_3)_2$ (4:4')
Dimethiodide M.P. 214°d. Yields quinone on oxidation. On adding solid KNO_3 to soln. in conc. H_2SO_4
at 0° yields dinitro deriv. M.P. 195°. Picrate M.P. 185°.

113° Antipyrine. See Hydrazine Derivatives.

127° Triphenylamine $(C_6H_5)_3N$
Does not combine with acids. Soln. in acetic acid
gives green colour with trace of HNO_3; soln. in conc.
H_2SO_4 gives with trace of HNO_3 violet colour changing
to blue. With (3 mols.) fuming HNO_3 in acetic acid
yields trinitro deriv. M.P. 280°. Forms no picrate.

174° Tetramethyldiaminobenzophenone (Michler's Ketone)
$(CH_3)_2N·C_6H_4·CO·C_6H_4·N(CH_3)_2$ (4:4')
Dimethiodide M.P. 105°. On distillation with Zn dust
yields tetramethyldiaminodiphenylmethane M.P. 90°.
On adding solid KNO_3 to soln. in conc. H_2SO_4 yields
mononitro deriv. M.P. 144°. Oxime M.P. 233°.
Phenylhydrazone M.P. 174°. Picrate M.P. 156°.

HETEROCYCLIC BASES

LIQUID

105° Piperidine   CH₂·CH₂·NH

CH₂·CH₂·CH₂

D. 0·876 (4°). Miscible with water. Hydrochloride
M.P. 237°. Acetyl deriv. B.P. 226°. Benzoyl deriv.
M.P. 48°, B.P. 320°. m-Nitrobenzoyl deriv. M.P. 83°.
Benzenesulphonyl deriv. M.P. 93°. p-Bromoben-
zenesulphonyl deriv. M.P. 88°. 2:4-Dinitrophenyl
deriv. M.P. 92°. Compound with phenyl isocyanate
M.P. 171°. Nitroso deriv. B.P. 218°.

115° Pyridine   CH·CH:N

CH·CH:CH

D. 0·989 (15°). Miscible with water. Characteristic
odour. Much weaker base than most trialkyl amines.
Hydrobromide M.P. 200°d. Platinichloride M.P.
241°. With 2:4-dinitrochlorobenzene forms addition
product M.P. 201° which gives purple colour with dil.
NaOH. Methiodide M.P. 117°. Ethiodide M.P. 90°.
With chloroacetic acid forms addition product M.P.
202°. Picrate M.P. 167°. Perchlorate M.P. 209°.

B.P.

129°   α-Picoline   CH·CH:N
                        ‖
                        CH·CH:C·CH$_3$

D. 0·950 (15°). Closely resembles pyridine. On boiling with dil. KMnO$_4$ yields picolinic acid M.P. 137°. Methiodide M.P. 224°. Ethiodide M.P. 123°. Picrate M.P. 169°.

238°   Quinoline   C$_6$H$_4$⟨CH:CH
                                  |
                                  N :CH

D. 1·094 (20°). Hydrochloride (+ ½H$_2$O) M.P. 93°, (anhydrous) M.P. 134°. Acid sulphate M.P. 164°. Bichromate M.P. 165°. Platinichloride M.P. 218°. Methiodide M.P. 72° (hydrated), 133° (anhydrous). Ethiodide M.P. 159°. No reaction with HNO$_2$. Reduced by Sn + HCl to tetrahydro deriv. B.P. 251° (*q.v.*). On adding bleaching powder soln. to soln. in boric acid yields chloroquinoline M.P. 112°, which with NaOH yields carbostyril M.P. 199°. Picrate M.P. 203°. Tartrate M.P. 126° is sparingly sol. in alc.

240°   *iso*Quinoline   C$_6$H$_4$⟨CH:CH
                                       |
                                       CH:N

M.P. 24°. D. 1·096 (25°). Stronger base than quinoline. Does not react with HNO$_2$. Acid sulphate M.P. 205°. Bichromate d. 150°. Platinichloride M.P. 263°d. Methiodide M.P. 159°. Ethiodide M.P. 148°. Picrate M.P. 222°.

247°   Quinaldine   C$_6$H$_4$⟨CH:CH
                                   |
                                   N :C·CH$_3$

D. 1·059 (20°). Acid sulphate M.P. 212°. Platinichloride M.P. 226°. Mercurichloride M.P. 165°. Bichromate M.P. 110° is almost insol. in cold water. Methiodide M.P. 195° and ethiodide M.P. 233° form more slowly than the corresponding quinoline derivs. No reaction with HNO$_2$. On heating to 190° with phthalic anhydride yields quinophthalone M.P. 239° (yellow). On boiling with conc. HNO$_3$ yields nitro-quinaldinic acid M.P. 219°. Picrate M.P. 191°.

251°   Tetrahydroquinoline   C$_6$H$_4$⟨CH$_2$·CH$_2$
                                           |
                                           NH· CH$_2$

D. 1·063 (15°). On long boiling with nitrobenzene yields quinoline B.P. 239°. Hydrochloride M.P. 181°.

Acid sulphate M.P. 136°. Platinichloride M.P. 200°.
Nitrosoamine (oil) yields 6-nitroso deriv. M.P. 134°
with HCl gas in alc. Acetyl deriv. B.P. 295°.
Benzoyl deriv. M.P. 75°. Benzenesulphonyl deriv.
M.P. 67°.

SOLID

M.P.
44° Piperazine Hydrate. See Piperazine M.P. 104°.
104° Piperazine $CH_2 \cdot NH \cdot CH_2$

$CH_2 \cdot NH \cdot CH_2$

B.P. 140°. Readily sol. in water, sparingly in ether.
Odourless. Forms a hydrate M.P. 44°. Diacetyl
deriv. M.P. 134°. Dibenzoyl deriv. M.P. 191°.
Dibenzenesulphonyl deriv. M.P. 282°. Dinitroso
deriv. M.P. 158°.

238° Carbazole C_6H_4
$\rangle$NH
C_6H_4

B.P. 351°. Very weak base ; salts with mineral acids
are hydrolysed by water, Forms K deriv. on fusion
with KOH. Yields NH_3 on ignition with soda-lime.
Soln in conc. H_2SO_4 gives green colour with trace of
$NaNO_2$. Gives red colour with pine chip moistened
with conc. HCl. Gives blue colour with dil. soln. of
isatin in conc. H_2SO_4. Nitrosoamine M.P. 84°.
Acetyl deriv. M.P. 69°. Benzoyl deriv. M.P. 98°.
Picrate M.P. 182°.

AMINOPHENOLS

SOLID

M.P.
75° *p*-Dimethylaminophenol $(CH_3)_2N \cdot C_6H_4 \cdot OH$ (1:4)
B.P. 165°/30 mm. Readily sol. in cold water and
ether. Sulphate M.P. 205° is extremely sol. in cold
water and conc. HCl. Oxalate M.P. 190° is moderately sol. in water and alc. Soln. in dil. NaOH darkens
in air, giving odour of methyl *iso*cyanide. Gives no
colour with $FeCl_3$ or $AgNO_3$ in cold ; odour of quinone
on warming. Soln in dil. acid gives brown colour and
evolves gas on adding $NaNO_2$. Acetyl deriv. M.P.
78°. Benzoyl deriv. M.P. 158°.
79°d. 2:4-Diaminophenol $HO \cdot C_6H_3(NH_2)_2$ (1:2:4)
Readily sol. in cold water. Rapidly oxidised by air.
Hydrochloride M.P. 295°d. is sparingly sol. in conc.
HCl. Oxalate M.P. 333°d. is slightly sol. in cold
water. Gives intense red colour with $FeCl_3$ or $AgNO_3$;

     no odour on warming.   Alk. soln darkens rapidly in air. Triacetyl deriv. M.P. 180°.   Tribenzoyl deriv. M.P. 231°.   Benzal deriv. is amorphous. Picrate M.P. 180°d.

85°   *p*-Methylaminophenol $HO \cdot C_6H_4 \cdot NH \cdot CH_3$ (1:4)
     Sol. in about 10 parts of cold water ; readily sol. in ether.   Sulphate M.P. 262°d. is sol. in 10 parts of cold water and in 3 parts of cold conc. HCl.   Alk. soln darkens in air, giving odour of methyl *iso*cyanide. Gives purple colour with $FeCl_3$ or $AgNO_3$ in cold ; odour of quinone on warming.   Nitrosoamine M.P. 136° is colourless and insol. in water.   Diacetyl deriv. M.P. 97° is sol. in cold water.   Monoacetyl deriv. M.P. 240° is insol. in cold water.   Dibenzoyl deriv. M.P. 175°.

96°   *o*-Methylaminophenol $HO \cdot C_6H_4 \cdot NH \cdot CH_3$ (1:2)
     Sparingly sol. in cold water.   Sulphate M.P. 240° is sol. in 3 parts of cold conc. HCl.   Alk. soln develops dark green colour in air, giving odour of methyl *iso*cyanide.   Gives purple colour with $FeCl_3$ in cold ; no odour on warming, colour changes to red-brown. Gives yellow-brown colour with $AgNO_3$ changing to red-brown on warming.   Nitrosoamine M.P. 130°d. is colourless and insol. in cold water.   Diacetyl deriv. is liquid, sol. in cold water.   Monoacetyl deriv. M.P. 150°.   Dibenzoyl deriv. M.P. 150°.

122°   *m*-Aminophenol $HO \cdot C_6H_4 \cdot NH_2$ (1:3)
     Sparingly sol. in cold water and benzene.   Hydrochloride M.P. 237° gives no characteristic colour with $FeCl_3$ in cold ; soln. darkens on warming.   Benzal deriv. is amorphous.   Diacetyl deriv. M.P. 101°. Monoacetyl deriv. M.P. 148°.   Dibenzoyl deriv. M.P. 153°.

174°   *o*-Aminophenol $HO \cdot C_6H_4 \cdot NH_2$ (1:2)
     Sparingly sol. in cold water, readily in ether.   Hydrochloride M.P. 210° is sparingly sol. in conc. HCl. Gives dark brown ppte. with $FeCl_3$; no odour of quinone on warming.   With $AgNO_3$ gives yellowbrown colour slowly in cold, rapidly on warming. Benzal deriv. M.P. 89°.   On boiling with acetic acid or anhydride yields methyl benzoxazole B.P. 200°, which on standing with very dil. HCl yields the monoacetyl deriv. M.P. 201°.   Dibenzoyl deriv. M.P. 182° (insol. in ligroin) on heating yields phenylbenzoxazole M.P. 103° (sol. in ligroin) and benzoic acid.

M.P.
176°d.   5-Amino-o-cresol $CH_3 \cdot C_6H_3(OH) \cdot NH_2(1:2:5)$
Sparingly sol. in cold water ; sol. in ether. Salts are almost insol. in cold conc. HCl. Alk. soln. darkens rapidly in air. With $FeCl_3$ or $AgNO_3$ gives purple colour in cold ; on warming, toluquinone M.P. 68° is formed. Benzal deriv. M.P. 208°. Diacetyl deriv. M.P. 103°. Monoacetyl deriv. M.P. 179°. Dibenzoyl deriv. M.P. 194°.

184°d. p-Aminophenol $HO \cdot C_6H_4 \cdot NH_2$ (1:4)
Sol. in about 100 parts of cold water ; sparingly sol. in ether. Hydrochloride M.P. 306°d. is almost insol. in cold conc. HCl. Alk. soln. darkens rapidly in air (no odour). With $FeCl_3$ or $AgNO_3$ gives purple colour in cold ; on warming, benzoquinone M.P. 116° is formed. Soln in dil. HCl gives ppte of quinonechloroimide M.P. 85° with NaOCl. Benzal deriv. M.P. 183°. Diacetyl deriv. M.P. 150°. Monoacetyl deriv. M.P. 168°. Dibenzoyl deriv. M.P. 234°.

199°   Carbostyril $C_6H_4 \bigg\langle {\substack{CH:CH \\ | \\ N \ :COH}}$

Almost insol. in cold water. Sol. in dil. NaOH ; Na salt crysts on adding excess conc. NaOH.   Ba salt is sparingly sol. in water. No colour with $FeCl_3$. On heating with Zn dust yields quinoline ($q.v.$). With conc. $HNO_3 + H_2SO_4$ yields 6-nitro deriv. M.P. 280°. With PCl_5 at 130° yields 2-chloroquinoline M.P. 37°, B.P. 275°.

ALDEHYDE-AMMONIAS

and Condensation Products of Aldehydes with Amines

SOLID

M.P.
54°   Benzalaniline $C_6H_5 \cdot CH:N \cdot C_6H_5$
B.P. about 300°. Insol. in water. Volatile with steam.   On boiling with HCl yields benzaldehyde B.P. 179° and aniline HCl ($q.v.$).   Forms a dibromide M.P. 142°d. which with pyridine (or NaOH in alc.) yields benzaldehyde and p-bromoaniline M.P. 63°.

93°   Acetaldehyde-Ammonia $CH_3 \cdot CH—NH——CH \cdot CH_3$
$$\substack{| \\ NH \cdot CH(CH_3) \cdot NH}$$
B.P. 123°d.   Readily sol. in water, sparingly in ether. Forms a trihydrate M.P. 70–80°.   Yields NH_3 on

O.A.   P

warming with dil. NaOH (not in cold). On warming
with dil. HCl yields acetaldehyde B.P. 21° and NH_4Cl.
On warming with ethyl acetoacetate yields ethyl
dihydrocollidinedicarboxylate M.P. 131°. With HNO_2
yields nitrosoparaldimine B.P. 95°/35 mm. (yellow,
insol. in water).

102°   Hydrobenzamide $C_6H_5 \cdot CH:N \cdot CH(C_6H_5)N:CH \cdot C_6H_5$
Insol. in water. With dil. HCl in cold yields benz-
aldehyde B.P. 179° and NH_4Cl. On warming with
aniline yields benzalaniline M.P. 54° and NH_3.

280°   Hexamethylenetetramine (Urotropine) $C_6H_{12}N_4$
Readily sol. in cold water. On warming with dil. HCl
yields formaldehyde (q.v.) and NH_4Cl. Soln. in very
dil. HCl yields trimethylenetrinitrosoamine M.P. 105°
with $NaNO_2$. On adding conc. HNO_3 to 25% soln.
in water at 0° yields a cryst. nitrate M.P. 165°. On
gradually adding to 95% HNO_3 at 20–30° and pouring
into ice-water yields trimethylenetrinitroamine M.P.
200°. Forms a red tetrabromide which on standing
in air loses bromine to form a yellow dibromide M.P.
196–200°d.

SIMPLE AMIDES AND IMIDES
Including Ureas and Guanidines

SOLID

M.P.
3°   Formamide $H \cdot CONH_2$
B.P. 105°/11 mm.; on heating under atm. press.
decomposes yielding NH_3, CO and H_2O. D. 1·337
(14°). Miscible in all proportions with water and alc.,
sparingly sol. in ether. Yields CO on heating with
conc. H_2SO_4. On heating with aniline yields formanilide M.P. 46° and NH_3; with α-naphthylamine
yields formyl α-naphthylamine M.P. 138°.

Guanidine $(NH_2)_2C:NH$
Alkaline, deliquescent solid. Carbonate M.P. 197°.
Nitrate M.P. 214°. Nitrite M.P. 77°. Acetate M.P.
229°. Hydrochloride M.P. 172°. Thiocyanate M.P.
118°. Picrate M.P. above 280° is almost insol. in
cold water. Rapidly oxidised by $KMnO_4$. On boiling with $Ba(OH)_2$ yields urea (q.v.) and NH_3. With
alk. NaOCl gives yellow colour changing to orange-
red. With conc. $HNO_3 + H_2SO_4$ in cold yields
nitroguanidine M.P. 230°d. (long needles from hot
water).

M.P.

—   Methylguanidine $(NH_2)_2C:N\cdot CH_3$
     Alkaline, deliquescent solid. Nitrate M.P. 150°.
     Sulphate M.P. 240°. Platinichloride M.P. 194° is
     readily sol. in water. Aurichloride M.P. 198°. Pic-
     rate M.P. 201°. On boiling with HCl yields NH_4Cl
     and methylamine HCl (q.v.). Rapidly oxidised by
     $KMnO_4$.

—   as-Dimethylguanidine $NH_2\cdot C(:NH)N(CH_3)_2$
     Resembles methylguanidine. Sulphate M.P. 285°d.
     Aurichloride M.P. 144°. Picrate M.P. 224°.

49°   Ethyl Carbamate. See Ester—Amides.

52°   Methyl Carbamate. See Ester—Amides.

54°   n-Butyl Carbamate. See Ester—Amides.

55°   isoButyl Carbamate. See Ester—Amides.

60°   n-Propyl Carbamate. See Ester—Amides.

64°   isoAmyl Carbamate. See Ester—Amides.

79°   Propionamide $CH_3\cdot CH_2\cdot CONH_2$
     B.P. 213°. Readily sol. in water, alc., and ether.
     With 75% H_2SO_4 at 120° yields propionic acid B.P.
     140°. On heating with aniline yields propionanilide
     M.P. 103° and NH_3; with α-naphthylamine yields
     propionyl α-naphthylamine M.P. 116°.

82°   Acetamide $CH_3\cdot CONH_2$
     B.P. 222°. Readily sol. in water and in alc.; almost
     insol. in ether. Forms a platinichloride M.P. 225°d.
     sparingly sol. in water and alc. Picrate M.P. 107°.
     On distilling with conc. H_2SO_4 yields acetic acid M.P.
     16°, B.P. 118°. On heating with aniline yields
     acetanilide M.P. 115° and NH_3; with α-naphthyl-
     amine yields acetyl α-naphthylamine M.P. 159°.

92°   isoPropyl Carbamate. See Ester—Amides.

96°   Semicarbazide. See Hydrazine Derivatives.

105°   Dicyandiamidine $NH_2\cdot C(:NH)\cdot NH\cdot CONH_2$
     Strong base. Sol. in water; sparingly sol. in cold
     alc., insol. in ether and in benzene. Hydrochloride
     M.P. 173°. Sulphate M.P. 194°. Picrate M.P. 265°
     is almost insol. in water. Evolves NH_3 on heating to
     160° or on boiling with water. On warming with
     $Ba(OH)_2$ soln. yields NH_3, CO_2 and urea (q.v.). With
     $CuSO_4 + NaOH$ yields a sparingly sol. red Cu salt.
     Ni salt is yellow and insol. in water.

114°   Ethyl Oxamate. See Ester—Amides.

M.P.

115°   *n*-Butyramide $CH_3 \cdot CH_2 \cdot CH_2 \cdot CONH_2$
B.P. 216°. Readily sol. in water, alc. and ether.
With 75% H_2SO_4 at 120° yields *n*-butyric acid B.P.
163°. On heating with aniline yields *n*-butyranilide
M.P. 90°; with α-naphthylamine yields *n*-butyryl
α-naphthylamine M.P. 120°.

125°   Succinimide $\begin{matrix} CH_2 \cdot CO \\ | \\ CH_2 \cdot CO \end{matrix} \Big\rangle NH$
B.P. 287°. On boiling with HCl yields succinic acid
M.P. 185° and NH_4Cl; on warming with $Ba(OH)_2$
soln. yields succinamic acid M.P. 157°. On igniting
with Zn dust yields pyrrole (vapours redden aniline
acetate paper). On heating with aniline yields succinanil M.P. 156° and NH_3.

128°   Benzamide $C_6H_5 \cdot CONH_2$
B.P. 290°. Sparingly sol. in cold water. With 75 %
H_2SO_4 at 120° yields benzoic acid M.P. 121°. On
heating with PCl_5 or $POCl_3$ yields benzonitrile B.P.
190° and HCl. On heating with aniline yields benzanilide M.P. 160° and NH_3.

129°   *iso*Butyramide $(CH_3)_2CH \cdot CONH_2$
B.P. 218°. Sol. in water, alc., and ether. With
75% H_2SO_4 at 120° yields *iso*butyric acid B.P. 155°.
On heating with aniline yields *iso*butyranilide M.P.
105° and NH_3.

132°   Urea (Carbamide) $CO(NH_2)_2$
Sol. in 1 part of water at 17°, in 5 parts of CH_3OH
at 20°, and in 20 parts of abs. alc. at 20°; almost
insol. in ether. Nitrate M.P. 163° is sparingly sol.
in HNO_3. Oxalate M.P. 171°. On heating to 150°
yields biuret M.P. 192° and NH_3. Evolves N_2 with
NaOBr soln. On boiling with HCl yields CO_2 and
NH_4Cl; slowly evolves NH_3 on boiling with dil. NaOH.
On warming with soln of aniline HCl yields phenylurea
M.P. 147° and carbanilide M.P. 238°; on heating
with aniline yields carbanilide and NH_3. On treating
extremely dil. soln. in 50% acetic acid with xanthydrol in alc. yields insol. dixanthenylurea M.P. 265°.

139°   Salicylamide $HO \cdot C_6H_4 \cdot CONH_2$ (1:2)
Sparingly sol. in cold water. Gives violet colour with
$FeCl_3$. Sol. in cold dil. NaOH; ppted unchanged
by CO_2. On boiling with NaOH yields salicylic acid
M.P. 155° and NH_3. Acetyl deriv. M.P. 143°.
Benzoyl deriv. M.P. 200°. Methyl ether M.P. 128°.

M.P.

147°   Phenylurea $C_6H_5 \cdot NH \cdot CONH_2$

Sol. in hot water. On heating above M.P. yields NH_3, CO_2 and carbanilide M.P. 238°. On heating with aniline or on boiling with soln of aniline HCl yields carbanilide. On boiling with HCl yields aniline HCl (q.v.) and NH_4Cl; with NaOH yields aniline and NH_3. Xanthenyl deriv. M.P. 225°.

147°   Diphenylguanidine $(C_6H_5 \cdot NH)_2 C:NH$

Insol. in water, sol. in dil. HCl. Nitrate and oxalate are sparingly sol. in cold water. On heating to 170–180° for 1 hour breaks down into NH_3, aniline B.P. 183° and triphenyldicarbimide M.P. 70–74° (soln. in ether has violet fluorescence). On boiling with HCl yields NH_4Cl and aniline HCl (q.v.). With acetic anhydride at 100° yields acetanilide M.P. 114° and s-acetylphenylurea M.P. 183°. Perchlorate M.P. 162°.

149°   Benzylurea $C_6H_5 \cdot CH_2 \cdot NH \cdot CONH_2$

Sol. in hot water. On heating to 200° yields CO_2, NH_3 and dibenzylurea M.P. 167°. On boiling with HCl yields benzylamine HCl (q.v.) and NH_4Cl.

154°   Phenylacetamide $C_6H_5 \cdot CH_2 \cdot CONH_2$

B.P. 262°d. Sparingly sol. in cold water. On boiling with HCl yields phenylacetic acid M.P. 76° and NH_4Cl. On heating with aniline yields phenylacetanilide M.P. 117° and NH_3.

170°   Malonamide $CH_2(CONH_2)_2$

Sol. in 10 parts of cold water; insol. in abs. alc. and in ether. Gives red colour with $CuSO_4$ + dil. NaOH. On boiling with conc. HCl yields acetic acid (q.v.) and NH_4Cl. On boiling with NaOH yields malonic acid M.P. 133° and NH_3. On heating with aniline yields malonanilide M.P. 224° and NH_3.

d.170°   Alloxan $\begin{matrix} CO \cdot CO \cdot CO \\ | \qquad | \\ NH \cdot CO \cdot NH \end{matrix} + H_2O$

Crystallises from water with $4H_2O$. On heating alone yields NH_3, CO_2 and CO. Very sol. in cold water; soln develops red colour on skin. On boiling with NaOH evolves NH_3. Gives blue colour with ferrous salts. Gives yellow colour with phenylhydrazine HCl soln. With $SnCl_2$ in dil. HCl yields insol. alloxantin, which gives a blue ppte with $Ba(OH)_2$ soln. On warming with $NH_2OH \cdot HCl$ soln. yields violuric acid, which forms a purple soln. in Na_2CO_3.

M.P.

173°   *p*-Phenetylurea ('Dulcin')

$C_2H_5O \cdot C_6H_4 \cdot NH \cdot CONH_2$ (1:4)

Sparingly sol. in cold water; soln. has sweet taste. On heating above M.P. yields NH_3, CO_2 and di-*p*-phenetylurea M.P. 235°. On boiling with HCl yields *p*-phenetidine HCl (*q.v.*) and NH_4Cl. On boiling with 48% HBr yields *p*-aminophenol HBr (*q.v.*), NH_4Br and ethyl bromide B.P. 38°.

181°   *p*-Tolylurea $CH_3 \cdot C_6H_4 \cdot NH \cdot CONH_2$ (1:4)

Sol. in hot water. On heating above M.P. yields NH_3, CO_2 and di-*p*-tolylurea M.P. 268°. On boiling with HCl yields *p*-toluidine HCl (*q.v.*) and NH_4Cl.

191°   *o*-Tolylurea $CH_3 \cdot C_6H_4 \cdot NH \cdot CONH_2$ (1:2)

Sol. in hot water. On heating above M.P. yields NH_3, CO_2 and di-*o*-tolylurea M.P. 250°. On boiling with HCl yields *o*-toluidine HCl (*q.v.*) and NH_4Cl. Xanthenyl deriv. M.P. 228°.

192°d.   Biuret $NH_2 \cdot CO \cdot NH \cdot CO \cdot NH_2$

Sol. in 65 parts of water at 15°, in 2·2 parts on boiling. On heating above M.P. yields NH_3. Gives red colour with trace of $CuSO_4$ + dil. NaOH; with excess of $CuSO_4$ colour is violet. On boiling with $Ba(OH)_2$ soln. yields NH_3, CO_2 (as $BaCO_3$) and urea (*q.v.*). On adding to conc. HNO_3 + H_2SO_4 at 0° and pouring on to ice yields nitro deriv. M.P. 165°d. On heating with aniline yields diphenylbiuret M.P. 210° and NH_3. Dixanthenyl deriv. M.P. 260°.

219°d.   Phthalamide $C_6H_4(CONH_2)_2$ (1:2)

On heating above M.P. yields phthalimide M.P. 233° and NH_3. On boiling with HCl yields phthalic acid M.P. 195° and NH_4Cl. On heating with aniline yields phthalanil M.P. 205° and NH_3.

226°   *l*-Asparagine. See Amino Acids, etc.

233°   Phthalimide $C_6H_4 \diagup_{CO}^{CO} \diagdown NH$

Almost insol. in cold water. On boiling with dil. NaOH yields phthalic acid M.P. 195° and NH_3; on warming with $Ba(OH)_2$ soln. yields phthalamidic acid M.P. 148°. On adding alc. KOH to soln. in alc. yields cryst. ppte of K deriv., which on heating with benzyl chloride yields benzylphthalimide M.P. 115°. On heating with aniline yields phthalanil M.P. 205° and NH_3.

M.P.

d.240° Barbituric Acid $CO{\cdot}CH_2{\cdot}CO$

| |

$NH{\cdot}CO{\cdot}NH$

Decomposes on heating, yielding NH_3. Readily sol. in hot water, sparingly in cold; sol. in cold dil. NaOH. On boiling with NaOH yields NH_3 and Na malonate. NH_4 salt is sparingly sol. in cold water. Gives yellow ppte with $AgNO_3$. With $NaNO_2$ soln. in cold yields Na violurate (purple soln.). With bromine in water yields dibromo deriv. M.P. 235°d. With acid diazobenzene soln. yields sparingly sol. alloxan phenylhydrazone M.P. 284° (sol. in K_2CO_3 with reddish yellow colour; soln. loses NH_3 on boiling giving a pure yellow soln. which with HCl gives a product M.P. 164°).

242° Succinamide $NH_2{\cdot}CO{\cdot}CH_2{\cdot}CH_2{\cdot}CO{\cdot}NH_2$

Sol. in about 200 parts of cold water, in 9 parts on boiling; insol. in abs. alc. and in ether. On heating above M.P. yields succinimide M.P. 125° and NH_3. On boiling with dil. NaOH yields succinic acid M.P. 185° and NH_3. On heating with aniline yields succinanil M.P. 156° and NH_3.

315°d. Creatine $NH_2{\cdot}C(:NH){\cdot}N(CH_3){\cdot}CH_2{\cdot}COOH$

Sol. in 75 parts of water at 18°; insol. in alc. and in ether. Yields NH_3 on boiling with dil. NaOH or $Ba(OH)_2$. On warming with mineral acids yields creatinine (*q.v.*). On adding $AgNO_3$ and then KOH gives a white ppte. sol. in excess of KOH; this soln. gelatinises on standing and darkens slowly in cold (rapidly on warming). With $HgCl_2$ and KOH gives similar ppte. which darkens on standing but is insol. in KOH.

315°d. Creatinine $NH{:}C{\cdot}NH{-}CO$

| |

$N(CH_3).\ CH_2$

Sol. in 11·5 parts of water at 16°; sparingly sol. in alc. Oxidised by $KMnO_4$ to oxalic acid and methylguanidine (*q.v.*). On saturating soln. with NO_2 and then adding NH_4OH yields insol. nitroso deriv. M.P. 210°. Reduces Fehling's soln. giving white flocculent ppte of creatinine-cuprous oxide. With nitroprusside + NaOH gives red colour changing to yellow; on adding acetic acid and warming, colour changes to blue. Gives red colour with picric acid + NaOH. Forms a compound with $ZnCl_2$, sol. in 54 parts of

M.P.

water at 15°, insol. in alc. Picrate M.P. 220° is almost insol. in water.

418° Oxamide $NH_2 \cdot CO \cdot CO \cdot NH_2$

M.P. observable in sealed tube; subl. in open tube. Almost insol. in cold water, alc. and ether. Gives red colour with $CuSO_4$ + dil. NaOH. On boiling with dil. NaOH yields oxalic acid (q.v.) and NH_3. On heating with aniline yields oxanilide M.P. 245° and NH_3.

d. Uric Acid. See Purines.

SUBSTITUTED AMIDES AND IMIDES

(ACYL AMINES)

(Including Guanidines)

LIQUID

B.P.

221° Formyl Piperidine $CH_2 \cdot CH_2 \cdot N \cdot CHO$

$\qquad\qquad CH_2 \cdot CH_2 \cdot CH_2$

D. 1·019 (23°). Miscible with water. Weak base. Hydrobromide M.P. 203°. On boiling with HCl yields formic acid (q.v.) and piperidine HCl (q.v.). Forms a compound with $HgCl_2$ M.P. 148°.

226° Acetyl Piperidine $CH_2 \cdot CH_2 \cdot N \cdot CO \cdot CH_3$

$\qquad\qquad CH_2 \cdot CH_2 \cdot CH_2$

D. 1·011 (9°). Miscible with water. Weak base. Hydrochloride M.P. 95°. Hydrobromide M.P. 131°. On boiling with HCl yields acetic acid B.P. 118° and piperidine HCl (q.v.).

SOLID

M.P.

47° Formanilide $C_6H_5 \cdot NH \cdot CHO$

B.P. 271°. Slightly sol. in cold water. On boiling with HCl yields formic acid (q.v.) and aniline HCl (q.v.). On heating with Zn dust yields CO, CO_2, aniline and benzonitrile (q.v.). With NaOH in alc. gives ppte of Na deriv.; on warming this with benzyl chloride yields benzylformanilide M.P. 48°, which on hydrolysis yields benzylaniline M.P. 37°. On warming with $CHCl_3$ + KOH in alc. gives odour of phenyl isocyanide.

M.P.

47°   Benzoyl Piperidine $CH_2 \cdot CH_2 \cdot N \cdot COC_6H_5$

$CH_2 \cdot CH_2 \cdot CH_2$

B.P. 320°. Insol. in water. On boiling with HCl yields benzoic acid M.P. 121° and piperidine HCl (q.v.). On slowly distilling with (1 mol.) PCl_5 yields 1:5-dichloropentane B.P. 177° (insol. in cold conc. H_2SO_4), benzonitrile B.P. 190° (sol. in cold conc. H_2SO_4) and $POCl_3$ (decomp. by cold water).

52°   Ethyl Carbanilate. See Ester—Amides.

54°   Ethylacetanilide $C_6H_5 \cdot N(C_2H_5) \cdot CO \cdot CH_3$

B.P. 249°. On boiling with HCl yields acetic acid B.P. 118° and ethylaniline HCl (q.v.). With conc. $HNO_3 + H_2SO_4$ at 40° yields p-nitro deriv. M.P. 118°, which on hydrolysis yields p-nitroethylaniline M.P. 95°.

66°   Ethyl Oxanilate. See Ester—Amides.

73°   Formyl Diphenylamine $(C_6H_5)_2N \cdot CHO$

On boiling with HCl yields formic acid (q.v.) and diphenylamine M.P. 54°. Soln. in conc. H_2SO_4 gives blue colour with trace of HNO_3.

79°   Diethylcarbanilide $C_6H_5 \cdot N(C_2H_5) \cdot CO \cdot N(C_2H_5) \cdot C_6H_5$

On boiling with HCl yields ethylaniline HCl (q.v.).

85°   Acetoacetanilide $CH_3 \cdot CO \cdot CH_2 \cdot CO \cdot NH \cdot C_6H_5$

Sol. in hot water. Gives violet colour with $FeCl_3$. On boiling with HCl yields acetic acid B.P. 118° and aniline HCl (q.v.). On heating with aniline yields acetone B.P. 56° and carbanilide M.P. 238°. On warming with conc. H_2SO_4 yields lepidone M.P. 224°.

90°   n-Butyranilide $CH_3 \cdot CH_2 \cdot CH_2 \cdot CO \cdot NH \cdot C_6H_5$

On boiling with HCl yields n-butyric acid B.P. 163° and aniline HCl (q.v.)

101°   Acetyl Diphenylamine $(C_6H_5)_2N \cdot CO \cdot CH_3$

On boiling with HCl yields acetic acid B.P. 118° and diphenylamine M.P. 54°. Soln. in conc. H_2SO_4 gives blue colour with trace of HNO_3.

102°   Methylacetanilide $C_6H_5 \cdot N(CH_3) \cdot CO \cdot CH_3$

B.P. 237°. On boiling with HCl yields acetic acid B.P. 118° and methylaniline HCl (q.v.). With conc. $HNO_3 + H_2SO_4$ at 40° yields p-nitro deriv. M.P. 153°, which on hydrolysis yields p-nitromethylaniline M.P. 152°.

103°   Propionanilide $CH_3 \cdot CH_2 \cdot CO \cdot NH \cdot C_6H_5$

On boiling with HCl yields propionic acid B.P. 140°

M.P.

and aniline HCl (*q.v.*). With conc. $HNO_3 + H_2SO_4$ at 0° yields *p*-nitro deriv. M.P. 182°, which on hydrolysis yields *p*-nitroaniline M.P. 147°.

112° *o*-Acetotoluidide $CH_3 \cdot C_6H_4 \cdot NH \cdot CO \cdot CH_3$ (1:2)
B.P. 303°. Sol. in hot water. On boiling with HCl yields acetic acid B.P. 118° and *o*-toluidine HCl (*q.v.*). With hot $KMnO_4$ soln yields acetylanthranilic acid M.P. 185°.

113° Antipyrine. See Hydrazine Derivatives.

114° Acetanilide $CH_3 \cdot CO \cdot NH \cdot C_6H_5$
B.P. 304°. Sol. in hot water. On boiling with HCl yields acetic acid B.P. 118° and aniline HCl (*q.v.*). With (1 mol.) bromine in acetic acid yields *p*-bromo deriv. M.P. 167°, which on hydrolysis yields *p*-bromoaniline M.P. 63°. With NaOCl soln yields *N*-chloro deriv. M.P. 91°, which with acetic acid + trace of HCl yields *p*-chloro deriv. M.P. 179°. With conc. $HNO_3 + H_2SO_4$ yields *p*-nitro deriv. M.P. 210°, which on hydrolysis yields *p*-nitroaniline M.P. 147°.

115° *iso*Valeranilide $(CH_3)_2CH \cdot CH_2 \cdot CO \cdot NH \cdot C_6H_5$
On boiling with HCl yields *iso*valeric acid B.P. 155° and aniline HCl (*q.v.*).

117° Phenylacetanilide $C_6H_5 \cdot CH_2 \cdot CO \cdot NH \cdot C_6H_5$
On boiling with HCl yields phenylacetic acid M.P. 76° and aniline HCl (*q.v.*). With conc. HNO_3 in cold yields oxides on nitrogen and 2:4-dinitrophenylacetic acid M.P. 189°.

120° Dimethylcarbanilide $C_6H_5 \cdot N(CH_3) \cdot CO \cdot N(CH_3) \cdot C_6H_5$
B.P. 350°. On boiling with HCl yields methylaniline HCl (*q.v.*).

127° Phenylmethylpyrazolone. See Hydrazine Derivatives.

128° Acetylphenylhydrazine. See Hydrazine Derivatives.

129° Piperine $(CH_2O_2){:}C_6H_3[\cdot CH{:}CH]_2 \cdot CO \cdot NC_5H_{10}$ (1:2:4)
On boiling with HCl yields piperic acid M.P. 216° and piperidine HCl (*q.v.*). With acid $KMnO_4$ soln. yields piperonal M.P. 37°.

133° 4-Aceto-*m*-xylidide $(CH_3)_2C_6H_3 \cdot NH \cdot CO \cdot CH_3$ (1:3:4)
On boiling with HCl yields acetic acid B.P. 118° and *m*-xylidine HCl (*q.v.*). With fuming HNO_3 yields 5-nitro deriv. M.P. 172°; on slowly adding KNO_4 to soln. in conc. H_2SO_4 yields 6-nitro deriv. M.P. 159°.

134° *β*-Acetnaphthylamide $C_{10}H_7 \cdot NH \cdot CO \cdot CH_3$ (2)
On boiling with HCl yields acetic acid B.P. 118° and

β-naphthylamine HCl (q.v.). With (1 mol.) bromine in acetic acid yields 1-bromo deriv. M.P. 140°. With fuming HNO_3 yields two dinitro derivs., one sol. in alc. M.P. 185°, the other insol. in alc. M.P. 235°.

135°   Aceto-p-phenetidide ('Phenacetine')
$$C_2H_5O \cdot C_6H_4 \cdot NH \cdot CO \cdot CH_3 \quad (1:4)$$
On boiling with HCl yields acetic acid B.P. 118° and p-phenetidine HCl (q.v.); on boiling with 48% HBr yields acetic acid, ethyl bromide B.P. 38° and p-aminophenol HCl (q.v.). On warming with (2 mols.) 10% HNO_3 yields 3-nitro deriv. M.P. 103°, which on hydrolysis yields nitrophenetidine M.P. 113°.

143° o-Benzotoluidide $CH_3 \cdot C_6H_4 \cdot NH \cdot CO \cdot C_6H_5$ (1:2)
On boiling with HCl yields benzoic acid M.P. 121° and o-toluidine HCl (q.v.). With hot $KMnO_4$ soln. yields benzoylanthranilic acid M.P. 177°.

145°   Triphenylguanidine $C_6H_5 \cdot N:C(NH \cdot C_6H_5)_2$
Insol. in water. Weak base. Hydrochloride M.P. 241°. Nitrate and oxalate are sparingly sol. in cold water. Picrate M.P. 180°. On heating yields aniline B.P. 183° and carbodiphenylimide B.P. 330°. On boiling with conc. KOH soln. yields aniline.

147° p-Acetotoluidide $CH_3 \cdot C_6H_4 \cdot NH \cdot CO \cdot CH_3$ (1:4)
B.P. 307°. On boiling with HCl yields acetic acid B.P. 118° and p-toluidine HCl (q.v.). On adding to conc. $HNO_3 + H_2SO_4$ at 30–40° yields 3-nitro deriv. M.P. 144°, which on hydrolysis yields nitrotoluidine M.P. 116°. With (1 mol.) bromine in acetic acid yields 3-bromo deriv. M.P. 117°. With hot $KMnO_4$ soln yields p-acetaminobenzoic acid M.P. 256°.

147°   Phenylurea. See Simple Amides.

147°   Diphenylguanidine. See Simple Amides.

148°   Oxanilic Acid. See Amino Acids, etc.

149°   Benzylurea. See Simple Amides.

153°   Cinnamanilide $C_6H_5 \cdot CH:CH \cdot CO \cdot NH \cdot C_6H_5$
On boiling with HCl yields cinnamic acid M.P. 133° and aniline HCl (q.v.). Yields benzaldehyde B.P. 179° and benzoic acid M.P. 121° with acid $KMnO_4$.

156°   Succinanil $\begin{array}{l} CH_2 \cdot CO \\ | \qquad\quad\ \ \rangle N \cdot C_6H_5 \\ CH_2 \cdot CO \end{array}$

On boiling with HCl yields succinic acid M.P. 185°

M.P.

and aniline HCl (*q.v.*). On warming with Ba(OH)$_2$ soln. yields succinanilic acid M.P. 148°.

158°   *p*-Benzotoluidide $C_6H_5 \cdot CO \cdot NH \cdot C_6H_4 \cdot CH_3$ (1:4)
On boiling with HCl yields benzoic acid M.P. 121° and *p*-toluidine HCl (*q.v.*). With fuming HNO$_3$ at 0° yields dinitro deriv. M.P. 186°. With CrO$_3$ in acetic acid yields *p*-benzoylaminobenzoic acid M.P. 278°.

159°   *α*-Acetnaphthylamide $C_{10}H_7 \cdot NH \cdot CO \cdot CH_3$ (1)
On boiling with HCl yields acetic acid B.P. 118° and *α*-naphthylamine HCl (*q.v.*). With fuming HNO$_3$ in acetic acid yields dinitro deriv. M.P. 250°. With (1 mol.) bromine in acetic acid yields 4-bromo deriv. M.P. 193°.

161°   Benzanilide $C_6H_5 \cdot CO \cdot NH \cdot C_6H_5$
On boiling with HCl yields benzoic acid M.P. 121° and aniline HCl (*q.v.*). On adding to 77% HNO$_3$ at 0° and at once pouring into water yields *o*-nitro deriv. M.P. 94° (sol. in cold alc.) and *p*-nitro deriv. M.P. 199° (insol. in cold alc.). With (1 mol.) bromine in acetic acid yields *p*-bromo deriv. M.P. 204°.

162°   *p*-Aminoacetanilide $CH_3 \cdot CO \cdot NH \cdot C_6H_4 \cdot NH_2$ (1:4)
On boiling with HCl yields acetic acid B.P. 118° and *p*-phenylenediamine HCl (*q.v.*). Sol. in hot water and in cold dil. HCl. On boiling with acetic acid or with cold acetic anhydride yields diacetyl-*p*-phenylenediamine M.P. 304°. Benzal deriv. M.P. 165°. Azo-*β*-naphthol deriv. M.P. 261°.

167°   *s*-Dibenzylurea $CO(NH \cdot CH_2 \cdot C_6H_5)_2$
On boiling with HCl yields benzylamine HCl (*q.v.*).

168°   *s*-Benzoylphenylhydrazine. See Hydrazine Derivs.

185°   Diacetyl-*o*-phenylenediamine $C_6H_4(NH \cdot CO \cdot CH_3)_2$ (1:2)
Readily sol. in hot water; insol. in benzene. On boiling with HCl yields acetic acid B.P. 118° and *o*-phenylenediamine HCl (*q.v.*). On heating above M.P. yields acetic acid and methylbenziminazole M.P. 175°.

187°   Hippuric Acid. See Amino Acids, etc.

191°   Diacetyl-*m*-phenylenediamine $C_6H_4(NH \cdot CO \cdot CH_3)_2$ (1:3)
Sol. in hot water. On boiling with HCl yields acetic acid B.P. 118° and *m*-phenylenediamine HCl (*q.v.*). With conc. HNO$_3$ at 0° in presence of urea yields dinitro deriv. M.P. 228°.

M.P.

199° Carbostyril. See Aminophenols.

205° Phthalanil $C_6H_4 \underset{CO}{\overset{CO}{<}} > N \cdot C_6H_5$ (1:2)

> On boiling with HCl yields phthalic acid M.P. 195°
> and aniline HCl (q.v.). On boiling with Ba(OH)₂ soln.
> and acidifying yields phthalanilic acid M.P. 169°.

226° Succinanilide $C_6H_5 \cdot NH \cdot CO \cdot CH_2 \cdot CH_2 \cdot CO \cdot NH \cdot C_6H_5$

> On boiling with HCl yields succinic acid M.P. 185°
> and aniline HCl (q.v.). On heating above M.P. yields
> aniline B.P. 183° and succinanil M.P. 156°.

238° Carbanilide $CO(NH \cdot C_6H_5)_2$

> B.P. 270°d. Almost insol. in water. On boiling with
> HCl yields aniline HCl (q.v.). On boiling with acetic
> anhydride + Na acetate yields acetanilide M.P. 115°.
> With conc. HNO₃ in cold yields di-m-nitro deriv. M.P.
> 248°, which on hydrolysis yields m-nitroaniline M.P.
> 114°.

245° Oxanilide $C_6H_5 \cdot NH \cdot CO \cdot CO \cdot NH \cdot C_6H_5$

> Insol. in hot water ; slightly sol. in cold alc. and ether.
> On boiling with HCl yields oxalic acid (q.v.) and aniline
> HCl (q.v.). On boiling with acetic anhydride + Na
> acetate yields vinylideneoxanilide M.P. 208°. With
> fuming HNO₃ in acetic acid yields di-p-nitro deriv.
> M.P. 260°, which on hydrolysis yields p-nitroaniline
> M.P. 147°.

250° s-Di-o-tolylurea $CH_3 \cdot C_6H_4 \cdot NH \cdot CO \cdot NH \cdot C_6H_4 \cdot CH_3$
(1:2:1′:2′)

> Almost insol. in water. On boiling with HCl yields
> o-toluidine HCl (q.v.). On boiling with acetic anhy-
> dride + Na acetate yields o-acetotoluidide M.P. 112°.

268° s-Di-p-tolylurea $CH_3 \cdot C_6H_4 \cdot NH \cdot CO \cdot NH \cdot C_6H_4 \cdot CH_3$
(1:4:1′:4′)

> Almost insol. in water. On boiling with HCl yields
> p-toluidine HCl (q.v.). On boiling with acetic
> anhydride + Na acetate yields p-acetotoluidide M.P.
> 147°.

304° Diacetyl-p-phenylenediamine $C_6H_4(NH \cdot CO \cdot CH_3)_2$ (1:4)

> Sol. in acetic acid ; sparingly sol. in other organic
> liquids. On boiling with HCl yields acetic acid B.P.
> 118° and p-phenylenediamine HCl (q.v.). With
> fuming HNO₃ at 0° yields dinitro deriv. M.P. 258°.

ESTER—AMIDES

SOLID

M.P.

49°   Ethyl Carbamate (Urethane) $NH_2 \cdot COOC_2H_5$
      B.P. 184°. Readily sol. in cold water, alc., and ether.
      On boiling with dil. HCl yields CO_2, ethyl alc. B.P. 78°
      and NH_4Cl. With cold alc. KOH yields cryst.
      KOCN. On boiling with aniline yields NH_3, ethyl
      alc. and carbanilide M.P. 238°.

52°   Ethyl Carbanilate $C_6H_5 \cdot NH \cdot COOC_2H_5$
      B.P. 237°d. Almost insol. in cold water. On boiling
      with HCl yields ethyl alc. B.P. 78° and aniline HCl
      (q.v.). On boiling with aniline yields ethyl alc. and
      carbanilide M.P. 238°. On heating with P_2O_5 yields
      phenyl isocyanate B.P. 166°.

52°   Methyl Carbamate $NH_2 \cdot COOCH_3$
      B.P. 177°. Readily sol. in cold water, alc. and ether.
      On boiling with dil. HCl yields CO_2, methyl alc.
      B.P. 65° and NH_4Cl. With cold alc. KOH yields
      cryst. KOCN. On boiling with aniline yields NH_3,
      methyl alc. and carbanilide M.P. 238°.

54°   n-Butyl Carbamate $NH_2 \cdot COOC_4H_9$
      Slightly sol. in cold water, readily in alc. and ether.
      On boiling with dil. HCl yields n-butyl alc. B.P. 117°
      and NH_4Cl. On boiling with aniline yields NH_3,
      butyl alc. and carbanilide M.P. 238°. Yields KOCN
      very slowly with cold alc. KOH.

60°   n-Propyl Carbamate $NH_2 \cdot COOC_3H_7$
      B.P. 195°. Sol. in cold water, alc., and ether. On
      boiling with dil. HCl yields n-propyl alc. B.P. 97° and
      NH_4Cl. On boiling with aniline yields NH_3, propyl
      alc. and carbanilide M.P. 238°. Yields KOCN slowly
      with cold alc. KOH.

60°   isoAmyl Carbamate $NH_2 \cdot COOC_5H_{11}$
      B.P. 220°. Sparingly sol. in cold water, readily in
      alc. and ether. On boiling with dil. HCl yields iso-
      amyl alc. B.P. 131° and NH_4Cl. On heating with
      aniline yields NH_3, isoamyl alc. and carbanilide M.P.
      238°. Yields KOCN very slowly with cold alc. KOH.

66°   Ethyl Oxanilate $C_6H_5 \cdot NH \cdot CO \cdot COOC_2H_5$
      Sol. in hot water. On boiling with dil. HCl yields
      oxalic acid (q.v.), ethyl alc. B.P. 78° and aniline HCl
      (q.v.). On heating with aniline yields ethyl alc. and

M.P.

oxanilide M.P. 245°. On boiling with alc. KOH rapidly yields K oxanilate (see oxanilic acid M.P. 149°) which on continued boiling slowly breaks down into aniline and K oxalate.

114° Ethyl Oxamate (Oxamethane) $NH_2 \cdot CO \cdot COOC_2H_5$
Sol. in hot water, forming acid soln. On boiling with dil. HCl yields oxalic acid (*q.v.*), ethyl alc. B.P. 78° and NH_4Cl. On heating with aniline yields NH_3, ethyl alc. and oxanilide M.P. 245°. Yields N_2 with alkaline NaOCl. On heating with P_2O_5 yields ethyl cyanoformate B.P. 115°.

AMINO ACIDS, ESTERS AND AMIDES

LIQUID

B.P.

255° Methyl Anthranilate M.P. 25°. See Amino Acids, etc.

267° Ethyl Anthranilate $NH_2 \cdot C_6H_4 \cdot COOC_2H_5$ (1:2)
M.P. 13°. On boiling with dil. acids or alkalies yields ethyl alc. B.P. 78° and anthranilic acid M.P. 144°. Hydrochloride M.P. 170°. Acetyl deriv. M.P. 61°. Benzoyl deriv. M.P. 98°. Benzenesulphonyl deriv. M.P. 92°. Forms compound with *s*-trinitrobenzene M.P. 71°.

294° Ethyl *m*-Aminobenzoate $NH_2 \cdot C_6H_4 \cdot COOC_2H_5$ (1:3)
On boiling with dil. acids or alkalies yields ethyl alc. B.P. 78° and *m*-aminobenzoic acid M.P. 174°. Hydrochloride M.P. 185°. Benzoyl deriv. M.P. 114°. Forms compound with *s*-trinitrobenzene M.P. 84°.

SOLID

M.P.

25° Methyl Anthranilate $NH_2 \cdot C_6H_4 \cdot COOCH_3$ (1:2)
Almost insol. in cold water; soln. in alc. has blue fluorescence. On boiling with dil. acids or alkalies yields methyl alc. B.P. 65° and anthranilic acid M.P. 144°. Hydrochloride M.P. 178°. Acetyl deriv. M.P. 101°. Benzoyl deriv. M.P. 100°. Benzenesulphonyl deriv. M.P. 107°. Forms compound with *s*-trinitrobenzene M.P. 106°.

89° Ethyl *p*-Aminobenzoate $NH_2 \cdot C_6H_4 \cdot COOC_2H_5$ (1:4)
On boiling with dil. acids or alkalies yields ethyl alc. B.P. 78° and *p*-aminobenzoic acid M.P. 186°. Acetyl deriv. M.P. 110°. Benzoyl deriv. M.P. 148°. Forms compound with *s*-trinitrobenzene M.P. 85°.

M.P.

126°   Phenylglycine $C_6H_5 \cdot NH \cdot CH_2 \cdot COOH$

Sol. in hot water; sparingly sol. in ether. Sol. in cold dil. alkalies and mineral acids (but not in acetic acid). On heating Ca salt (sparingly sol. in cold water) alone or with Ca formate gives odour of indole. On fusion with NaOH in presence of air gives blue colour of indigo. Acetyl deriv. M.P. 194°. Benzoyl deriv. M.P. 63°. Addition product with phenyl *iso*cyanate M.P. 195°. Nitrosoamine M.P. 105°d.

144°   Anthranilic Acid $NH_2 \cdot C_6H_4 \cdot COOH$ (1:2)

Sol. in water and in alc., with blue fluorescence. On heating yields aniline B.P. 183°. On gently heating with $CaCl_2$, product gives red soln. in alc. developing violet fluorescence on standing; fusion with $ZnCl_2$ gives yellow product forming yellow soln in alc. With bromine water yields dibromo deriv. M.P. 227°. Hydrochloride M.P. 193°. Acetyl deriv. M.P. 185°. Benzoyl deriv. M.P. 181°. Benzenesulphonyl deriv. M.P. 214°. Benzal deriv. M.P. 128°. Phenacyl deriv. M.P. 190°. Azo-β-naphthol deriv. M.P. 276°. Methyl ester M.P. 25°, B.P. 255°. *p*-Nitrobenzyl ester M.P. 205°d. Phenacyl ester M.P. 181°. Amide M.P. 108°. Anilide M.P. 126°. Forms compound with *s*-trinitrobenzene M.P. 192°.

148°   Oxanilic Acid $C_6H_5 \cdot NH \cdot CO \cdot COOH$

Sol. in hot water; very sol. in alc. and in ether, sparingly in benzene. Soln. in conc. H_2SO_4 is coloured blue-violet by trace of $K_2Cr_2O_7$. On boiling with acids or alkalies yields aniline B.P. 183° and oxalic acid (*q.v.*). On boiling with aniline yields oxanilide M.P. 245°. Na and NH_4 salts are sparingly sol. in cold water. Aniline salt M.P. 140–160°. β-Naphthylamine salt M.P. 151°. Pyridine salt M.P. 132°. Quinoline salt M.P. 122°.

174°   *m*-Aminobenzoic Acid $NH_2 \cdot C_6H_4 \cdot COOH$ (1:3)

Sol. in hot water and in alc. On gently heating with $CaCl_2$, product gives red soln in alc. without fluorescence; fusion with $ZnCl_2$ yields violet product giving brown soln. in alc. Acetyl deriv. M.P. 250°. Benzal deriv. M.P. 119°. Phenacyl deriv. M.P. 202°. Methyl ester M.P. 37°. *p*-Nitrobenzyl ester M.P. 201°. Amide M.P. 75°. Anilide M.P. 129°. Forms a compound with *s*-trinitrobenzene M.P. 118°.

186°   *p*-Aminobenzoic Acid $NH_2 \cdot C_6H_4 \cdot COOH$ (1:4)

Sol. in hot water and in alc. Fusion with $CaCl_2$ and

M.P.

with $ZnCl_2$: same as with m-aminobenzoic acid.
Acetyl deriv. M.P. 252°. Benzoyl deriv. M.P. 278°.
Benzenesulphonyl deriv. M.P. 212°. Benzal deriv.
M.P. 193°. Phenacyl deriv. M.P. 211°. Methyl ester
M.P. 112°. p-Nitrobenzyl ester M.P. 248°. Amide
M.P. 183°. Forms a compound with s-trinitrobenzene
M.P. 151°.

187° Hippuric Acid $C_6H_5 \cdot CO \cdot NH \cdot CH_2 \cdot COOH$
Sol. in hot water and in alc. ; insol. in benzene and
in ligroin. On boiling with HCl yields benzoic acid M.P.
121° and glycine HCl ($q.v.$). Methyl ester M.P. 80°.
Ethyl ester M.P. 60°. p-Nitrobenzyl ester M.P. 136°.
p-Bromophenacyl ester M.P. 151°. With conc.
$HNO_3 + H_2SO_4$ yields m-nitro deriv. M.P. 162°.

198° d-Glutamic Acid $COOH \cdot CH_2 \cdot CH_2 \cdot CH(NH_2) \cdot COOH$
Sol. in 100 parts of water at 16° ; insol. in alc.
$[a]_D = + 12°$ in water, $+ 30°$ in HCl, $—4°$ in $Ba(OH)_2$.
Hydrochloride M.P. 203° is almost insol. in cold conc.
HCl. On heating at 150–160° yields levorotatory
pyrrolidonecarboxylic acid M.P. 160°. Hydantoic
acid M.P. 150° is sol. in 150 parts of water and in
80 parts of alc. at 20°. a-Naphthylhydantoic acid
M.P. 236°.

210°d. Sarcosine $CH_3 \cdot NH \cdot CH_2 \cdot COOH$
Sol. in water, insol. in alc. On heating yields anhydride M.P. 149°, B.P. 350°, and some dimethylamine
($q.v.$). Hydrochloride M.P. 169°. Hydrobromide
M.P. 186°. Nitrate M.P. 70°d. Phenylhydantoic
acid M.P. 102°. Ethyl ester B.P. 43°/10 mm. forms
a picrate M.P. 149°.

226° l-Asparagine $COOH \cdot CH(NH_2) \cdot CH_2 \cdot CONH_2 + H_2O$
Loses water of crystallisation above 100°. Sol. in
56 parts of water at 10°. $[a]_D = — 5 \cdot 4°$. On boiling
with dil. alkali yields NH_3 and l-aspartic acid ($q.v.$).
Gives blue colour with dil. NaOH + trace of $CuSO_4$.
Cu salt is almost insol. in cold water. Picrate d.180°.
a-Naphthylhydantoic acid M.P. 199°.

232°d. Glycine (Glycocoll) $NH_2 \cdot CH_2 \cdot COOH$
Sol. in 4 parts of cold water ; insol. in alc. Gives
blue colour with trace of $CuSO_4$; red colour with
$FeCl_3$. Cu salt is sol. in 174 parts of cold water.
Hydrochloride is hygroscopic. Nitrate M.P. 145°d.
Picrate M.P. 190° is sparingly sol. in cold water. On
boiling with alc. + HCl gas yields ethyl ester HCl

M.P.

M.P. 144°. On warming with acetic anhydride yields
acetyl deriv. M.P. 206°. Benzoyl deriv. M.P. 187°.
Benzenesulphonyl deriv. M.P. 165°. Hydantoic acid
M.P. 163° is sol. in 32 parts of water and in 200
parts of alc. at 20°. α-Naphthylhydantoic acid M.P.
191°.

248°   p-Hydroxyphenylglycine $HO \cdot C_6H_4 \cdot NH \cdot CH_2 \cdot COOH$ (1:4)
Sparingly sol. in cold water and in alc. ; insol. in
ether. Sol. in dil. alkalies and mineral acids (not in
acetic acid). Gives no colour with $FeCl_3$ in cold ;
odour of quinone on warming. With $AgNO_3$ soln
gives black ppte. in cold; soln. becomes purple on
heating. Acetyl deriv. is very sol. in cold water.

270°   l-Aspartic Acid $COOH \cdot CH_2 \cdot CH(NH_2) \cdot COOH$
Sol. in 250 parts of water at 10° ; insol. in alc. $[\alpha]_D$
$= + 6°$ in water, $+ 25°$ in HCl, $-1°$ in NaOH.
Benzoyl deriv. M.P. 180°. Hydantoic acid M.P. 162°
is sol. in 270 parts of water and in 1,000 parts of alc.
at 20°.

273°   dl-Phenylalanine $C_6H_5 \cdot CH_2 \cdot CH(NH_2) \cdot COOH$
Sparingly sol. in cold water ; insol. in alc. On heating
alone yields phenyl-lactimide M.P. 290° and some
β-phenylethylamine B.P. 197°. On oxidation yields
benzoic acid M.P. 121°. Benzoyl deriv. M.P. 187°.
Hydantoic acid M.P. 190°. Phenylhydantoic acid
M.P. 182°d.

subl.
280°   α-Aminoisobutyric Acid $(CH_3)_2C(NH_2) \cdot COOH$
Readily sol. in cold water ; almost insol. in alc.
On oxidation by (1 mol.) NaOCl yields acetone B.P.
56°. Benzoyl deriv. M.P. 198°. Hydantoic acid
M.P. 162° is sol. in 100 parts of water at 20° and
readily in alc. α-Naphthylhydantoic acid M.P. 198°.

283°   5-Aminosalicylic Acid $COOH \cdot C_6H_3(OH) \cdot NH_2$ (1:2:5)
Sparingly sol. in cold water ; insol. in alc. Sulphate
M.P. 334°. With $FeCl_3$ gives red colour changing to
brown ppte. Acetyl deriv. M.P. 197°. On long
warming at 100° with benzyl chloride + Na acetate
yields dibenzyl deriv. M.P. 168°. p-Nitrobenzyl ester
M.P. 245°d. Azo-β-naphthol deriv. M.P. 201°.

294°d.   l-Leucine $(CH_3)_2CH \cdot CH_2 \cdot CH(NH_2) \cdot COOH$
Sol. in 4·5 parts of water at 20°. $[\alpha]_D = - 10°$ in
water, $+ 16°$ in HCl. On heating yields isoamyl-
amine B.P 95°. On oxidation by $KMnO_4$ yields iso-

valeric acid B.P. 176°. Cu salt is almost insol. in cold water. Benzoyl deriv. M.P. 118°. Hydantoic acid M.P. 189° is sol. in 1700 parts of water and in 250 parts of alc. at 20°. α-Naphthylhydantoic acid M.P. 163°.

295°d. *dl*-Alanine $CH_3 \cdot CH(NH_2) \cdot COOH$
Sol. in 4·6 parts of water at 17°; insol. in alc. With conc. H_2SO_4 yields CO above 180°. On warming in water with PbO_2 yields acetaldehyde B.P. 21° and NH_3. Cu salt is fairly sol. in water. On boiling with alc. + HCl gas yields ester hydrochloride (methyl M.P. 157°, ethyl M.P. 64–68°). Picrate is readily sol. in water. Benzoyl deriv. M.P. 165°. Benzenesulphonyl deriv. M.P. 126°. β-Naphthalenesulphonyl deriv. M.P. 152°. Hydantoic acid M.P. 157° is sol. in 46 parts of water and in 100 parts of alc. at 20°. Phenylhydantoic acid M.P. 190°d. α-Naphthylhydantoic acid M.P. 198°.

298°d. *dl*-Valine $(CH_3)_2CH \cdot CH(NH_2) \cdot COOH$
Sol. in 11·7 parts of water at 15° and in 14·1 parts at 25°. On heating alone yields anhydride M.P. 304°. Oxidised by (1 mol.) NaOCl to *iso*butyraldehyde B.P. 63°. Hydrochloride M.P. 189°. Cu salt is sparingly sol. in water. Benzoyl deriv. M.P. 132°. Hydantoic acid M.P. 176° is sol. in 213 parts of water at 20° and readily in alc. α-Naphthylhydantoic acid M.P. 204°.

307°d. *dl*-α-Amino-*n*-butyric Acid $CH_3 \cdot CH_2 \cdot CH(NH_2) \cdot COOH$
Sol. in 3·5 parts of cold water; almost insol. in alc. Cu salt is sparingly sol. in cold water. Benzoyl deriv. M.P. 143°. Benzenesulphonyl deriv. M.P. 148°. Hydantoic acid M.P. 177°. Phenylhydantoic acid M.P. 170°d. α-Naphthylhydantoic acid M.P. 194°.

310° *l*-Tyrosine $HO \cdot C_6H_4 \cdot CH_2 \cdot CH(NH_2) \cdot COOH$ (1:4)
Sol. in about 2,500 parts of cold and about 154 parts of hot water. Cu salt is almost insol. in cold water. On warming with conc. HNO_3 yields dinitro deriv. (yellow leaflets insol. in cold water). Gives red colour with dil. soln. of acetaldehyde in conc. H_2SO_4. On fusion with NaOH yields *p*-hydroxybenzoic acid M.P. 213°. Dibenzoyl deriv. M.P. 211°. Hydantoic acid M.P. 218°d. is sol. in 36 parts of water at 20° and readily sol. in alc. α-Naphthylhydantoic acid M.P. 205°.

PURINES

SOLID

M.P.

234° Caffeine (1:3:7-Trimethylxanthine)

$$CH_3 \cdot N \cdot CO$$
$$CO \quad C \cdot N \diagdown CH_3$$
$$CH_3 \cdot N \cdot C \cdot N \diagup CH$$

Readily sol. in water or $CHCl_3$, fairly sol. in alc. or benzene, sparingly in ether or CCl_4. Can be sublimed unchanged. Decomposed on boiling with aqueous KOH. On boiling with alcoholic KOH yields CO_2, NH_3, CH_3NH_2, HCOOH, and sarcosine M.P. 210°d. Unchanged on boiling with conc. HCl. Yields Prussian Blue on warming with $K_4Fe(CN)_6$ and HNO_3. Boil 0·1 g. with 2 c.c. water and 1 c.c. conc. HCl, add 10 c.c. saturated bromine water, boil until colourless, dilute with water to the original volume : on adding to 2 c.c. of this soln. 1 drop of 5% $FeSO_4$ and 2 or 3 drops of NH_4OH, blue colour results. Gives ppte. M.P. 215° with iodine in KI.

264° Theophylline (1:3-Dimethylxanthine) $C_7H_8O_2N_4$
Readily sol. in warm water, sparingly in cold alc. On warming in CH_3OH with KOH and CH_3I yields caffeine M.P. 234°. Gives blue colour with HCl + Br_2, then $FeSO_4 + NH_4OH$, etc., like caffeine.

Subl.
290° Theobromine (3:7-Dimethylxanthine) $C_7H_8O_2N_4$
M.P. 329° (in closed tube). Almost insol. in cold water, alc., ether, $CHCl_3$, CCl_4, or ligroin. Slightly sol. in hot water. Unchanged on boiling with aqueous KOH. On warming in CH_3OH with KOH and CH_3I yields caffeine M.P. 234°. Gives blue colour with HCl + Br_2, then $FeSO_4 + NH_4OH$, etc., like caffeine. Yields cryst. ppte with $AgNO_3$ in dil. HNO_3.

d.   Uric Acid

$$NH \cdot CO$$
$$CO \quad C \cdot NH \diagdown CO$$
$$NH \cdot C \cdot NH \diagup$$

On heating alone yields NH_3, HCN, and other products. Sol. in 10,000–15,000 parts of water at 20°, in about 1,900 at 100°. Insol. in alc. Sol. in Na acetate soln. and in glycerol. Sol. without decomp. in conc. H_2SO_4. On oxidation by 7% HNO_3 at

M.P.

60–70° yields alloxan (*q.v.*). Reduces acid₁ KMnO₄ in cold and Fehling's soln. on long boiling. Reduces ammon. AgNO₃. With CuSO₄ + NaHSO₃ gives white ppte. of cuprous urate.

ALDOXIMES

SOLID

M.P.

33° α-Benzaldoxime $C_6H_5 \cdot CH:NOH$ ('*Anti*')
B.P. 123°/14 mm. Sparingly sol. in water, readily in benzene and in dil. NaOH. On boiling with dil. HCl yields benzaldehyde B.P. 179° and $NH_2OH \cdot HCl$. With HCl gas in well-cooled ether yields hydrochloride M.P. 103°; in warm ether yields β-hydrochloride M.P. 66°. Forms cryst. compound (sol. in water, insol. in alc.) with $NaHSO_3$. With conc. alc. $NaOC_2H_5$ yields ppte. of Na deriv. Gives no colour with either $FeCl_3$ or Cu acetate in alc. With acetic anhydride in cold yields acetyl deriv. M.P. 14°; on boiling yields benzonitrile B.P. 190°. With PCl_5 yields benzonitrile.

47° α-Acetaldoxime $CH_3 \cdot CH:NOH$ ('*Anti*')
B.P. 114°. Sol. in water, alc., and ether. On boiling with dil. HCl yields acetaldehyde B.P. 21° and $NH_2OH \cdot HCl$. With acetic anhydride or acetyl chloride in cold yields acetonitrile B.P. 81°.

128° β-Benzaldoxime $C_6H_5 \cdot CH:NOH$ ('*Syn*')
Sparingly sol. in cold water and in cold benzene; sol. in dil. NaOH. On boiling with dil. HCl yields benzaldehyde B.P. 179° and $NH_2OH \cdot HCl$; with HCl gas in ether yields hydrochloride M.P. 66°. Gives no ppte with conc. alc. C_2H_5ONa. Gives red colour with $FeCl_3$ in alc.; green with Cu acetate. With acetic anhydride in cold yields acetyl deriv. M.P. 55°. With PCl_5 yields benzonitrile B.P. 190°.

KETOXIMES

SOLID

M.P.

59° Acetoxime $(CH_3)_2C:NOH$
B.P. 135°. Readily sol. in water, alc., and ether. On boiling with dil. HCl yields acetone B.P. 56° and $NH_2OH \cdot HCl$. With HCl gas in dry ether yields hydrochloride M.P. 98–101°. Forms cryst. compound with $NaHSO_3$. With methyl sulphate + dil. NaOH

yields methyl deriv. B.P. 72°. With conc. H_2SO_4 in acetic acid yields methylamine sulphate (*q.v.*).

59°   Acetophenoneoxime $C_6H_5 \cdot C(:NOH) \cdot CH_3$

Volatile with steam. Sparingly sol. in cold water; readily in dil. NaOH and in organic liquids. On adding formaldehyde to cold soln. in conc. HCl yields acetophenone M.P. 20°, B.P. 202°. On warming to 100° with conc. H_2SO_4, or with HCl gas in acetic acid, yields acetanilide M.P. 114°. With acetic anhydride at 100° yields acetyl deriv. M.P. 55°. With methyl sulphate + dil. NaOH yields methyl deriv. B.P. 215°.

118°   *d*-Camphoroxime $C_{10}H_{16}:NOH$

B.P. 250°d. Insol. in water; sol. in dil. acids and alkalies, and in alc. Optically active: $[\alpha]_D = -42°$ in alc. Stable towards boiling dil. HCl. With HCl gas in dry ether yields hydrochloride M.P. 162°. With $SOCl_2$ or acetyl chloride in cold yields campholenonitrile B.P. 226°, which with alc. KOH yields campholenamide M.P. 130°. On warming with conc. HCl + formaldehyde yields camphor M.P. 175°. With acetic anhydride in cold yields liquid acetyl deriv.; on heating yields campholenonitrile. With methyl sulphate + dil. NaOH yields methyl deriv. B.P. 209°. With $AgNO_3$ in dil. HNO_3 yields an addition compound M.P. 157° (insol. in water; sol. in alc., ether and benzene).

126°d   Quinonemonoxime. See *p*-Nitrosophenol.

143°   Benzophenoneoxime $(C_6H_5)_2C:NOH$

Insol. in cold water; readily sol. in ether, less so in benzene. Sol. in conc. HCl, ppted. on dilution; sol. in dil. NaOH. With HCl gas in dry ether yields unstable hydrochloride. On adding formaldehyde to soln. in conc. HCl yields benzophenone M.P. 48°. With conc. H_2SO_4 at 100° yields benzanilide M.P. 161°. On warming with acetyl chloride yields acetyl deriv. M.P. 102°.

237°d.   *a*-Benzildioxime $C_6H_5 \cdot C(:NOH) \cdot C(:NOH) \cdot C_6H_5$

Insol. in water, almost insol. in alc., ether, and acetic acid; sol. in dil. NaOH and is pptd. by CO_2 or NH_4Cl. Gives yellow ppte. in NH_4OH with $AgNO_3$. Forms red insol. ppte. with Ni salts. With conc. HCl at 100° yields benzil M.P. 95° and $NH_2OH \cdot HCl$. On boiling with acetic anhydride yields diacetate M.P. 147°.

M.P.
245° Dimethylglyoxime (Diacetyldioxime)

$$CH_3 \cdot C(:NOH) \cdot C(:NOH) \cdot CH_3$$

Insol. in water; sol. in alc. and in ether; sol. in dil.
NaOH and is ppted by CO_2 or NH_4Cl. On boiling
with 25% H_2SO_4 yields diacetyl B.P. 88° (yellow
liquid, sol. in 4 parts of cold water) and NH_2OH
sulphate. Forms bright red ppte. in alc. with Ni
salts. On warming with acetic anhydride yields
diacetyl deriv. M.P. 115°.

SIMPLE NITRILES

LIQUID

B.P.
81° Acetonitrile $CH_3 \cdot CN$

D. 0·804 (0°). Miscible with water; separates on
adding $CaCl_2$. On boiling with dil. acids or alkalies
yields acetic acid B.P. 118° and NH_3. With (1 mol.)
alc. + HCl gas yields acetiminoethyl ether HCl M.P.
98°d. (free base B.P. 92–95°). With Zn + dil. HCl
yields ethylamine HCl (q.v.).

98° Propionitrile $C_2H_5 \cdot CN$

D. 0·802 (0°). Readily sol. in water; separates on
adding $CaCl_2$. On boiling with dil. acids or alkalies
yields propionic acid B.P. 140° and NH_3. With
(1 mol.) alc. + HCl gas yields propioniminoethyl
ether HCl M.P. 92°d. On boiling with alc. + H_2SO_4
yields ethyl propionate B.P. 98°.

117° n-Butyronitrile $CH_3 \cdot CH_2 \cdot CH_2 \cdot CN$

D. 0·796 (15°). Sol. in water. On boiling with dil.
acids or alkalies yields n-butyric acid B.P. 163° and
NH_3. On boiling with alc. + H_2SO_4 yields ethyl
n-butyrate B.P. 120°.

140° n-Valeronitrile $CH_3 \cdot CH_2 \cdot CH_2 \cdot CH_2 \cdot CN$

D. 0·801 (18°). Slightly sol. in water. On boiling
with dil. acids or alkalies yields n-valeric acid B.P.
186° and NH_3. On boiling with alc. + H_2SO_4 yields
ethyl n-valerate B.P. 144°.

190° Benzonitrile $C_6H_5 \cdot CN$

D. 1·000 (25°). Insol. in water. Odour resembles
that of nitrobenzene. With conc. H_2SO_4 at 100°,
or on shaking with dil. NaOH + H_2O_2 in cold, yields
benzamide M.P. 128°. On boiling with 75% H_2SO_4
yields benzoic acid M.P. 121°. On boiling with
CH_3OH + conc. H_2SO_4 yields methyl benzoate B.P.

B.P.

198°. With conc. $HNO_3 + H_2SO_4$ yields *m*-nitro deriv. M.P. 117°.

204°   *o*-Tolunitrile $CH_3 \cdot C_6H_4 \cdot CN$ (1:2)
D. 1·006 (4°). Insol. in water. With conc. H_2SO_4 at 100°, or on shaking with dil. $NaOH + H_2O_2$ in cold, yields *o*-toluamide M.P. 142°. On boiling with 75% H_2SO_4 yields *o*-toluic acid M.P. 102°. On boiling with $CH_3OH + H_2SO_4$ yields methyl *o*-toluate B.P. 207°. With conc. $HNO_3 + H_2SO_4$ yields nitro deriv. M.P. 105°.

231°   Phenylacetonitrile (Benzyl Cyanide) $C_6H_5 \cdot CH_2 \cdot CN$
D. 1·017 (17°). Insol. in water. With conc. H_2SO_4 at 100° yields phenylacetamide M.P. 154°; on boiling with 75% H_2SO_4 yields phenylacetic acid M.P. 76°. On boiling with $CH_3OH + H_2SO_4$ yields methyl phenylacetate B.P. 220°. With conc. $HNO_3 + H_2SO_4$ yields *p*-nitro deriv. M.P. 116°.

SOLID

M.P.
29°   *p*-Tolunitrile $CH_3 \cdot C_6H_4 \cdot CN$ (1:4)
B.P. 217°. With conc. H_2SO_4 at 100°, or on shaking with dil. $NaOH + H_2O_2$ in cold, yields *p*-toluamide M.P. 158°. On boiling with 75% H_2SO_4 yields *p*-toluic acid M.P. 177°. On boiling with $CH_3OH + H_2SO_4$ yields methyl *p*-toluate M.P. 32°, B.P. 217°. With conc. $HNO_3 + H_2SO_4$ yields nitro deriv. M.P. 107°.

33°   *a*-Naphthonitrile $C_{10}H_7 \cdot CN$ (1)
B.P. 297°. On heating with 75% H_2SO_4 rapidly yields *a*-naphthoamide M.P. 202°, which on prolonged boiling is converted into *a*-naphthoic acid M.P. 160°.

66°   *β*-Naphthonitrile $C_{10}H_7 \cdot CN$ (2)
B.P. 305°. On heating with 75% H_2SO_4 rapidly yields *β*-naphthoamide M.P. 192°, which on prolonged boiling is converted into *β*-naphthoic acid M.P. 182°.

SUBSTITUTED NITRILES

LIQUID

B.P.
d.   Acetone Cyanohydrin $(CH_3)_2C(OH) \cdot CN$
B.P. 82°/23 mm. D. 0·932 (19°). Miscible with water, alc., and ether; insol. in light petroleum. With conc. HCl yields *a*-hydroxy*iso*butyric acid M.P. 78° and NH_4Cl. With KOH yields acetone

B.P. 56° and KCN. On evaporating aqueous soln. yields HCN and diacetone cyanohydrin M.P. 162°. With acetyl chloride yields acetyl deriv. B.P. 181°. On warming with NH_3 in alc. yields α-amino*iso*-butyronitrile B.P. 49°/12 mm. (hydrochloride M.P. 145°) which on hydrolysis yields α-amino*iso*butyric acid (*q.v.*).

183°d. Acetaldehyde Cyanohydrin $CH_3 \cdot CH(OH) \cdot CN$

B.P. 90°/17 mm. D. 0·984 (25°). Miscible with water, alc., and ether ; insol. in light petroleum and carbon disulphide. With conc. HCl yields lactic acid (*q.v.*) and NH_4Cl. With KOH yields acetaldehyde resin and KCN. With acetyl chloride at 0° yields acetyl deriv. B.P. 172°. With NH_3 in alc. yields unstable aminopropionitrile (hydrochloride M.P. 115°, picrate M.P. 141°d.) which on boiling with $Ba(OH)_2$ or with HCl yields *dl*-alanine (*q.v.*) and NH_3.

207° Ethyl Cyanoacetate $CN \cdot CH_2 \cdot COOC_2H_5$

D. 1·063 (20°). Insol. in water ; sol. in dil. NaOH and NH_4OH ; latter soln. on evaporation yields cyanoacetamide M.P. 118°. On boiling with alc. + H_2SO_4 yields ethyl malonate B.P. 198°. With C_2H_5ONa in abs. alc. yields Na deriv., which with benzyl chloride yields ethyl benzylcyanoacetate B.P. 176°/20 mm. ; this on hydrolysis yields benzylmalonic acid M.P. 117°d., which on heating yields hydrocinnamic acid M.P. 48°.

SOLID

21° Benzaldehyde Cyanohydrin $C_6H_5 \cdot CH(OH) \cdot CN$

Usually an oil ; D. 1·124. On heating to 170° decomposes into benzaldehyde B.P. 179° and HCN. Insol. in water ; sol. in alc. and ether. Forms red soln in conc. H_2SO_4. On warming with HCl yields *dl*-mandelic acid M.P. 118°. Acetyl deriv. B.P. 138°/11 mm. Benzoyl deriv. M.P. 62°. Carbanilate M.P. 105°.

69° Cyanoacetic Acid $CN \cdot CH_2 \cdot COOH$

Very sol. in water. On heating to 165° yields acetonitrile B.P. 81° and CO_2. On boiling with NaOH yields NH_3 and Na malonate (*q.v.*). On warming with conc. HCl yields NH_4Cl and malonic acid M.P. 133°, which on prolonged boiling breaks down into acetic acid B.P. 118° and CO_2. On boiling with alc. +

H_2SO_4 yields ethyl malonate B.P. 198°. On warming with benzaldehyde yields α-cyanocinnamic acid M.P. 180°.

*ISO*CYANATES

LIQUID

B.P.
166°   Phenyl *iso*Cyanate (Carbanil) $C_6H_5 \cdot N:C:O$
D. 1·092 (15°). Sharp odour. Insol. in water; on standing with water or with aniline yields carbanilide M.P. 238°. With alc. yields ethyl carbanilate M.P. 52°. With NH_3 yields phenylurea M.P. 147°. With phenol yields phenyl carbanilate M.P. 126°. On boiling with HCl yields aniline HCl (*q.v.*).

269°   α-Naphthyl *iso*Cyanate $C_{10}H_7 \cdot N:C:O$
D. 1·177 (16°). Insol. in water; on standing with water yields di-α-naphthylurea M.P. 314°. With alc. yields ethyl α-naphthylcarbamate M.P. 79°. With NH_3 yields α-naphthylurea M.P. 213°. With aniline yields phenyl-α-naphthylurea M.P. 222°. With phenol yields phenyl α-naphthylcarbamate M.P. 136°. On boiling with HCl yields α-naphthylamine HCl (*q.v.*).

HYDRAZINE DERIVATIVES

LIQUID

B.P.
227°   Methylphenylhydrazine $C_6H_5 \cdot N(CH_3) \cdot NH_2$
D. 1·023 (26°). Almost insol. in water. Reduces Fehling's soln. on warming, yielding N_2 and methyl-aniline B.P. 193°. On boiling with Zn + HCl yields methylaniline HCl and NH_4Cl. Soln. in dil. acids, on treatment with $NaNO_2$, yields methylphenylnitroso-amine (yellow) M.P. 12°, B.P. 121°/13 mm. Soln. in HCl gives green colour with formaldehyde. On adding acetic acid to cold soln. in dil. acetic acid yields acetyl deriv. M.P. 92°. Benzoyl deriv. M.P. 153°. Benzal deriv. M.P. 106°.

SOLID

M.P.
19°   Phenylhydrazine $C_6H_5 \cdot NH \cdot NH_2$
B.P. 243°. D. 1·097 (22°). Slightly sol. in water. Hydrochloride M.P. 240°. Reduces Fehling's soln. in cold, yielding benzene B.P. 80° and N_2. On warming soln in HCl with $CuSO_4$ yields chlorobenzene B.P. 132°.

With excess of iodine yields iodobenzene B.P. 188°.
On heating with acetamide, or on treating cold soln.
in dil. acetic acid with acetic anhydride, yields acetyl
deriv. M.P. 128°.   Benzoyl deriv. M.P. 168°.   Benzal
deriv. M.P. 156°.

34°   Diphenylhydrazine $(C_6H_5)_2N\cdot NH_2$
        Insol. in water ; readily sol. in alc.   Forms blue soln.
        in conc. H_2SO_4.   Hydrochloride M.P. 167°.   Reduces
        ammon. $AgNO_3$.   With Sn + HCl yields diphenyl-
        amine M.P. 54°.   Acetyl deriv. M.P. 184°.   Benzoyl
        deriv. M.P. 192°.   Benzal deriv. M.P. 122°.

65° p-Tolylhydrazine $CH_3\cdot C_6H_4\cdot NH\cdot NH_2$ (1:4)
        B.P. 240–244°d.   Reduces Fehling's soln. in cold,
        yielding toluene B.P. 110° and N_2.   With excess
        iodine yields p-iodotoluene M.P. 35°, B.P. 211°.
        Acetyl deriv. M.P. 121°.   Benzoyl deriv. M.P. 146°.
        Benzal deriv. M.P. 125°.

96°   Semicarbazide $NH_2\cdot CO\cdot NH\cdot NH_2$
        Very sol. in water and alc. ; insol. in ether, benzene,
        and $CHCl_3$.   Neutral to litmus.   Hydrochloride M.P.
        173°d.   Acid sulphate M.P. 144°.   Nitrate M.P. 123°.
        On boiling with conc. HCl yields NH_4Cl and hydrazine
        HCl.   Reduces Fehling's soln. and ammon. $AgNO_3$.
        With acetone forms *iso*propenyl deriv. M.P. 187°.
        Benzal deriv. M.P. 214°.

113°   Antipyrine   CH$_3$·N———N·C$_6$H$_5$

                       CH$_3$·C:CH·CO
        Readily sol. in cold water and alc. ; sparingly in
        ether.   Fairly strong base.   Unsaturated ;   with
        bromine in $CHCl_3$ forms a dibromide (ppted. by ether)
        M.P. about 150°, which with cold water yields bromo-
        antipyrine M.P. 117°.   On adding $NaNO_2$ to soln. in
        dil. HCl yields nitroso deriv. (green crysts.) M.P.
        200°d.   Gives orange colour with $FeCl_3$.   On boiling
        with KOH yields s-methylphenylhydrazine B.P. 230°.
        On nitration yields p-nitro deriv. M.P. 273°.

127°   1-Phenyl-3-methyl-5-pyrazolone   NH — N·C$_6$H$_5$

                               CH$_3$·C : CH·CO
        Insol. in cold water, ether, and light petroleum ; sol.
        in hot water, cold dil. acids or alkalies, alc., and
        benzene.   Gives red colour on boiling with acetone.
        On boiling with $FeCl_3$ in water gives purple ppte. of
        pyrazole blue.   Gives red colour with $FeCl_3$ in alc.

M.P.

Acetyl deriv. B.P. 200°/10 mm. Benzoyl deriv. M.P. 75°. Benzal deriv. M.P. 107°. With (2 mols.) bromine in hot acetic acid yields dibromo deriv. M.P. 80°. With N_2O_3 yields *iso*nitroso deriv. M.P. 157°.

128° Acetyl Phenylhydrazine $C_6H_5 \cdot NH \cdot NH \cdot CO \cdot CH_3$
Sol. in hot water. On boiling with conc. HCl yields phenylhydrazine HCl (*q.v.*) and acetic acid B.P. 118°. Reduces Fehling's soln. With (2 mols.) bromine in conc. HCl yields dibromo deriv. M.P. 146°.

131° Hydrazobenzene $C_6H_5 \cdot NH \cdot NH \cdot C_6H_5$
Insol. in water; sol. in alc. and ether. Slowly oxidised by air (rapidly in alk. alc. soln.) to orange azobenzene M.P. 68°. Weak base. Converted by hot conc. HCl to benzidine HCl (*q.v.*). Diacetyl deriv. M.P. 105°. Dibenzoyl deriv. M.P. 138°.

168° Benzoyl Phenylhydrazine $C_6H_5 \cdot NH \cdot NH \cdot CO \cdot C_6H_5$
Slightly sol. in hot water and ether; readily sol. in warm dil. KOH. On oxidation by HgO or N_2O_3 yields red benzoylazobenzene M.P. 80°. On boiling with conc. HCl yields phenylhydrazine HCl (*q.v.*) and benzoic acid M.P. 121°.

HYDRAZONES

SOLID

M.P.

42° Acetonephenylhydrazone $(CH_3)_2C:N \cdot NH \cdot C_6H_5$
B.P. 165°/91 mm. Slightly sol. in water; forms a hydrate M.P. 15°. With dry HCl in ether yields hydrochloride M.P. 142°. On boiling with conc. HCl yields acetone B.P. 56° and phenylhydrazine HCl (*q.v.*). On warming with hydroxylamine HCl yields acetoxime M.P. 59°, B.P. 135° and phenyl-hydrazine HCl. On heating with $ZnCl_2$ yields α-methylindole M.P. 59°, B.P. 268°.

93° Benzalazine $C_6H_5 \cdot CH:N \cdot N:CH \cdot C_6H_5$
Yellow. On heating alone yields stilbene M.P. 125°, B.P. 306° and N_2. With dry HCl in ether yields hydrochloride M.P. 150°. On boiling with conc. HCl yields benzaldehyde B.P. 179° and hydrazine HCl. On reduction with Zn + acetic acid yields dibenzylamine B.P. 315° and NH_3. With bromine in CCl_4 yields an unstable tetrabromide M.P. 134°. Forms an addition product with methyl sulphate, which with water yields benzaldehyde and methylhydrazine B.P. 87°.

M.P.

105° Acetophenonephenylhydrazone

$CH_3 \cdot C(C_6H_5):N \cdot NH \cdot C_6H_5$

Insol. in water ; not very sol. in cold alc., readily in
ether. On long boiling with conc. HCl yields acetophenone M.P. 20°, B.P. 202° and phenylhydrazine
HCl (q.v.). On warming with hydroxylamine HCl
yields acetophenoneoxime M.P. 59° and phenylhydrazine HCl.

137° Benzophenonephenylhydrazone $(C_6H_5)_2C:N \cdot NH \cdot C_6H_5$

Insol. in water ; slightly sol. in alc. On long boiling
with conc. HCl yields benzophenone M.P. 48° and
phenylhydrazine HCl (q.v.). Unchanged on warming
with hydroxylamine HCl.

158° Benzaldehydephenylhydrazone $C_6H_5 \cdot CH:N \cdot NH \cdot C_6H_5$

Yellow. On long boiling with conc. HCl yields benzaldehyde B.P. 179° and phenylhydrazine HCl (q.v.).
On boiling with acetic anhydride + trace conc.
H_2SO_4 yields labile modification M.P. 136°. Oxidised
in alk. alc. soln. to benzilosazone M.P. 225°. With
amyl nitrite yields dibenzaldiphenylhydrotetrazone
M.P. 180° (forms blue soln. in conc. H_2SO_4).

ALIPHATIC NITRO-HYDROCARBONS

LIQUID

B.P.

101° Nitromethane $CH_3 \cdot NO_2$

D. 1·138 (20°). Sol. in 9 vols of cold water ; soln.
reacts acid to litmus. Miscible with organic liquids.
On heating with fuming H_2SO_4 yields CO and hydroxylamine sulphate. Reduced by $SnCl_2$ or $Na_2S_2O_4$ to
methylamine (q.v.). With C_2H_5ONa in alc. yields
ppte. of Na deriv. (expl. with trace of water). With
chloral hydrate + dil. K_2CO_3 yields trichloronitro-
isopropyl alc. M.P. 42°.

114° Nitroethane $C_2H_5 \cdot NO_2$

D. 1·056 (15°). Sol. in 24 vols of cold water, readily
in dil. NaOH. On adding excess of HCl to alk. soln.
yields acetaldehyde B.P. 21°. Reduced by Fe +
acetic acid to ethylamine (q.v.). On standing with
benzaldehyde + trace of ethylamine yields β-nitro-
α-phenylpropylene M.P. 64°. Soln. in dil. NaOH with
diazobenzene yields benzeneazonitroethane M.P. 141°.

126° Tetranitromethane $C(NO_2)_4$

M.P. 13°. D. 1·650 (13°). Gives orange colour in
alc. with pyridine ; light yellow with unsaturated

B.P.

hydrocarbons. With C_2H_5ONa in alc. yields tri-
nitromethane M.P. 15° (forms yellow soln. in water,
decolorised by strong acids) and ethyl nitrate B.P. 87°.

226°d. Phenylnitromethane $C_6H_5 \cdot CH_2 \cdot NO_2$
B.P. 118°/16 mm. D. 1·160 (20°). Yellow. Insol.
in water ; sol. in dil. NaOH. With alc. NaOH yields
Na deriv., which with excess HCl yields phenyl-
*iso*nitromethane M.P. 84°. Reduced by Sn + HCl to
benzylamine B.P. 185°. With benzaldehyde + trace
methylamine in alc. yields α-nitrostilbene M.P. 75°.

AROMATIC NITRO-HYDROCARBONS

LIQUID

B.P.
210°   Nitrobenzene $C_6H_5 \cdot NO_2$
M.P. 5°. D. 1·197 (25°). Very pale yellow. Odour
like bitter almond. Almost insol. in water ; miscible
with organic liquids. Reduced by Sn (or $SnCl_2$) +
HCl to aniline B.P. 183°. On boiling with dil. Na
arsenite yields azoxybenzene M.P. 36°. On warming with fuming HNO_3 + H_2SO_4 yields *m*-dinitro-
benzene M.P. 90°. On warming with bromine +
$FeBr_3$ (or $FeCl_3$) yields *m*-bromo deriv. M.P. 54°.

220°   *o*-Nitrotoluene $CH_3 \cdot C_6H_4 \cdot NO_2$ (1:2)
D. 1·162 (20°). Very pale yellow. Odour like nitrobenzene. Almost insol. in water ; miscible with
organic liquids. Reduced by Sn + HCl to *o*-toluidine
B.P. 197°. Not attacked by boiling $K_2Cr_2O_7$ + dil.
H_2SO_4 ; oxidised by boiling dil. $KMnO_4$ to *o*-nitro-
benzoic acid M.P. 147°. With (1 mol.) conc. HNO_3
+ H_2SO_4 yields 2:4-dinitrotoluene M.P. 70°; on heating with excess fuming HNO_3 + H_2SO_4 yields 2:4:6-
trinitrotoluene M.P. 82°.

230°   *m*-Nitrotoluene $CH_3 \cdot C_6H_4 \cdot NO_2$ (1:3)
M.P. 16°. D. 1·160 (17°). Very pale yellow. Odour
like nitrobenzene. Almost insol. in water ; miscible
with organic liquids. Reduced by Sn (or $SnCl_2$) +
HCl to *m*-toluidine B.P. 199°. Readily oxidised by
boiling $K_2Cr_2O_7$ + dil. H_2SO_4 or by $KMnO_4$ soln. to
m-nitrobenzoic acid M.P. 140°. On boiling with
fuming HNO_3 + H_2SO_4 yields 2:4:5-trinitrotoluene
M.P. 104° (insol. in CS_2) and β-trinitrotoluene
M.P. 112° (sol. in CS_2).

244°   4-Nitro-*m*-xylene $(CH_3)_2C_6H_3 \cdot NO_2$ (1:3:4)
D. 1·126 (17°). Reduced by Sn + HCl to 4-*m*-
xylidine B.P. 212°. On boiling with $KMnO_4$ soln.

yields 4-nitro*iso*phthalic acid M.P. 258°. With fuming HNO_3 in cold yields 4:6-dinitro-*m*-xylene M.P. 93°; with warm conc. $HNO_3 + H_2SO_4$ yields trinitro-*m*-xylene M.P. 125°.

264°   2-Nitrocymene $(CH_3)_2CH\cdot C_6H_3(CH_3)\cdot NO_2$ (4:1:2)
D. 1·085 (15°). Reduced by Sn + HCl to 2-amino-cymene B.P. 241° (acetyl deriv. M.P. 115°; benzoyl deriv. M.P. 102°). On oxidation ,by alk. $KMnO_4$ soln yields 2-nitro-4-hydroxy*iso*propylbenzoic acid M.P. 168°. On warming with conc. $HNO_3 + H_2SO_4$ yields 2:6-dinitrocymene M.P. 54°.

SOLID

41°   Nitromesitylene $(CH_3)_3C_6H_2\cdot NO_2$ (1:3:5:2)
B.P. 255°. Reduced by Sn + HCl to mesidine B.P. 229° (acetyl deriv. M.P. 216°; benzoyl deriv. M.P. 204°). With CrO_3 in acetic acid at 60–70° yields *p*-nitromesitylenic acid M.P. 219–225°. On warming with fuming HNO_3 yields dinitromesitylene M.P. 86°; with cold conc. $HNO_3 + H_2SO_4$ yields trinitro-mesitylene M.P. 235°.

54°   *p*-Nitrotoluene $CH_3\cdot C_6H_4\cdot NO_2$ (1:4)
B.P. 238°. Very pale yellow. Odour like nitro-benzene. Reduced by Sn + HCl to *p*-toluidine M.P. 45°, B.P. 200°. Readily oxidised by $K_2Cr_2O_7$ in dil. H_2SO_4 or by $KMnO_4$ soln to *p*-nitrobenzoic acid M.P. 241°. On warming with (1 mol.) conc. $HNO_3 + H_2SO_4$ yields 2:4-dinitrotoluene M.P. 70°; on heating with excess fuming $HNO_3 + H_2SO_4$ yields 2:4:6-trinitrotoluene M.P. 82°.

61°   α-Nitronaphthalene $C_{10}H_7\cdot NO_2$ (1)
B.P. 304°. Readily sol. in organic liquids; forms dark red soln in conc. H_2SO_4. Reduced by Sn + HCl to α-naphthylamine M.P. 50°. Oxidised by CrO_3 in acetic acid to 3-nitrophthalic acid M.P. 218°. With (1 mol.) conc. $HNO_3 + H_2SO_4$ in cold yields 1:5-dinitronaphthalene M.P. 214° (sol. in 125 parts of cold pyridine) and 1:8-dinitronaphthalene M.P. 170° (sol. in 10 parts of cold pyridine). On warming with excess conc. $HNO_3 + H_2SO_4$ yields 1:3:8-trinitro-naphthalene M.P. 218° (sparingly sol. in organic liquids).

70°   2:4-Dinitrotoluene $CH_3\cdot C_6H_3(NO_2)_2$ (1:2:4)
Sparingly sol. in cold alc. or ether, readily in benzene

M P.

Reduced by (3 mols.) $SnCl_2$ + HCl in alc. to 2-amino-4-nitrotoluene M.P. 107°; with excess Sn + HCl yields *m*-toluylenediamine M.P. 99°. Oxidised by CrO_3 in conc. H_2SO_4 or by $KMnO_4$ soln. to 2:4-dinitrobenzoic acid M.P. 179°. On warming with fuming HNO_3 + H_2SO_4 yields 2:4:6-trinitrotoluene M.P. 82°. With acetone + KOH gives blue colour, changed to violet by acetic acid. With benzaldehyde + a little piperidine (or diethylamine) yields dinitrostilbene M.P. 139°. Forms addition compound with naphthalene (in benzene) M.P. 60°.

82°   2:4:6-Trinitrotoluene $CH_3 \cdot C_6H_2(NO_2)_3$ (1:2:4:6)
Very pale yellow. Slightly sol. in hot water; readily sol. in most organic liquids, sparingly in CS_2. Reduced by Sn + HCl to unstable triaminotoluene. Oxidised by CrO_3 in conc. H_2SO_4 to trinitrobenzoic acid M.P. 220°. With benzaldehyde + pyridine yields trinitrostilbene M.P. 158°. Forms addition compound with naphthalene (in alc.) M.P. 97°.

90°   *m*-Dinitrobenzene $C_6H_4(NO_2)_2$ (1:3)
B.P. 302°. Very pale yellow. Volatile with steam. Slightly sol. in hot water; sol. in 30 parts of cold alc., in 15 parts of cold CH_3OH, in 2·5 parts of cold benzene, in 3 parts of cold $CHCl_3$. Reduced by NH_4SH in alc. to *m*-nitroaniline M.P. 114°; by Sn + HCl to *m*-phenylenediamine M.P. 63°. On boiling with alk. $K_3Fe(CN)_6$ yields 2:4-dinitrophenol M.P. 114°. On adding trace of $SnCl_2$ (or dextrose) to soln. in boiling very dil. NaOH gives violet colour. Forms addition compound with naphthalene (in benzene) M.P. 52°.

93°   4:6-Dinitro-*m*-xylene $(CH_3)_2C_6H_2(NO_2)_2$ (1:3:4:6)
Sparingly sol. in cold alc. Reduced by NH_4SH in alc. to nitroxylidine M.P. 123°; by Sn + HCl to diaminoxylene M.P. 104°. On warming with conc. HNO_3 + H_2SO_4 yields trinitroxylene M.P. 125°.

118°   *o*-Dinitrobenzene $C_6H_4(NO_2)_2$ (1:2)
B.P. 319°. Volatile with steam. Slightly sol. in hot water; sol. in 50 parts of cold alc., in 30 parts of cold CH_3OH, in 18 parts of cold benzene, in 4 parts of cold $CHCl_3$. With NH_4SH in alc., or on boiling with NH_3 in alc., yields *o*-nitroaniline M.P. 71°. Reduced by Sn + HCl to *o*-phenylenediamine M.P. 102°. On boiling with dil. NaOH yields *o*-nitrophenol M.P. 44°. With aniline at 100° yields *o*-nitrodiphenylamine M.P. 75°.

M.P.

122° 1:3:5-Trinitrobenzene $C_6H_3(NO_2)_3$ (1:3:5)
Very pale yellow. Slightly sol. in hot water ; sol. in 55 parts of cold alc., in 20 parts of cold CH_3OH, in 70 parts cold ether, in 16 parts of cold benzene or $CHCl_3$. With dil. NaOH gives red colour, discharged by acid. With Na_2CO_3 soln. $+ K_3Fe(CN)_6$ yields picric acid M.P. 122°. Reduced by Sn $+$ HCl to unstable triaminobenzene (triacetyl deriv. M.P. 208°). Forms addition compound with naphthalene (in alc.) M.P. 152°.

170° 1:8-Dinitronaphthalene $C_{10}H_6(NO_2)_2$ (1:8)
Sol. at 19° in 140 parts of benzene, in 90 parts of $CHCl_3$, in 10 parts of pyridine. On boiling for 5 mins. with fuming $HNO_3 + H_2SO_4$ yields 1:3:8-trinitronaphthalene M.P. 218°. Reduced by Sn $+$ HCl in alc. to 1:8-diaminonaphthalene M.P. 66°.

172° p-Dinitrobenzene $C_6H_4(NO_2)_2$ (1:4)
B.P. 299°. Volatile with steam. Slightly sol. in hot water ; sol. in 250 parts of cold alc., in 140 parts of cold CH_3OH, in 40 parts of cold benzene, in 50 parts of cold $CHCl_3$. On boiling with 5% NaOH yields p-nitrophenol M.P. 114°. Reduced by Sn $+$ HCl to p-phenylenediamine M.P. 140° ; by NH_4SH in alc. to p-nitroaniline M.P. 147°. Forms addition compound with naphthalene (in alc.) M.P. 118°.

214° 1:5-Dinitronaphthalene $C_{10}H_6(NO_2)_2$ (1:5)
Sparingly sol. in cold in most organic liquids ; sol. in 125 parts of cold, and in 10 parts of boiling, pyridine. On boiling for 5 mins. with (5 parts) fuming $HNO_3 +$ (5 parts) conc. H_2SO_4 yields 1:4:5-trinitronaphthalene M.P. 154°. Reduced by Sn $+$ HCl in alc. to 1:5-diaminonaphthalene M.P. 189° (diacetyl deriv. M.P. above 360°). On passing (3 mols.) H_2S into cold soln in alc. NH_3 yields 1-amino-5-nitronaphthalene M.P. 118°.

NITROETHERS

LIQUID

B.P.

265° o-Nitroanisole $CH_3O \cdot C_6H_4 \cdot NO_2$ (1:2)
M.P. 9°. D. 1·254 (20°). Insol. in water, miscible with organic liquids. On reduction by Sn $+$ HCl yields o-anisidine B.P. 218°. With conc. $HNO_3 + H_2SO_4$ at 0° yields 2:4-dinitroanisole M.P. 88° ; on warming, trinitroanisole M.P. 68° is formed. With

O.A. R

B.P.

chlorine in acetic acid yields 4-chloro deriv. M.P. 97°. On boiling with 48% HBr yields o-nitrophenol M.P. 44° and methyl bromide B.P. 4°. On long boiling with conc. NaOH yields o-nitrophenol and methyl alc. B.P. 65°.

268°   o-Nitrophenetole $C_2H_5O \cdot C_6H_4 \cdot NO_2$ (1:2)

Insol. in water, miscible with organic liquids. With Sn + HCl yields o-phenetidine B.P. 229°. With cold conc. $HNO_3 + H_2SO_4$ yields 2:4-dinitrophenetole M.P. 86°; on warming, trinitrophenetole M.P. 78° is formed. On boiling with 48% HBr yields o-nitrophenol M.P. 44° and ethyl bromide B.P. 38°. On long boiling with conc. NaOH yields o-nitrophenol and ethyl alc. B.P. 78°.

SOLID

M.P.

38°   m-Nitroanisole $CH_3O \cdot C_6H_4 \cdot NO_2$ (1:3)

B.P. 258°. Almost insol. in water, readily sol. in organic liquids. With Sn + HCl yields m-anisidine B.P. 251° (acetyl deriv. M.P. 80°). On boiling with 48% HBr yields m-nitrophenol M.P. 97° and methyl bromide B.P. 4°. Unchanged on boiling with 10% NaOH.

54°   p-Nitroanisole $CH_3O \cdot C_6H_4 \cdot NO_2$ (1:4)

B.P. 274°. Volatile with steam. Almost insol. in water, readily sol. in alc. and ether, sparingly in cold light petroleum. With Sn + HCl yields p-anisidine M.P. 57°. With fuming HNO_3 at 0° yields 2:4-dinitroanisole M.P. 88°; on warming with conc. $HNO_3 + H_2SO_4$ yields trinitroanisole M.P. 68°. On boiling with 48% HBr yields p-nitrophenol M.P. 114° and methyl bromide B.P. 4°. On long boiling with conc. NaOH yields p-nitrophenol and methyl alc. B.P. 65°.

59°   p-Nitrophenetole $C_2H_5O \cdot C_6H_4 \cdot NO_2$ (1:4)

B.P. 283°. Insol. in water; sparingly sol. in cold alc., readily in ether. With Sn + HCl yields p-phenetidine B.P. 254°. With conc. $HNO_3 + H_2SO_4$ in cold yields 2:4-dinitrophenetole M.P. 86°; on warming, trinitrophenetole M.P. 78° is formed. With $KClO_3$ + HCl yields 2-chloro deriv. M.P. 78°. On boiling with 40% HBr yields p-nitrophenol M.P. 114° and ethyl bromide B.P. 38°. On long boiling with conc. NaOH yields p-nitrophenol and ethyl alc. B.P. 78°.

M.P.
68°   2:4:6-Trinitroanisole $CH_3O·C_6H_2(NO_2)_3$ (1:2:4:6)
Insol. in water, sparingly sol. in cold alc., sol. in benzene and acetic acid. On boiling with dil. NaOH yields picric acid M.P. 122° and methyl alc. B.P. 65°. With C_2H_5ONa in abs. alc. yields an addition compound (red needles) which with acid yields a mixture of trinitroanisole and trinitrophenetole M.P. 78°. With NH₃ in alc. yields picramide M.P. 188°. On warming with aniline yields trinitrodiphenylamine M.P. 177°.

78°   2:4:6-Trinitrophenetole $C_2H_5O·C_6H_2(NO_2)_3$ (1:2:4:6)
Insol. in water, readily sol. in ether and benzene. On boiling with dil. NaOH yields picric acid M.P. 122° and ethyl alc. B.P. 78°. With NH₃ in alc. yields picramide M.P. 188°. On warming with aniline yields trinitrodiphenylamine M.P. 177°.

88°   2:4-Dinitroanisole $CH_3O·C_6H_3(NO_2)_2$ (1:2:4)
Insol. in water, readily sol. in alc. and ether. On boiling with conc. NaOH yields 2:4-dinitrophenol M.P. 114° and methyl alc. B.P. 65°. On warming with conc. $HNO_3 + H_2SO_4$ yields trinitroanisole M.P. 68°. On heating with aniline yields dinitrodiphenylamine M.P. 156°.

NITROALCOHOLS

SOLID

M.P.
27°   *m*-Nitrobenzyl Alcohol $NO_2·C_6H_4·CH_2OH$ (1:3)
On heating to 250° yields di-*m*-nitrobenzyl ether M.P. 114°. With Zn dust + dil. $CaCl_2$ yields *m*-aminobenzyl alc. M.P. 97°. With acid $KMnO_4$ yields *m*-nitrobenzaldehyde M.P. 58° and *m*-nitrobenzoic acid M.P. 140°.

74°   *o*-Nitrobenzyl Alcohol $NO_2·C_6H_4·CH_2OH$ (1:2)
B.P. 270°d. On heating at 230° slowly decomposes, yielding hydroxyindazylbenzoic lactone M.P. 295°. Sparingly sol. in water, readily in alc. and ether. With Zn dust + dil. $CaCl_2$ yields *o*-aminobenzyl alc. M.P. 82°. Oxidised by conc. HNO_3 to *o*-nitrobenzaldehyde M.P. 46°; with $K_2Cr_2O_7$ + dil. H_2SO_4 yields *o*-nitrobenzoic acid M.P. 144°. Acetate M.P. 35°. Benzoate M.P. 94°.

93°   *p*-Nitrobenzyl Alcohol $NO_2·C_6H_4·CH_2OH$ (1:4)
B.P. 185°/12 mm. Decomposes on heating to 250°. Readily sol. in hot water, sparingly in cold. With.

Zn dust + dil. CaCl$_2$ yields p-aminobenzyl alc. M.P. 65°. On oxidation yields p-nitrobenzoic acid M.P. 241°. Acetate M.P. 78°. Benzoate M.P. 89°.

NITROPHENOLS

SOLID

M.P.
44° o-Nitrophenol   NO$_2$·C$_6$H$_4$·OH (1:2)

B.P. 215°. Bright yellow. Volatile with steam. Characteristic odour. Readily sol. in hot water and in most organic liquids. Sol. in dil. NaOH with orange colour ; red Na salt is readily sol. in cold 5% NaOH. With Zn dust + dil. CaCl$_2$ yields o-amino-phenol M.P. 174°. On gently warming with 60% HNO$_3$ yields 2:4-dinitrophenol M.P. 114° ; with conc. HNO$_3$ + H$_2$SO$_4$ yields picric acid M.P. 122°. On adding (2 mols.) bromine to soln. in dil. NaOH yields 4:6-dibromo deriv. M.P. 117°. Methyl ether M.P. 9°, B.P. 265°. p-Nitrobenzyl ether M.P. 130°. Acetate M.P. 40°, B.P. 253°d. Benzoate M.P. 142°. Benzenesulphonate M.P. 75°.

97° m-Nitrophenol   NO$_2$·C$_6$H$_4$·OH (1:3)

B.P. 186°/12 mm. Pale yellow. Odourless and not volatile with steam. Readily sol. in hot water and most organic liquids. Sol. in dil. NaOH with orange-yellow colour. With Zn dust + dil. CaCl$_2$ yields m-aminophenol M.P. 122°. With conc. HNO$_3$ + H$_2$SO$_4$, at first in cold and finally at 50°, yields tetranitrophenol M.P. 140°. On warming with (2 mols.) bromine yields dibromo deriv. M.P. 91°. Methyl ether M.P. 38°, B.P. 258°. Benzoate M.P. 95°. Benzenesulphonate M.P. 72°. Carbanilate M.P. 129°.

114° p-Nitrophenol   NO$_2$·C$_6$H$_4$·OH (1:4)

Colourless. Odourless and not volatile with steam. Readily sol. in hot water (melts), alc. and ether. Sol. in dil. NaOH with bright yellow colour ; yellow Na salt is sparingly sol. in cold 5% NaOH. With Zn dust + dil. CaCl$_2$ yields p-aminophenol M.P. 184°d. On gently warming with 60% HNO$_3$ yields 2:4-dinitrophenol M.P. 114° ; with conc. HNO$_3$ + H$_2$SO$_4$ yields picric acid M.P. 122°. With (2 mols.) bromine in acetic acid at 100° yields 2:6-dibromo deriv. M.P. 142°. Methyl ether M.P. 54°. p-Nitrobenzyl ether M.P. 187°. Acetate M.P. 81°. Benzoate M.P. 142°. Benzenesulphonate M.P. 82°.

M.P.
114°   2:4-Dinitrophenol $(NO_2)_2C_6H_3 \cdot OH$ (2:4:1)
       Colourless. Sol. in hot water, alc. and ether. Aque-
       ous soln. is yellow ; colour is discharged by HCl.
       Sol. in dil. NaOH with bright yellow colour ; yellow
       Na salt is sparingly sol. in cold 5% NaOH.   With
       Sn + HCl yields 2:4-diaminophenol M.P. 79°d. ; with
       NH_4SH yields 4-nitro-2-aminophenol M.P. 142°
       (forms violet soln. in dil. NaOH).   On heating with
       urea or acetamide at 200° in a current of NH_3 yields
       2:4-dinitroaniline M.P. 187°.   On warming with conc.
       HNO_3 + H_2SO_4 yields picric acid M.P. 122°.   With
       bromine water yields 6-bromo deriv. M.P. 118°.
       Methyl ether M.P. 88°.   p-Nitrobenzyl ether M.P.
       248°. Acetate M.P. 72°. Benzoate M.P. 132°.
       Benzenesulphonate M.P. 118°. NH_4 salt M.P. 220°.

122°   Picric Acid $(NO_2)_3C_6H_2 \cdot OH$ (2:4:6:1)
       Light yellow. Sol. in 90 parts of water at 20°, in
       14 parts at 100°.   Sol. in alc. and benzene, very readily
       in acetone, sparingly in ether.   Forms yellow soln
       in water (colour discharged by HCl) and in alc. ;
       colourless in acetic acid, $CHCl_3$ and ligroin.   Reduced
       by NH_4SH in alc., or by Zn dust in NH_4OH, to 4:6-
       dinitro-2-aminophenol (picramic acid) M.P. 168°.
       With PCl_5 yields picryl chloride M.P. 83°.   With
       cold alk. NaOCl soln yields chloropicrin B.P. 112°.
       Forms addition compounds with benzene (M.P. 84°)
       and naphthalene (M.P. 149°).

138°   2:4-Dinitro-α-naphthol $(NO_2)_2C_{10}H_5 \cdot OH$ (2:4:1)
       Yellow. Insol. in water ; sparingly sol. in alc.,
       ether, and benzene. With Sn + HCl yields 2:4-
       diamino-α-naphthol (triacetyl deriv. M.P. 280°d.).
       With conc. H_2SO_4 + fuming HNO_3 in cold yields
       2:4:5-trinitro-α-naphthol M.P. 189° (forms sparingly
       sol. K salt) and 2:4:7-trinitro-α-naphthol M.P. 145°
       (forms sparingly sol. Na salt).

NITROALDEHYDES

SOLID

M.P.
44°   o-Nitrobenzaldehyde $NO_2 \cdot C_6H_4 \cdot CHO$ (1:2)
      B.P. 153°/23 mm. Yellow. Volatile with steam.
      Slightly sol. in water, readily in most organic liquids.
      Sol. (with gradual decomposition) in dil. NaOH, from
      which it is ppted by acids. With conc. $NaHSO_3$

M.P.

yields a cryst. addition compound, readily sol. in water. With $KMnO_4$ soln yields o-nitrobenzoic acid M.P. 144°. With $SnCl_2$ + HCl yields anthranil B.P. 210–215°d. (99°/13 mm). On exposure in benzene soln. to sunlight is converted into o-nitrosobenzoic acid M.P. 213°d. On boiling with acetic anhydride + Na acetate yields o-nitrocinnamic acid M.P. 240°. With dil. acetone + trace NaOH yields blue ppte of indigotin. Oxime M.P. 102°. Phenylhydrazone M.P. 156°. p-Nitrophenylhydrazone M.P. 263°. 2:4-Dinitrophenylhydrazone M.P. 192°. Semicarbazone M.P. 256°. With hydrazine sulphate in dil. alc. yields azine M.P. 205°. Anil. M.P. 69°.

58°   **m-Nitrobenzaldehyde $NO_2 \cdot C_6H_4 \cdot CHO$ (1:3)**

B.P. 164°/23 mm. Pale yellow. Slightly sol. in water, readily in organic liquids. Sol. in dil. NaOH with gradual decomposition ; is ppted. from this soln by acids. With $NaHSO_3$ forms an addition compound sol. in water. With $KMnO_4$ soln. yields m-nitrobenzoic acid M.P. 140°. With Sn + acetic acid yields a yellow condensation product of m-aminobenzaldehyde, which with acetic anhydride yields m-acetaminobenzaldehyde M.P. 84°. On heating with acetic anhydride + Na acetate yields m-nitrocinnamic acid M.P. 196°. On boiling with acetic anhydride alone yields diacetate M.P. 72°. Oxime M.P. 120°. Phenylhydrazone M.P. 120°. p-Nitrophenylhydrazone M.P. 247°. 2:4-Dinitrophenylhydrazone M.P. 268°d. Semicarbazone M.P. 246°. With hydrazine sulphate yields azine M.P. 195°. Anil M.P. 61°. With benzene + conc. H_2SO_4 in cold yields m-nitrotriphenylmethane M.P. 90°.

106°   **p-Nitrobenzaldehyde $NO_2 \cdot C_6H_4 \cdot CHO$ (1:4)**

Slightly sol. in water and light petroleum, sparingly in ether, readily in alc. and benzene. Sol. in dil. NaOH with gradual decomposition ; is ppted. from this soln. by acids. Resists oxidation by dil. HNO_3 ; oxidised by $K_2Cr_2O_7$ + dil. H_2SO_4 to p-nitrobenzoic acid M.P. 241°. Forms a cryst. compound (very sol. in water) with $NaHSO_3$; on heating with $NaHSO_3$ soln. yields p-aminobenzaldehyde M.P. 70°. With Sn + HCl yields a mixture. On boiling with acetic anhydride + Na acetate yields p-nitrocinnamic acid M.P. 285° ; with acetic anhydride alone yields diacetate M.P. 126°. Oxime M.P. 129°.

Phenylhydrazone M.P. 159°. *p*-Nitrophenylhydra-
zone M.P. 249°. Semicarbazone M.P. 221°. With
hydrazine sulphate soln. yields azine M.P. 304°.
Anil M.P. 93°.

NITROCARBOXYLIC ACIDS

SOLID

M.P.

125°   3-Nitrosalicylic $NO_2 \cdot C_6H_3(OH) \cdot COOH + H_2O$ (3:2:1)
Anhydrous acid has M.P. 144°. Yellow. Sparingly
sol. in cold water, readily in organic liquids. Gives
red colour with $FeCl_3$. On heating with lime yields
o-nitrophenol M.P. 44°. With Sn + acetic acid yields
3-aminosalicylic acid M.P. 235°d. (hydrochloride M.P.
250°). Ethyl ester M.P. 118°. With PCl_5 yields
chloride M.P. 60°. Amide M.P. 145°. Ba salt is
almost insol. in water.

140°   *m*-Nitrobenzoic $NO_2 \cdot C_6H_4 \cdot COOH$ (1:3)
Colourless. Sol. in boiling water (melts), sparingly in
cold. On heating with soda-lime yields n trobenzene
B.P. 210°. With Sn + HCl yields *m*-aminobenzoic
acid M.P. 174°. Methyl ester M.P. 78°. Ethyl ester
M.P. 47°. *p*-Nitrobenzyl ester M.P. 141°. Chloride
M.P. 30°, B.P. 154°/18 mm. Amide M.P. 142°.
Anilide M.P. 153°. Ba salt is sparingly sol. in cold
water.

144°   *o*-Nitrobenzoic $NO_2 \cdot C_6H_4 \cdot COOH$ (1:2)
Colourless. Sol. in boiling water. On heating with
soda-lime yields nitrobenzene B.P. 210°. With Sn +
HCl yields anthranilic acid M.P. 144°. Methyl ester
B.P. 275° (169°/19 mm.). Ethyl ester M.P. 30°.
Chloride occasionally explodes on distillation under
reduced pressure. Amide M.P. 174°. Anilide M.P.
155°. Ba salt is very sol. in cold water.

144°   3-Nitrosalicylic (Anhydrous)   See Hydrated Acid M.P.
125°.

173°   3:5-Dinitrosalicylic $(NO_2)_2C_6H_2(OH) \cdot COOH$ (3:5:2:1)
Colourless. Readily sol. in hot water (yellow soln.),
alc. and ether, sparingly in HCl. Gives red colour
with $FeCl_3$. Soln. in dil. NaOH gives orange-red
colour with dextrose, yielding by partial reduction
3-amino-5-nitrosalicylic acid M.P. 220°. Methyl ester
M.P. 127°. Ethyl ester M.P. 99°. With PCl_5 yields
chloride M.P. 69°.

M.P.

179°   2:4-Dinitrobenzoic $(NO_2)_2C_6H_3\cdot COOH$ (2:4:1)
Colourless. Sol. in hot water. With Sn + HCl
yields m-phenylenediamine M.P. 63°. Methyl ester
M.P. 70°. Ethyl ester M.P. 41°. p-Nitrobenzyl ester
M.P. 142°. Chloride M.P. 41°. Amide M.P. 203°.

199°   m-Nitrocinnamic $NO_2\cdot C_6H_4\cdot CH{:}CH\cdot COOH$ (1:3)
Colourless. Unsaturated. On oxidation by $KMnO_4$
yields m-nitrobenzoic acid M.P. 140°. With $SnCl_2$ +
HCl yields m-aminocinnamic acid M.P. 180°. Methyl
ester M.P. 123°. Ethyl ester M.P. 78°. p-Nitrobenzyl
ester M.P. 174°.

202°   3:5-Dinitrobenzoic $(NO_2)_2C_6H_3\cdot COOH$ (3:5:1)
Colourless. Sol. in hot water. With Sn + HCl yields
3:5-diaminobenzoic acid M.P. 236°. Methyl ester M.P.
107°. Ethyl ester M.P. 92°. Chloride M.P. 74°.
Amide M.P. 183°. Anilide M.P. 234°.

218°   3-Nitrophthalic $NO_2\cdot C_6H_3(COOH)_2$ (3:1:2)
Colourless. Sol. in hot water, readily in alc. and
ether ; insol. in $CHCl_3$. On heating above M.P. yields
anhydride M.P. 163°. Methyl ester M.P. 69°. Ethyl
ester M.P. 45°. p-Nitrobenzyl ester M.P. 189°.
Imide M.P. 217°. Anil M.P. 136°. p-Tolil M.P. 149°.

220°d.   2:4:6-Trinitrobenzoic $(NO_2)_3C_6H_2\cdot COOH$ (2:4:6:1)
Very pale yellow. Sol. in hot water and in most
organic liquids. On boiling with water, or on melting,
yields CO_2 and trinitrobenzene M.P. 122°. With dil.
NaOH gives red colour, discharged by acids. Methyl
ester M.P. 157°. Ethyl ester M.P. 155°. Chloride
M.P. 158°. Amide M.P. 264°d.

230°   5-Nitrosalicylic $NO_2\cdot C_6H_3(OH)\cdot COOH$ (5:2:1)
Colourless. Almost insol. in cold water ; sol. in hot
water, readily in alc. Gives red colour with $FeCl_3$.
On heating with lime yields p-nitrophenol M.P. 114°.
On boiling with conc. HNO_3 yields picric acid M.P.
122°. With Sn + HCl yields 5-aminosalicylic acid
M.P. 283°. Methyl ester M.P. 117°. Ethyl ester M.P.
118°. Methyl ether M.P. 148°. Amide M.P. 225°.
Anilide M.P. 224°. Ba salt is readily sol. in water.

237°   o-Nitrocinnamic $NO_2\cdot C_6H_4\cdot CH{:}CH\cdot COOH$ (1:2)
Colourless. Almost insol. in cold water. Unsatu-
rated ; with bromine slowly yields dibromide M.P.
180°d. With $KMnO_4$ soln. yields o-nitrobenzaldehyde
M.P. 44° and o-nitrobenzoic acid M.P. 144°. With Sn +
HCl in alc. yields o-aminocinnamic acid M.P. 158°d.

M.P.

Methyl ester M.P. 72°. Ethyl ester M.P. 42°. *p*-Nitrobenzyl ester M.P. 132°. Chloride M.P. 64°. Amide M.P. 185°.

241° *p*-Nitrobenzoic NO₂·C₆H₄·COOH (1:4)

Colourless. Sparingly sol. in cold water and alc., sol. in ether, almost insol. in benzene. On heating with. soda-lime yields nitrobenzene B.P. 210°. With Sn + HCl yields *p*-aminobenzoic acid M.P. 186°. Methyl ester M.P. 96°. Ethyl ester M.P. 57°. *p*-Nitrobenzyl ester M.P. 168°. Phenacyl ester M.P. 128°. Chloride M.P. 75°. Amide M.P. 201°. Anilide M.P. 204°.

285° *p*-Nitrocinnamic NO₂·C₆H₄·CH:CH·COOH (1:4)

Colourless. Almost insol. in cold water, alc. and ether. Unsaturated ; with bromine slowly forms dibromide M.P. 217°. With conc. HNO₃ + H₂SO₄ yields *p*-nitrobenzaldehyde M.P. 106° ; with alk. KMnO₄ yields *p*-nitrobenzoic acid M.P. 241°. With Sn + HCl in alc. yields *p*-aminocinnamic acid M.P. 175°d. (acetyl deriv. M.P. 259°). Methyl ester M.P. 161°. Ethyl ester M.P. 138°. *p*-Nitrobenzyl ester M.P. 168°. Amide M.P. 160°.

NITROSO COMPOUNDS
(Including Nitrosoamines)

LIQUID

B.P.

227°d. Methylphenylnitrosoamine C₆H₅·N·(CH₃)·NO.

M.P. 12°. B.P. 121°/13 mm. D. 1·125 (25°). Pale yellow. Volatile with steam. Insol. in water, miscible with organic liquids. With Sn + HCl yields methylaniline B.P. 193° ; with Zn. dust + acetic acid yields methylphenylhydrazine B.P. 227°. With HCl gas in ether yields *p*-nitrosomethylaniline M.P. 115°.

236°d. Ethylphenylnitrosoamine C₆H₅·N(C₂H₅)·NO

B.P. 134°/16 mm. D. 1·086 (22°). Pale yellow. Volatile with steam. Insol. in water, miscible with organic liquids. With Sn + HCl yields ethylaniline B.P. 206° ; with Zn dust + acetic acid yields ethylphenylhydrazine B.P. 237° (benzal deriv. M.P. 49°). With HCl gas in ether yields *p*-nitrosoethylaniline M.P. 78°.

SOLID

M.P.

67° Diphenylnitrosoamine (C₆H₅)₂N·NO

Pale yellow. Insol. in water and dil. acids, sol. in

M.P.

organic liquids. Gives blue colour on adding a trace to conc. H_2SO_4. On boiling with Sn + HCl in alc. yields diphenylamine M.P. 54°; on warming with Zn dust + acetic acid yields diphenylhydrazine M.P. 34°. With HCl gas in ether or alc. yields *p*-nitrosodiphenyl-amine M.P. 144°.

67°   Nitrosobenzene $C_6H_5 \cdot NO$
B.P. 58°/18 mm. Sharp odour. Colourless ; green in fused state. Insol. in water, sol. in organic liquids with green colour. Reduced by Sn + HCl to aniline B.P. 183° (with some chloroanilines), by alk. NaOH to azoxybenzene M.P. 36°. Oxidised by alk. H_2O_2 to nitrobenzene B.P. 210°. With aniline in acetic acid yields azobenzene M.P. 68°.

84°   *p*-Nitrosodiethylaniline $(C_2H_5)_2N \cdot C_6H_4 \cdot NO$ (1:4)
Dark green. Insol. in water, sol. in dil. acids and in organic liquids. Forms a yellow cryst. hydrochloride. With Sn + HCl yields *p*-aminodiethylaniline B.P. 261°. On boiling with conc. NaOH yields *p*-nitroso-phenol M.P. 126°d. and diethylamine B.P. 55°. With $KMnO_4$ or $K_3Fe(CN)_6$ yields *p*-nitrodiethylaniline M.P. 77°.

85°   *p*-Nitrosodimethylaniline $(CH_3)_2N \cdot C_6H_4 \cdot NO$ (1:4)
Dark green. Insol. in water, sol. in dil. acids and in organic liquids. Forms a yellow cryst. hydrochloride. With Sn + HCl yields *p*-aminodimethylaniline M.P. 41°. On boiling with conc. NaOH yields *p*-nitroso-phenol M.P. 126°d. and dimethylamine (*q.v.*). With $KMnO_4$ or $K_3Fe(CN)_6$ yields *p*-nitrodimethylaniline M.P. 163°.

109°   1-Nitroso-2-naphthol $NO \cdot C_{10}H_6 \cdot OH$ (1:2)
Dull yellow. Almost insol. in water, sol. in dil. alkali and in most organic liquids. Volatile with steam. Forms a sparingly sol. green Na salt, and gives (in 50% acetic acid) brown and red pptes. with Cu and Co salts (but not with Ni). Forms an addition product M.P. 130° with (1 mol.) bromine in $CHCl_3$. With NH_4SH yields 1-amino-2-naphthol (colourless leaflets, sparingly sol. in hot water ; picrate M.P. 109°, mono-acetyl deriv. M.P. 235°, diacetyl deriv. M.P. 206°). On boiling with HCl yields hydroxylamine HCl and some *β*-naphthoquinone d. 115–120°. With dil. HNO_3 in cold yields 1-nitro-2-naphthol M.P. 103° ; with fuming HNO_3 at 40–50° yields 1:6-dinitro-2-naphthol M.P. 195°d.

M.P.

115° *p*-Nitrosomethylaniline $CH_3 \cdot NH \cdot C_6H_4 \cdot NO$ (1:4)
Green with blue reflex. Insol. in water, sol. in dil.
acids and alkalies and in most organic liquids. Forms
a yellow cryst. hydrochloride. With Sn + HCl
yields *p*-aminomethylaniline M.P. 35°, B.P. 258°
(dibenzoyl deriv. M.P. 164°). On boiling with conc.
NaOH yields *p*-nitrosophenol M.P. 126°d, and
methylamine (*q.v.*).

126°d. *p*-Nitrosophenol $HO \cdot C_6H_4 \cdot NO$ (1:4)
(Decomposition sets in at about 124°). Nearly
colourless. Appreciably sol. ın cold water, readily in
alc. and in ether, giving green solns. ; sparingly sol. in
benzene, giving yellow soln. Sol. in dil. NaOH,
giving red-brown soln. Reduced by NH_4SH to
p-aminophenol M.P. 184°d. Oxidised by conc. HNO_3
or by $K_3Fe(CN)_6$ to *p*-nitrophenol M.P. 114°. With
acetic anhydride at 100° yields yellow acetyl deriv.
M.P. 107°. On warming with aniline acetate yields
p-hydroxyazobenzene M.P. 152°. With 2:4-dinitro-
chlorobenzene + Na acetate in alc. yields 2:4-dinitro-
phenyl deriv. M.P. 165°. On methylation in alk.
soln yields quinone methoxime M.P. 83°.

144° *p*-Nitrosodiphenylamine $C_6H_5 \cdot NH \cdot C_6H_4 \cdot NO$ (1:4)
Green. Insol. in water ; sol. in dil. NaOH and in
organic liquids. With Zn dust + acetic acid yields
p-aminodiphenylamine M.P. 66°. On boiling with
conc. NaOH yields *p*-nitrosophenol M.P. 126°d. and
aniline B.P. 183°.

AZO COMPOUNDS

SOLID

M.P.

55° *o*-Azotoluene $CH_3 \cdot C_6H_4 \cdot N{:}N \cdot C_6H_4 \cdot CH_3$ (2:2′)
Red. With Zn dust + NaOH in dil. alc. yields
o-hydrazotoluene M.P. 165° which with conc. HCl
yields *o*-toluidine M.P. 129°. With $Na_2S_2O_4$ + NaOH
in dil. alc. yields *o*-toluidine B.P. 197°.

68° Azobenzene $C_6H_5 \cdot N{:}N \cdot C_6H_5$
B.P. 293°. Orange-red. With Zn dust + NaOH in
dil. alc. yields hydrazobenzene M.P. 131°, which with
conc. HCl yields benzidine M.P. 127°. With SO_2 in
alc. yields benzidine. With $Na_2S_2O_4$ + NaOH in dil.
alc. yields aniline B.P. 183°. With (2 mols.) bromine
in acetic acid yields dibromo deriv. M.P. 187°. With
benzaldehyde at 200° yields benzanilide M.P. 161°.

M.P.

100°   Aminoazo-*o*-toluene

$$CH_3 \cdot C_6H_4 \cdot N:N \cdot C_6H_3(CH_3) \cdot NH_2 \quad (2:3':4')$$

Purple crysts. Sol. in organic liquids (yellow soln.) and in dil. acids (red soln.). Dyes wool yellow. With Sn + HCl yields *o*-toluidine B.P. 197° and *p*-toluylene-diamine M.P. 64°, B.P. 273° (diacetyl deriv. M.P. 220°). Acetyl deriv. M.P. 185°. Azo-β-naphthol deriv. M.P. 186°.

115°   *p*-Dimethylaminoazobenzene

$$C_6H_5 \cdot N:N.C_6H_4 \cdot N(CH_3)_2 \quad (4)$$

Orange. Sol. in organic liquids (yellow soln.) and in dil. acids (red soln.). Dyes wool yellow. With Sn + HCl yields aniline B.P. 183° and *p*-aminodimethyl-aniline M.P. 41°, B.P. 262°.

125°   *p*-Aminoazobenzene $C_6H_5 \cdot N:N \cdot C_6H_4 \cdot NH_2$ (4)

Yellow with bluish reflex. Sol. in organic liquids (yellow soln.) and in dil. acids (red soln). Dyes wool yellow. With Sn + HCl yields aniline B.P. 183° and *p*-phenylenediamine M.P. 140°. Acetyl deriv. M.P. 144°. Benzal deriv. M.P. 127°. Azo-β-naphthol deriv. M.P. 202°.

128°   Benzeneazo-*o*-cresol $C_6H_5 \cdot N:N \cdot C_6H_3(CH_3) \cdot OH$ (3:4)

Yellow. Sol. in organic liquids (yellow soln.) and in dil. NaOH (orange soln.). With Sn + HCl yields aniline B.P. 183° and 5-amino-*o*-cresol M.P. 176°d. Acetyl deriv. M.P. 87°. Benzoyl deriv. M.P. 110°.

131°   Benzeneazo-β-naphthol $C_6H_5 \cdot N:N \cdot C_{10}H_6 \cdot OH$ (1:2)

Orange. Sol. in organic liquids (yellow soln) ; insol. in dil. NaOH. Sol. in conc. H_2SO_4 (magenta soln). With Sn + HCl yields aniline B.P. 183° and 1-amino-2-naphthol (colourless leaflets, sparingly sol. in hot water ; picrate M.P. 109°, monoacetyl deriv. M.P. 235°, diacetyl deriv. M.P. 206°). Acetyl deriv. M.P. 117°. Benzoyl deriv. M.P. 125°.

144°   *p*-Azotoluene $CH_3 \cdot C_6H_4 \cdot N:N \cdot C_6H_4 \cdot CH_3$ (4:4')

Orange. With Zn dust + NaOH in dil. alc. yields *p*-hydrazotoluene M.P. 133° ; with Sn + HCl yields *p*-toluidine M.P. 45°.

152°   *p*-Hydroxyazobenzene $C_6H_5 \cdot N:N \cdot C_6H_4 \cdot OH$ (4)

Yellow. Sol. in organic liquids (yellow soln.) and in dil. NaOH (orange soln.). With Sn + HCl yields aniline B.P. 183° and *p*-aminophenol M.P. 184°d. Acetyl deriv. M.P. 84°. Benzoyl deriv. M.P. 138°. Methyl ether M.P. 56°.

AZOXY COMPOUNDS

SOLID

M.P.

36° Azoxybenzene $C_6H_5\cdot N{:}NO\cdot C_6H_5$
Light yellow. With Zn dust + NaOH in dil. alc. yields first azobenzene M.P. 68° and then hydrazo-benzene M.P. 131°; with $SnCl_2$ + HCl yields aniline B.P. 183°. On warming with conc. H_2SO_4 yields p-hydroxyazobenzene M.P. 152°.

59° o-Azoxytoluene $CH_3\cdot C_6H_4\cdot N{:}NO\cdot C_6H_4\cdot CH_3$ (2:2′)
Light yellow. With Zn dust + NaOH in dil. alc. yields first o-azotoluene M.P. 55° and then o-hydr-azotoluene M.P. 165°; with $SnCl_2$ + HCl yields o-toluidine B.P. 197°.

75° p-Azoxytoluene $CH_3\cdot C_6H_4\cdot N{:}NO\cdot C_6H_4\cdot CH_3$ (4:4′)
Light yellow. With Zn dust + NaOH in dil. alc. yields first p-azotoluene M.P. 144°, and then p-hydr-azotoluene M.P. 133°; with $SnCl_2$ + HCl yields p-toluidine M.P. 45°.

NITROAMINO COMPOUNDS

SOLID

M.P.

71° o-Nitraniline $NH_2\cdot C_6H_4\cdot NO_2$ (1:2)
Orange. Volatile with steam. Sol. in hot water. With Zn dust + NaOH in dil. alc. yields o-phenylene-diamine M.P. 102°. Acetyl deriv. M.P. 92°. Benzoyl deriv. M.P. 94°. Benzenesulphonyl deriv. M.P. 104°. Azo-β-naphthol deriv. M.P. 212°.

72° 2-Nitro-p-toluidine $CH_3\cdot C_6H_3(NH_2)\cdot NO_2$ (1:4:2)
Yellow. Sol. in hot water. With Sn. + HCl yields m-toluylenediamine M.P. 99°. Acetyl deriv. M.P. 93°. Benzoyl deriv. M.P. 172°. Benzenesulphonyl deriv. M.P. 160°. Azo-β-naphthol deriv. M.P. 162°.

92° 6-Nitro-o-toluidine $CH_3\cdot C_6H_3(NH_2)\cdot NO_2$ (1:2:6)
Light yellow. Slightly sol. in hot water. With Sn + HCl yields toluylene-2:6-diamine M.P. 104° (diacetyl deriv. M.P. 202°). Acetyl deriv. M.P. 157°. Benzoyl deriv. M.P. 167°. Azo-β-naphthol deriv. M.P. 215°.

97° 3-Nitro-o-toluidine $CH_3\cdot C_6H_3(NH_2)\cdot NO_2$ (1:2:3)
Orange. Almost insol. in hot water. With Sn + HCl yields toluylene-2:3-diamine M.P. 61°, B.P. 255°. Acetyl deriv. M.P. 158°. Azo-β-naphthol deriv. M.P. 168°.

M.P.

107°   4-Nitro-o-toluidine $CH_3 \cdot C_6H_3(NH_2) \cdot NO_2$ (1:2:4)
Yellow. With Sn + HCl yields m-toluylenediamine
M.P. 99°. Acetyl deriv. M.P. 150°. Benzene-
sulphonyl deriv. M.P. 172°.

114° m-Nitroaniline $NH_2 \cdot C_6H_4 \cdot NO_2$ (1:3)
B.P. 285°. Yellow. Volatile with steam. Sol. in
hot water. Stable towards hot NaOH soln. With
Sn + HCl yields m-phenylenediamine M.P. 63°.
Acetyl deriv. M.P. 155°. Benzoyl deriv. M.P. 155°.
Benzenesulphonyl deriv. M.P. 136°. Benzal deriv.
M.P. 73°. Azo-β-naphthol deriv. M.P. 194°.

116°   3-Nitro-p-toluidine $CH_3 \cdot C_6H_3(NH_2) \cdot NO_2$ (1:4:3)
Red. Volatile with steam. Almost insol. in hot
water. With Zn dust + NaOH in dil. alc. yields
toluylene-3:4-diamine M.P. 88° (diacetyl deriv. M.P.
210°). Acetyl deriv. M.P. 144°. Benzoyl deriv.
M.P. 143°. Benzenesulphonyl deriv. M.P. 99°. Azo-
β-naphthol deriv. M.P. 278°.

130°   5-Nitro-o-toluidine $CH_3 \cdot C_6H_3(NH_2) \cdot NO_2$ (1:2:5)
Light yellow. Almost insol. in hot water, readily sol.
in alc. With Sn + HCl yields p-toluylenediamine
M.P. 64° (diacetyl deriv. M.P. 220°). Acetyl deriv.
M.P. 196°. Azo-β-naphthol deriv. M.P. 248°.

138°   2:6-Dinitroaniline $NH_2 \cdot C_6H_3(NO_2)_2$ (1:2:6)
Yellow. Slightly sol. in cold alc. With Sn + HCl
yields 1:2:3-triaminobenzene M.P. 103°, B.P. 336°.
Acetyl deriv. M.P. 197°.

147° p-Nitroaniline $NH_2 \cdot C_6H_4 \cdot NO_2$ (1:4)
Yellow. Not volatile with steam. Sol. in hot water.
With Sn + HCl yields p-phenylenediamine M.P.
140°. On long boiling with conc. Na H yields NH_3
and p-nitrophenol M.P. 114°. Acetyl deriv. M.P.
215°. Benzoyl deriv. M.P. 199°. Benzenesulphonyl
deriv. M.P. 139°. Benzal deriv. M.P. 117°. Azo-β-
naphthol deriv. M.P. 250°.

157°d. p-Nitrophenylhydrazine $NO_2 \cdot C_6H_4 \cdot NH \cdot NH_2$ (1:4)
Orange-red leaflets. With Sn + HCl yields p-phenyl-
enediamine M.P. 140°. With CuSO. soln. yields
nitrobenzene M.P. 5°, B.P. 210° and N_2. Acetyl
deriv. M.P. 205°. Benzoyl deriv. M.P. 193°. Benzal
deriv. M.P. 192°. With acetone yields isopropylidene
deriv. M.P. 148°. Forms a picrate M.P. 119°.

168°   Picramic Acid $(NO_2)_2C_6H_2(OH) \cdot NH_2$ (4:6:1:2)
Brownish red. Slightly sol. in water, sol. in dil.

NaOH with orange colour. Slightly sol. in ether and $CHCl_3$, sol. in alc., readily in benzene. With Sn + HCl yields triaminophenol (readily oxidised by air; triacetyl deriv. M.P. 279°d., tetra-acetyl deriv. M.P. 255°d., tetrabenzoyl deriv. M.P. 256°, picrate M.P. 196°). Monoacetyl deriv. M.P. 201°. Monobenzoyl deriv. M.P. 220°.

176°   2:4-Dinitroaniline $(NO_2)_2C_6H_3 \cdot NH_2$ (2:4:1)
Yellow, with blue reflex. Slightly sol. in hot water. Forms no salts with acids. With Sn + HCl yields 1:2:4-triaminobenzene M.P. below 100°, B.P. 340°. On boiling with conc. NaOH rapidly yields NH_3 and 2:4-dinitrophenol M.P. 114°. Acetyl deriv. M.P. 120°. Benzoyl deriv. M.P. 220°. Azo-β-naphthol deriv. M.P. 302°.

188°   Picramide $(NO_2)_3C_6H_2 \cdot NH_2$ (2:4:6:1)
Yellow, with blue reflex. On boiling with dil. NaOH readily yields NH_3 and picric acid M.P. 122°. Can be diazotised only in conc. H_2SO_4 soln. (or in conc. H_2SO_4 + acetic acid). With Sn + HCl yields NH_4Cl and triaminophenol (cf. Picramic acid M.P. 168° above). Forms a compound with naphthalene (in alc.) M.P. 168°.

198°d.   2:4-Dinitrophenylhydrazine

                      $(NO_2)_2C_6H_3 \cdot NH \cdot NH_2$ (2:4:1)
Red. Sparingly sol. in cold alc., ether and benzene, readily in hot ethyl acetate. Almost insol. in cold dil. acids, salts being hydrolysed by water. With Sn + HCl yields 1:2:4-triaminobenzene M.P. below 100°, B.P. 340°. On boiling with conc. NaOH yields 2:4-dinitrophenol M.P. 114° and NH_3. With $CuSO_4$ soln yields m-dinitrobenzene M.P. 90° and N_2. Benzal deriv. M.P. 235°. With acetone yields isopropylidene deriv. M.P. 128°.

NITRO CARBOXYLIC AMIDES
Simple and Substituted
SOLID

92°   o-Nitroacetanilide $NO_2 \cdot C_6H_4 \cdot NH \cdot CO \cdot CH_3$ (1:2)
Yellow. Sol. in hot water. Sol. in a 10% soln. of KOH in 8% aqueous alc.; soln. on standing deposits o-nitroaniline M.P. 71°.

143°   m-Nitrobenzamide $NO_2 \cdot C_6H_4 \cdot CONH_2$ (1:3)
Colourless.. Sol. in hot water. On boiling with dil.

M.P.

NaOH yields NH_3 and *m*-nitrobenzoic acid M.P. 140°. On warming with PCl_5 or P_2O_5 yields *m*-nitrobenzonitrile M.P. 117°.

144° 3-Nitro-4-acetaminotoluene
$$CH_3 \cdot C_6H_3(NO_2) \cdot NH \cdot CO \cdot CH_3 \ (1:3:4)$$
Yellow. Sol. in hot water. On boiling with dil. NaOH yields 3-nitro-*p*-toluidine M.P. 116° and Na acetate. On boiling with dil. $KMnO_4$ yields 3-nitro-4-acetaminobenzoic acid M.P. 220°.

153° *m*-Nitrobenzanilide $NO_2 \cdot C_6H_4 \cdot CO \cdot NH \cdot C_6H_5 \ (1:3)$
Colourless. Slightly sol. in hot water. On boiling with acids or alkalies yields *m*-nitrobenzoic acid M.P. 140° and aniline B.P. 183°.

155° *m*-Nitroacetanilide $NO_2 \cdot C_6H_4 \cdot NH \cdot CO \cdot CH_3 \ (1:3)$
Colourless. Insol. in water and in 30% KOH; on boiling with dil. NaOH yields *m*-nitroaniline M.P. 114° and Na acetate. On boiling with Sn + HCl yields *m*-phenylenediamine M.P. 63°.

176° *o*-Nitrobenzamide $NO_2 \cdot C_6H_4 \cdot CONH_2 \ (1:2)$
Colourless. Sol. in hot water. On boiling with dil. NaOH yields NH_3 and *o*-nitrobenzoic acid M.P. 144°. With Sn + HCl yields anthranilic acid M.P. 144°. On warming with PCl_5 yields *o*-nitrobenzonitrile M.P. 110°.

196° 5-Nitro-2-acetaminotoluene
$$CH_3 \cdot C_6H_3(NO_2) \cdot NH \cdot CO \cdot CH_3 \ (1:5:2)$$
Colourless. Sparingly sol. in hot water. On boiling with dil. NaOH yields 5-nitro-*o*-toluidine M.P. 130° and Na acetate; on long boiling with conc. NaOH yields 5-nitro-*o*-cresol M.P. 94° and NH_3. On boiling with dil. $KMnO_4$ yields 5-nitro-2-acetaminobenzoic acid M.P. 215°.

201° *p*-Nitrobenzamide $NO_2 \cdot C_6H_4 \cdot CONH_2 \ (1:4)$
Colourless. Sol. in hot water. On boiling with dil. NaOH yields NH_3 and *p*-nitrobenzoic acid M.P. 241°. On boiling with Sn + HCl yields *p*-aminobenzoic acid M.P. 186°. On warming with PCl_5 yields *p*-nitrobenzonitrile M.P. 147°.

210° *p*-Nitroacetanilide $NO_2 \cdot C_6H_4 \cdot NH \cdot CO \cdot CH_3 \ (1:4)$
Colourless. Insol. in a 10% soln of KOH in 8% aqueous alc., but sol. (with gradual decomposition) in 30% KOH. On boiling with dil. NaOH yields *p*-nitroaniline M.P. 147° and Na acetate; on long boiling with conc. NaOH yields NH_3 and *p*-nitro-

phenol M.P. 114°. On boiling with Sn + HCl yields
p-phenylenediamine M.P. 140°; with Fe filings + dil.
acetic acid yields p-aminoacetanilide M.P. 162°.

ALKYL NITRATES AND NITRITES

LIQUID

	Nitrate			Nitrite	
	B.P.	D.		B.P.	D.
Methyl	65°	1·232 (5°)	—	—	
Ethyl	87°	1·130 (4°)	17°	0·900 (15°)	
n-Propyl	110°	1·075 (5°)	44°	0·998 (0°)	
isoButyl	123°	1·033 (4°)	67°	0·888 (4°)	
n-Butyl	136°	1·048 (0°)	75°	0·911 (0°)	
isoAmyl	147°	1·000 (7°)	99°	0·880 (15°)	

HALOGEN SUBSTITUTED AMINES

LIQUID

B.P.

207° o-Chloroaniline $Cl.C_6H_4.NH_2$ (1:2)

D. 1·213 (20°). Hydrochloride M.P. 235°. On adding
(1 mol.) KNO_3 to soln. in conc. H_2SO_4 yields 5-nitro
deriv. M.P. 117°. By Sandmeyer's reaction yields
o-dichlorobenzene B.P. 179°. Acetyl deriv. M.P.
87°. Benzoyl deriv. M.P. 99°. Benzenesulphonyl
deriv. M.P. 129°. p-Bromobenzenesulphonyl deriv.
M.P. 105°. m-Nitrobenzenesulphonyl deriv. M.P.
153°. Azo-β-naphthol deriv. M.P. 167°.

230° m-Chloroaniline $Cl.C_6H_4.NH_2$ (1:3)

D. 1·216 (20°). Sulphate is sparingly sol. in cold
water. By Sandmeyer's reaction yields m-dichloro-
benzene B.P. 172°. Acetyl deriv. M.P. 72°. Benzoyl
deriv. M.P. 120°. Benzenesulphonyl deriv. M.P. 121°.
Benzal deriv. B.P. 338°.

SOLID

M.P.

18° m-Bromoaniline $Br.C_6H_4.NH_2$ (1:3)

B.P. 251°. By Sandmeyer's reaction yields m-
chlorobromobenzene B.P. 196°. Acetyl deriv. M.P.
87°. Benzoyl deriv. M.P. 120°.

31° o-Bromoaniline $Br.C_6H_4.NH_2$ (1:2)

B.P. 250°. By Sandmeyer's reaction yields o-chloro-
bromobenzene B.P. 195°. Acetyl deriv. M.P. 99°.
Benzoyl deriv. M.P. 116°.

M.P.
63°   2:4-Dichloroaniline $Cl_2C_6H_3 \cdot NH_2$ (2:4:1)
B.P. 245°. By Sandmeyer's reaction yields 1:2:4-tri-chlorobenzene M.P. 16°, B.P. 213°. Acetyl deriv. M.P. 145°. Benzoyl deriv. M.P. 117°. Benzene-sulphonyl deriv. M.P. 128°. Azo-β-naphthol deriv. M.P. 183°.

66°   p-Bromoaniline $Br \cdot C_6H_4 \cdot NH_2$ (1:4)
B.P. 245°d. By Sandmeyer's reaction yields p-chlorobromobenzene M.P. 67°, B.P. 196°. Acetyl deriv. M.P. 167°. Benzoyl deriv. M.P. 204°. Ben-zenesulphonyl deriv. M.P. 134°. m-Nitrobenzene-sulphonyl deriv. M.P. 120°. Benzal deriv. M.P. 67°.

70°   p-Chloroaniline $Cl \cdot C_6H_4 \cdot NH_2$ (1:4)
B.P. 230°. Sulphate is sparingly sol. in cold water. By Sandmeyer's reaction yields p-dichlorobenzene M.P. 53°. Acetyl deriv. M.P. 179°. Benzoyl deriv. M.P. 192°. Benzenesulphonyl deriv. M.P. 121°. p-Bromobenzenesulphonyl deriv. M.P. 134°. m-Ni-trobenzenesulphonyl deriv. M.P. 119°. Benzal deriv. M.P. 62°. Azo-β-naphthol deriv. M.P. 160°.

77°   2:4:6-Trichloroaniline $Cl_3C_6H_2 \cdot NH_2$ (2:4:6:1)
B.P. 262°. Insol. in HCl, salts being hydrolysed by water. By Sandmeyer's reaction yields 1:2:3:5-tetrachlorobenzene M.P. 50°, B.P. 246°. On diazo-tising in alc. + H_2SO_4 and then warming yields 1:3:5-trichlorobenzene M.P. 63°, B.P. 208°. Acetyl deriv. M.P. 204°. Benzoyl deriv. M.P. 174°.

80°   2:4-Dibromoaniline $Br_2C_6H_3 \cdot NH_2$ (2:4:1)
By Sandmeyer's reaction yields 2:4-dibromochloro-benzene M.P. 27°, B.P. 258°. Acetyl deriv. M.P. 146°. Benzoyl deriv. M.P. 134°.

106°   p-Bromophenylhydrazine $Br \cdot C_6H_4 \cdot NH \cdot NH_2$ (1:4)
With $SnCl_2$ + HCl yields p-bromoaniline M.P. 66° (with some aniline). With $CuSO_4$ soln yields bromo-benzene B.P. 157° and N_2. Acetyl deriv. M.P. 167°. Benzoyl deriv. M.P. 156°d. Benzal deriv. M.P. 127°. With acetone yields isopropylidene deriv. M.P. 98°.

119°   2:4:6-Tribromoaniline $Br_3C_6H_2 \cdot NH_2$ (2:4:6:1)
B.P. 300°. Insol. in HCl, salts being hydrolysed by water. By Sandmeyer's reaction yields 2:4:6-tri-bromochlorobenzene M.P. 90°. On diazotising in alc. + H_2SO_4 and then warming yields 1:3:5-tribromo-benzene M.P. 119°. On boiling with acetic anhy-dride yields diacetyl deriv. M.P. 127°, which on gentle

hydrolysis with dil. NaOH yields monoacetyl deriv.
M.P. 232°. Benzoyl deriv. M.P. 198°.

HALOGEN SUBSTITUTED AMIDES
Simple and Substituted

SOLID

M.P.
119°   Chloroacetamide $Cl \cdot CH_2 \cdot CONH_2$
       B.P. 224°d. Readily sol. in water and alc., slightly in
       ether. On boiling with HCl yields NH_4Cl and
       chloroacetic acid M.P. 63°. On warming with P_2O_5
       yields chloroacetonitrile B.P. 124° (sharp odour).
       Forms a compound with hexamethylenetetramine (in
       acetone) M.P. 160°d. On boiling with alc. + conc.
       H_2SO_4 yields ethyl chloroacetate B.P. 144°.

167° p-Bromoacetanilide $CH_3 \cdot CO \cdot NH \cdot C_6H_4 \cdot Br$ (1:4)
       On boiling with dil. acids or alkalies yields p-bromo-
       aniline M.P. 66° and acetic acid. With fuming HNO_3
       + acetic acid yields 2-nitro deriv. M.P. 104°, which
       on hydrolysis yields 2-nitro-4-bromoaniline M.P. 111°.

179° p-Chloroacetanilide $CH_3 \cdot CO \cdot NH \cdot C_6H_4 \cdot Cl$ (1:4)
       On boiling with dil. acids or alkalies yields p-chloro-
       aniline M.P. 70° and acetic acid. With fuming HNO_3
       + acetic acid yields 2-nitro deriv. M.P. 104°, which
       on hydrolysis yields 2-nitro-4-chloroaniline M.P. 115°.

HALOGEN SUBSTITUTED NITRO HYDROCARBONS
LIQUID

B.P.
112°   Chloropicrin $NO_2 \cdot CCl_3$
       D. 1·651 (23°). Highly irritating odour. Insol. in
       water. On boiling with dil. KOH yields KCl and
       KNO_2. On warming 1 drop with thymol + KOH in
       alc. gives yellow colour ; with resorcinol in place of
       thymol, red colour. With Fe + acetic acid yields
       methylamine (q.v.). On boiling with thiocarbanilide
       in alc. yields sulphur and a product M.P. 252°.

SOLID

M.P.
32° o-Nitrochlorobenzene $Cl \cdot C_6H_4 \cdot NO_2$ (1:2)
       Pale yellow. B.P. 245°. With Zn dust + dil. acetic
       acid yields o-chloroaniline B.P. 207°. On warming
       with conc. H_2SO_4 + HNO_3 yields 2:4-dinitrochloro-
       benzene M.P. 53°. On boiling with KOH in CH_3OH

M.P.

yields o-nitroanisole M.P. 9°, B.P. 265° (with a little 2:2′-dichloroazoxybenzene M.P. 56°). On gradually adding (0·5 mol.) Na_2S to soln in boiling alc. yields di-o-nitrophenyl sulphide M.P. 122°.

41°   o-Nitrobromobenzene $Br \cdot C_6H_4 \cdot NO_2$ (1:2)
Pale yellow. B.P. 264°. Sol. in cold fuming H_2SO_4. With Sn + HCl yields o-bromoaniline M.P. 31°, B.P. 250°. On warming with conc. H_2SO_4 + HNO_3 yields 2:4-dinitrobromobenzene M.P. 72°. For replacement reactions cf. o-Nitrochlorobenzene M.P. 32°.

44°   m-Nitrochlorobenzene $Cl \cdot C_6H_4 \cdot NO_2$ (1:3)
Pale yellow. B.P. 235°. With Sn + HCl yields m-chloroaniline B.P. 230°. With conc. H_2SO_4 + fuming HNO_3 yields 3:4-dinitrochlorobenzene M.P. 72°. Gives no replacement reactions; on boiling with KOH or Na_2S in CH_3OH yields 3:3′-dichloro-azoxybenzene M.P. 97°.

48°   o-Nitrobenzyl Chloride $NO_2 \cdot C_6H_4 \cdot CH_2Cl$ (1:2)
On adding to $SnCl_2$ + HCl at 40–50°, and then adding Zn dust, yields o-toluidine B.P. 197°. With $KMnO_4$ soln yields o-nitrobenzoic acid M.P. 144°. With conc. HNO_3 + H_2SO_4 yields 2:4-dinitrobenzyl chloride M.P. 34°. On warming with Na_2CO_3 soln. yields o-nitrobenzyl alc. M.P. 74°. On boiling with conc. Na acetate soln. yields o-nitrobenzyl acetate M.P. 35°. With phenol + NaOH in alc. yields o-nitrobenzyl phenyl ether M.P. 63°. On boiling with KCNS in 90% alc. yields the thiocyanate M.P. 75°.

53°   2:4-Dinitrochlorobenzene $Cl \cdot C_6H_3(NO_2)_2$ (1:2:4)
Pale yellow. B.P. 315°. Sparingly sol. in cold alc., readily in ether and benzene. With $SnCl_2$ + HCl yields chloro-m-phenylenediamine M.P. 91° (diacetyl deriv. M.P. 242°, dibenzoyl deriv. M.P. 178°). On warming with fuming HNO_3 + fuming H_2SO_4 yields picryl chloride M.P. 183°. On boiling with dil. NaOH yields 2:4-dinitrophenol M.P. 114°; with KOH in CH_3OH yields 2:4-dinitroanisole M.P. 88°. On boiling with dimethylaniline yields 2:4-dinitrophenyl methyl-aniline M.P. 167°.

54°   Nitro-p-dichlorobenzene $NO_2 \cdot C_6H_3Cl_2$ (2:1:4)
Pale yellow. B.P. 266°. Sparingly sol. in cold alc., readily in benzene. With Sn + HCl yields 2:5-dichloroaniline M.P. 50°, B.P. 251° (acetyl deriv. M.P. 143°, benzoyl deriv. M.P. 120°). On warming with conc. HNO_3 + H_2SO_4 yields 1:3-dinitro-2:5-dichloro-

M.P.

benzene M.P. 104°. On boiling with (1 mol.) KOH in CH_3OH yields 2-nitro-4-chloroanisole M.P. 97°.

54° *m*-Nitrobromobenzene $Br\cdot C_6H_4\cdot NO_2$ (1:3)
Pale yellow. B.P. 257°. Readily sol. in alc. With Sn + HCl yields *m*-bromoaniline M.P. 18°, B.P. 251°. On heating with large excess conc. $HNO_3 + H_2SO_4$ yields 3:4-dinitrobromobenzene M.P. 59°. Gives no replacement reactions; on boiling with KOH or Na_2S in CH_3OH yields 3:3'-dibromoazoxybenzene M.P. 111°.

71° *p*-Nitrobenzyl Chloride $NO_2\cdot C_6H_4\cdot CH_2Cl$ (1:4)
Readily sol. in alc. With $SnCl_2$ + HCl, followed by Zn dust, yields *p*-toluidine M.P. 45°. With pyrogallol + KOH in alc. yields *p*-nitrotoluene M.P. 54°. On boiling with $KMnO_4$ soln. yields *p*-nitrobenzoic acid M.P. 241°. With cold conc. $HNO_3 + H_2SO_4$ yields 2:4-dinitrobenzyl chloride M.P. 34°. On boiling with KOH in CH_3OH yields two 4:4'-dinitrostilbenes M.P. 293° and 213°, with some *p*-nitrobenzyl methyl ether M.P. 29°. On boiling with conc. K acetate soln. yields *p*-nitrobenzyl acetate M.P. 78°, which on hydrolysis yields *p*-nitrobenzyl alc. M.P. 93°. With phenol + NaOH in alc. yields *p*-nitrobenzyl phenyl ether M.P. 91°. β-Naphthyl ether M.P. 106°.

72° 2:4-Dinitrobromobenzene $Br\cdot C_6H_3(NO_2)_2$ (1:2:4)
Pale yellow. With Sn + HCl yields *m*-phenylenediamine M.P. 63°. Replacement reactions like those of 2:4-dinitrochlorobenzene M.P. 53°. Forms an unstable compound with benzene M.P. 65°.

83° *p*-Nitrochlorobenzene $Cl\cdot C_6H_4\cdot NO_2$ (1:4)
Very pale yellow. B.P. 242°. With Sn + HCl yields *p*-chloroaniline M.P. 70°. On warming with conc. $HNO_3 + H_2SO_4$ yields 2:4-dinitrochlorobenzene M.P. 53°. On long boiling with conc. NaOH yields *p*-nitrophenol M.P. 114°. On long boiling with KOH in $CH_3OH + H_2O$ yields *p*-nitroanisole M.P. 54°, and some 4:4'-dichloroazoxybenzene M.P. 155°. On slowly adding (0·5 mol.) Na_2S to soln. in boiling alc. yields di-*p*-nitrophenyl sulphide M.P. 154°.

83° Picryl Chloride $Cl\cdot C_6H_2(NO_2)_3$ (1:2:4:6)
Yellow. Sparingly sol. in ether and light petroleum, readily in hot alc. and benzene. With Sn + HCl yields unstable 1:3:5-triaminobenzene (triacetyl deriv. M.P. 208°). On boiling with dil. NaOH yields picric acid M.P. 122°; with KOH in CH_3OH yields trinitro-

anisole M.P. 68°; with KOH in alc. yields trinitrophenetole M.P. 78°. With NH₃ in alc. yields picramide M.P. 188°. On warming with aniline yields
trinitrodiphenylamine M.P. 177°. Forms a compound
with naphthalene M.P. 150°.

99°   p-Nitrobenzyl Bromide $NO_2 \cdot C_6H_4 \cdot CH_2Br$
Replacement reactions like those of p-Nitrobenzyl
chloride, M.P. 71°.

126°   p-Nitrobromobenzene $Br \cdot C_6H_4 \cdot NO_2$ (1:4)
Very pale yellow. B.P. 259°. Sparingly sol. in alc.
With $SnCl_2$ + HCl yields p-bromoaniline M.P. 66°
(with a little aniline). On warming with conc.
HNO_3 + H_2SO_4 yields 2:4-dinitrobromobenzene M.P.
72°. For replacement reactions cf. p-Nitrochloro-
benzene M.P. 83°.

MERCAPTANS

B.P.   LIQUID
36°   Ethyl Mercaptan $C_2H_5 \cdot SH$
D. 0·839 (20°). Almost insol. in water; forms a cryst.
hydrate below 8°. Sol. in dil. NaOH; soln on boiling
very slowly gives up mercaptan. Soln. in dil. NaOH
gives purple colour with nitroprusside. Alc. soln. gives
transient blue colour with $FeCl_3$. Gives yellow ppte. with
$AgNO_3$, colourless ppte. with $HgCl_2$. With HgO or
$Hg(CN)_2$ yields normal Hg salt M.P. 76°. With Pb
acetate yields yellow Pb salt M.P. 150°. With iodine
+ H_2O (or with conc. H_2SO_4) yields ethyl disulphide
B.P. 153°. Acetyl deriv. B.P. 116°. Benzoyl deriv.
B.P. 252°.

67°   n-Propyl Mercaptan $CH_3 \cdot CH_2 \cdot CH_2 \cdot SH$
D. 0·838 (20°). Sol. in dil. NaOH; soln. on boiling
gradually gives up mercaptan. Soln. in dil. NaOH
gives purple colour with nitroprusside. Normal Hg
salt M.P. 68°. With iodine + H_2O yields disulphide
B.P. 192°. Acetyl deriv. B.P. 136°.

88°   isoButyl Mercaptan $(CH_3)_2CH \cdot CH_2 \cdot SH$
D. 0·830 (20°). Sol. in dil. NaOH; soln. on boiling
readily gives up mercaptan. Soln. in dil. NaOH gives
purple colour with nitroprusside. With iodine + H_2O
yields disulphide B.P. 220°. Acetyl deriv. B.P. 149°.

97°   n-Butyl Mercaptan $CH_3 \cdot CH_2 \cdot CH_2 \cdot CH_2 \cdot SH$
D. 0·858 (0°). Sol. in dil. NaOH; can be readily
distilled out of alk. soln. Soln in dil. NaOH gives

B.P.

purple colour with nitroprusside.   With iodine + H_2O yields disulphide B.P. 234°.

117°   *iso*Amyl Mercaptan $(CH_3)_2CH \cdot CH_2 \cdot CH_2 \cdot SH$
D. 0·835 (20°). Sol. in dil. NaOH ; can be readily distilled out of alk. soln. Soln. in dil. NaOH gives purple colour with nitroprusside.   With iodine + H_2O yields disulphide B.P. 256°.

169°   Thiophenol $C_6H_5 \cdot SH$
D. 1·078 (24°). Sol. in dil. NaOH ; cannot be distilled out of alk. soln. Soln in dil. NaOH gives with nitroprusside a transient purple colour followed immediately by a turbidity. Soln. in conc. H_2SO_4 becomes red and then blue on warming. With dil. NaOH + iodine, or with H_2O_2, yields phenyl disulphide M.P. 60°. Gives colourless ppte. with $HgCl_2$; yellow pptes with Cu, Pb, and Ag salts. With NaOH + methyl sulphate (or iodide) yields methyl phenyl sulphide B.P. 188°, which with $KMnO_4$ in acetic acid yields sulphone M.P. 88°. With dil. NaOH + Na chloroacetate yields phenylthioglycollic acid M.P. 61°. With NaOH in alc. + benzyl chloride yields benzyl phenyl sulphide M.P. 42°. Acetyl deriv. B.P. 228°. Benzoyl deriv. M.P. 56°. With NaOH + benzenesulphochloride yields phenyl disulphide M.P. 60° and phenyl disulphone M.P. 193°.

194°   Benzyl Mercaptan $C_6H_5 \cdot CH_2 \cdot SH$
D. 1·058 (20°). Odour of onion. Soln in dil. NaOH gives with nitroprusside a purple colour which slowly fades. With dil. NaOH + iodine, or with bromine in ether, yields benzyl disulphide M.P. 71°. Oxidised by HNO_3 to benzoic acid M.P. 121° and some benzaldehyde B.P. 179°. Gives a sparingly sol. ppte. with $HgCl_2$ in alc. Benzoyl deriv. M.P. 30°. 2:4-Dinitrophenyl deriv. M.P. 128°.

SOLID

M.P.
43°   *p*-Thiocresol $CH_3 \cdot C_6H_4 \cdot SH$ (1:4)
B.P. 195°. With dil. NaOH + iodine, or with H_2O_2, yields *p*-tolyl disulphide M.P. 48°. Dissolves in warm conc. H_2SO_4 with blue colour, yielding dimethylthianthrene M.P. 123°. With dil. NaOH + methyl sulphate yields methyl *p*-tolyl sulphide B.P. 209°, which with $KMnO_4$ in acetic acid yields sulphone M.P. 86°. With dil. NaOH + Na chloroacetate yields *p*-tolylthioglycollic acid M.P. 93°. Acetyl deriv. B.P. 242°. Benzoyl deriv. M.P. 75°.

SULPHIDES AND DISULPHIDES

B.P.   LIQUID

37°   Methyl Sulphide $(CH_3)_2S$
        D. 0·870 (0°).   With $KMnO_4$ soln. yields sulphone M.P.
        109°, B.P. 238°.   Forms addition compounds with
        $HgCl_2$ M.P. 150°, with HgI_2 M.P. 75°.   With methyl
        iodide yields trimethylsulphonium iodide d. 215°
        (forms compound with iodoform M.P. 162°).   With
        (1 mol.) HgI_2 + methyl iodide yields addition
        compound M.P. 165°.

46°   Carbon Disulphide CS_2
        D. 1·292 (0°).   Insol. in water.   Highly inflammable ;
        burns with blue flame.   Slowly dissolves in NaOH
        soln., yielding Na trithiocarbonate (soln. gives deep red
        colour with nitroprusside).   With KOH in alc. yields
        cryst. K xanthate (gives yellow ppte. with $CuSO_4$).
        On shaking with aniline + conc. NaOH yields
        thiocarbanilide M.P. 153°.   With Zn + HCl yields
        trithioformaldehyde M.P. 218°.

92°   Ethyl Sulphide $(C_2H_5)_2S$
        D. 0·837 (20°).   With $KMnO_4$ soln. yields sulphone
        M.P. 70°, B.P. 248°.   Forms addition compounds with
        $HgCl_2$ M.P. 119°, with HgI_2 M.P. 52°.   Forms addi-
        tion compounds with methyl iodide + HgI_2 M.P. 67°,
        with ethyl iodide + HgI_2 M.P. 112°.

110° Methyl Disulphide $(CH_3)_2S_2$
        D. 1·046 (18°).   With Zn + HCl yields methyl
        mercaptan B.P. 6° (forms yellow Pb and Ag salts,
        colourless normal Hg salt M.P. 175°d.).

142° n-Propyl Sulphide $(CH_3 \cdot CH_2 \cdot CH_2)_2S$
        D 0·841 (17°).   With $KMnO_4$ soln. yields sulphone
        M.P. 29°, B.P. 260°.

153° Ethyl Disulphide $(C_2H_5)_2S_2$
        D. 0·993 (20°).   With Zn + HCl yields ethyl mer-
        captan B.P. 36°.

172° isoButyl Sulphide $[(CH_3)_2CH \cdot CH_2]_2S$
        D. 0·836 (10°).   With $KMnO_4$ soln. yields sulphone
        M.P. 17°, B.P. 265°.

182° n-Butyl Sulphide $(CH_3 \cdot CH_2 \cdot CH_2 \cdot CH_2)_2S$
        D. 0·839 (16°).   With $KMnO_4$ soln. yields sulphone
        M.P. 43°, B.P. 288°.

215° isoAmyl Sulphide $[(CH_3)_2CH \cdot CH_2 \cdot CH_2]_2S$
        D. 0·839 (16°).   With $KMnO_4$ soln. yields sulphone
        M.P. 31°, B.P. 295°.

B.P.
295°   Phenyl Sulphide $(C_6H_5)_2S$
D. $1\cdot118$ ($15°$). With conc. HNO_3, or $K_2Cr_2O_7$ + dil.
H_2SO_4, or $KMnO_4$ in acetic acid, yields sulphone M.P.
$128°$. With (2 mols.) bromine yields 4:4'-dibromo
deriv. M.P. $112°$.

SOLID

M.P.
48°   p-Tolyl Disulphide $(CH_3 \cdot C_6H_4)_2S_2$ (1:4)
With Zn + HCl yields p-thiocresol M.P. $43°$. Dissolves in warm conc. H_2SO_4 with blue colour, yielding
dimethylthianthrene M.P. $123°$.

49°   Benzyl Sulphide $(C_6H_5 \cdot CH_2)_2S$
Dec. above $185°$. With $KMnO_4$ in acetic acid yields
sulphone M.P. $150°$. With cold 48% HNO_3 yields
sulphoxide M.P. $134°$ (with some benzoic acid M.P.
$121°$). Compound with HgI_2 M.P. $37°$. With (1 mol.)
HgI_2 + methyl iodide in acetone yields addition
compound M.P. $155°$; with ethyl iodide, M.P. $115°$.

57°   p-Tolyl Sulphide $(CH_3 \cdot C_6H_4)_2S$ (1:4)
With $KMnO_4$ in acetic acid yields sulphone M.P. $158°$.

60°   Phenyl Disulphide $(C_6H_5)_2S_2$
B.P. $310°$. On long boiling yields phenyl sulphide
B.P. $295°$ and sulphur. With Zn + HCl yields thiophenol B.P. $169°$. With conc. HNO_3 yields benzenesulphonic acid (q.v.). On warming with conc. H_2SO_4
gives red and then blue colour, yielding thianthrene
M.P. $157°$. On boiling with conc. alc. KOH yields
thiophenol and benzenesulphinic acid M.P. $83°$.

71°   Benzyl Disulphide $(C_6H_5 \cdot CH_2)_2S_2$
Dec. above $270°$. With Zn + HCl yields benzyl
mercaptan B.P $194°$. With $KMnO_4$ soln. yields
benzoic acid M.P. $121°$. Forms a cryst. addition
product with $AgNO_3$ (in alc.).

SULPHOXIDES AND SULPHONES

SOLID

M.P.
70°   Phenyl Sulphoxide $(C_6H_5)_2SO$
B.P. $340°$d. Readily sol. in alc., ether, and benzene;
sparingly in cold ligroin. Gives a transient blue
colour with conc. H_2SO_4. With $KMnO_4$ in acetic
acid yields sulphone M.P. $128°$. With Zn + HCl
yields sulphide B.P. $295°$.

76°   Trional $(C_2H_5 \cdot SO_2)_2C(CH_3) \cdot C_2H_5$
Sol. in 320 parts of cold water, in 17 parts of cold alc.,

and in 15 parts of cold ether. Bitter taste. Resembles sulphonal M.P. 127° in general behaviour.

92°   p-Tolyl Sulphoxide $(CH_3 \cdot C_6H_4)_2SO$ (1:4)
Readily sol. in alc., ether, and benzene ; sparingly in cold ligroin. With $KMnO_4$ yields sulphone M.P. 158°, which on prolonged oxidation yields phenyl sulphone dicarboxylic acid M.P above 300°. With Zn + HCl yields sulphide M.P. 57°.

127°   Sulphonal $(C_2H_5 \cdot SO_2)_2C(CH_3)_2$
B.P. 300°d. Sol. at 15° in 500 parts of water, in 65 parts of alc., and in 133 parts of ether. Unaltered by strong acids, alkalies, oxidising agents, and bromine. On fusion with KCN gives odour of mercaptan, yielding KSCN.

128°   Phenyl Sulphone $(C_6H_5)_2SO_2$
B.P. 379°. Slightly sol. in hot water, sparingly in cold alc. ; sol. in benzene. Unaltered by oxidising and reducing agents. With conc. $HNO_3 + H_2SO_4$ yields di-m-nitro deriv. M.P. 201°. With PCl_5 at 160–170° yields chlorobenzene B.P. 132° and benzene-sulphochloride M.P. 14°, B.P. 246°d.

134°   Benzyl Sulphoxide $(C_6H_5 \cdot CH_2)_2SO$
d. 210°. Sol. in hot water, readily in alc. With $KMnO_4$ in acetic acid yields sulphone M.P. 150° and some benzoic acid M.P. 121°. On boiling with 48% HNO_3 yields benzoic acid. With Zn + HCl yields sulphide M.P. 49°.

150°   Benzyl Sulphone $(C_6H_5 \cdot CH_2)_2SO_2$
d. 290°. Insol. in water ; sparingly sol. in alc. On boiling with 48% HNO_3 yields benzoic acid M.P. 121°. On boiling with formaldehyde + NaOH yields a compound M.P. 188°.

158°   p-Tolyl Sulphone $(CH_3 \cdot C_6H_4)_2SO_2$ (1:4)
B.P. 405°. Sparingly sol. in cold alc. and ether, sol. in benzene and $CHCl_3$. On long treatment with $KMnO_4$ in acetic acid yields phenyl sulphone dicarboxylic acid M.P. above 300°.

SIMPLE SULPHONIC ACIDS

SOLID

M.P.

—   m-Benzenedisulphonic $C_6H_4(SO_3H)_2 + 2\frac{1}{2}H_2O$ (1:3)
Very hygroscopic crysts. On grinding Na salt with PCl_5 yields the chloride M.P. 63°, B.P. 195°/10 mm.,

which with NH_3 yields the amide M.P. 229°. On fusion with KOH yields resorcinol M.P. 118°.

—   2:7-Naphthalenedisulphonic $C_{10}H_6(SO_3H)_2$ (2:7)
Very hygroscopic needles. Ba salt is sol. in 82 parts of water at 19°. Chloride M.P. 162°. Amide M.P. 242°. On fusion with KOH yields 2:7-dihydroxy-naphthalene M.P. 184° (diacetate M.P. 136°, dibenzoate M.P. 138°, dimethyl ether M.P. 139°). Benzyl-pseudo-thiourea salt M.P. 199°.

—   2:6-Naphthalenedisulphonic $C_{10}H_6(SO_3H)_2$ (2:6)
Somewhat hygroscopic leaflets. Chloride M.P. 226° is sol. in 220 parts of cold benzene. Amide M.P. above 305°. On fusion with KOH yields 2:6-dihydroxynaphthalene M.P. 218° (diacetate M.P. 175°, dimethyl ether M.P. 150°). Benzyl-pseudo-thiourea salt d. 200° (without melting).

43°   Benzenesulphonic (Hydrated)
See anhydrous acid M.P. 65°.

57°   o-Toluenesulphonic $CH_3 \cdot C_6H_4 \cdot SO_3H + 2H_2O$ (1:2)
Hygroscopic leaflets. Ba salt is sol. in 26 parts of cold water. Chloride M.P. 10°, B.P. 126°/10 mm. Amide M.P. 153°. Anilide M.P. 136°. With $KMnO_4$ soln yields o-sulphobenzoic acid M.P. 134°. On fusion with KOH yields o-cresol M.P. 31° and some salicylic acid M.P. 155°. With conc. $HNO_3 + H_2SO_4$ yields 4-nitro deriv. M.P. 133°.

65°   Benzenesulphonic $C_6H_5 \cdot SO_3H$
Very sol. in water. On boiling under reflux with 80% H_2SO_4 yields benzene B.P. 80°. On grinding Na salt with PCl_5 yields chloride M.P. 14°, B.P. 246° d. (116°/10 mm.), which with NH_3 yields amide M.P. 153°. Anilide M.P. 105°. On fusion with KOH yields phenol M.P. 42°.

85–90°   α-Naphthalenesulphonic $C_{10}H_7 \cdot SO_3H$ (1)
On warming with conc. H_2SO_4 yields β-naphthalenesulphonic acid M.P. 124°. With Na amalgam + dil. acid yields naphthalene M.P. 80°. On boiling with $KMnO_4$ soln yields phthalic acid M.P. 195° d. Chloride M.P. 68°. Amide M.P. 150°. Anilide M.P. 112°. On fusion with KOH yields α-naphthol M.P. 94°. Benzyl-pseudo-thiourea salt M.P. 136°.

92°   p-Toluenesulphonic $CH_3 \cdot C_6H_4 \cdot SO_3H$ (1:4)
Ba salt is sol. in 5 parts of cold water. On distilling with 80% H_2SO_4 yields toluene B.P. 110°. On boiling

M.P.

with $KMnO_4$ yields p-sulphobenzoic acid M.P. 94°.
Chloride M.P. 69°. Amide M.P. 137°. Anilide M.P.
103°. On fusion with KOH yields p-cresol M.P. 35°.
Aniline salt M.P. 240°.

124° β-Naphthalenesulphonic $C_{10}H_7 \cdot SO_3H$ (2)
Unchanged on warming with conc. H_2SO_4 or on
treatment with Na amalgam. Chloride M.P. 76°.
Amide M.P. 217°. Anilide M.P. 132°. On fusion
with KOH yields β-naphthol M.P. 122°. Benzyl-
pseudo-thiourea salt M.P. 188°.

SUBSTITUTED SULPHONIC ACIDS

SOLID

M.P.

— p-Phenolsulphonic $HO \cdot C_6H_4 \cdot SO_3H$ (1:4)
Hygroscopic liquid. On distilling with MnO_2 + dil.
H_2SO_4 yields benzoquinone M.P. 115°. On heating
with PCl_5 yields p-dichlorobenzene M.P. 53°. On
warming with conc. HNO_3 yields 2:4-dinitrophenol
M.P. 114°. On warming with bromine water yields
tribromophenol M.P. 95°. Aniline salt M.P. 170° on
heating yields phenol M.P. 42° and sulphanilic acid
($q.v.$).

— 2-Naphthol-3:6-disulphonic (R Acid)

$HO \cdot C_{10}H_5(SO_3H)_2$ (2:3:6)
Deliquescent needles, very sol. in water. Na salt
(insol. in 90% alc.) reduces $AgNO_3$ soln. at once.
Benzeneazo deriv. is an orange dye. On distilling
with PCl_5 yields 2:3:6-trichloronaphthalene M.P. 90°.

— 2-Naphthol-6:8-disulphonic (G Acid)

$HO \cdot C_{10}H_5(SO_3H)_2$ (2:6:8)
Hygroscopic crysts. Na salt (sol. in 90% alc.)
reduces $AgNO_3$ soln only after several minutes.
Benzeneazo deriv. is an orange-yellow dye. On
distilling with PCl_5 yields 1:3:7-trichloronaphthalene
M.P. 113°.

70° o-Sulphobenzoic (Hydrated)
See anhydrous acid M.P. 134°.

94° p-Sulphobenzoic (Hydrated)
See anhydrous acid M.P. 259°.

96° m-Sulphobenzoic (Hydrated)
See anhydrous acid M.P. 141°.

120° 5-Sulphosalicylic $COOH \cdot C_6H_3(OH) \cdot SO_3H$ (1:2:5)
Readily sol. in water. Gives red colour with $FeCl_3$.

M.P.

On fusion with KOH yields salicylic acid M.P. 155°
and some phenol M.P. 42°.   On warming with phenol
+ POCl₃ yields diphenyl ester M.P. 177°.

122°d.   2-Naphthol-6-sulphonic (Schaeffer's)

$$HO \cdot C_{10}H_6 \cdot SO_3H \quad (2:6)$$

Soln. in water has blue fluorescence.   Gives pale green
colour with FeCl₃.   On fusion with KOH yields
2:6-dihydroxynaphthalene M.P. 218°.   On heating
with PCl₅ yields 2:6-dichloronaphthalene M.P. 136°.
With methyl sulphate + NaOH soln. yields methyl
ether (chloride M.P. 93°, amide M.P. 199°).

134°   o-Sulphobenzoic $COOH \cdot C_6H_4 \cdot SO_3H$

On warming with SOCl₂ or acetyl chloride yields anhydride M.P. 128°; with PCl₅ yields chloride M.P. 79°.
Imide M.P. 220°.   Anil M.P. 190°.   On fusion with
KOH yields salicylic acid M.P. 155°.   With phenol +
trace of H₂SO₄ at 120° yields red melt which gives red
soln. in alkalies, yellow in acids.   Aniline salt M.P.
165°.

141°   m-Sulphobenzoic $COOH \cdot C_6H_4 \cdot SO_3H \quad (1:3)$

Readily sol. in water.   Acid Ba salt is sparingly sol.
in water.   Amide M.P. 170°.   On fusion with KOH
yields m-hydroxybenzoic acid M.P. 200°.   Nitro deriv.
M.P. 96° (hydrated), M.P. 159° (anhydrous).

170°d.   1-Naphthol-4-sulphonic (Neville and Winther's)

$$HO \cdot C_{10}H_6 \cdot SO_3H \quad (1:4)$$

Does not melt sharply.   Gives transient blue colour
with FeCl₃.   Na salt (sol in 90% alc.) on heating
yields α-naphthol M.P. 94°.   On warming with conc.
HNO₃ yields 2:4-dinitro-1-naphthol M.P. 178°.   On
heating with PCl₅ yields 1:4-dichloronaphthalene M.P.
67°.

195°   d-Camphor-β-sulphonic $C_{10}H_{15}O \cdot SO_3H$

Readily sol. in water.   Optically active, $[a]_D = + 21°$
(10% in water).   With SOCl₂ yields the chloride M.P.
67°, which with dil. NH₄OH yields an amide M.P.
223°, and with conc. NH₄OH yields an amide M.P.
132°.   Anilide M.P. 119°.   Methyl ester M.P. 61°.
Ethyl ester M.P. 47°.

259°   p-Sulphobenzoic $COOH \cdot C_6H_4 \cdot SO_3H \quad (1:4)$

Readily sol. in water; forms a hydrate M.P. 94°.
Acid Ba salt is sparingly sol. in cold water.   Amide
M.P. 230°.   On fusion with KOH yields p-hydroxy-
benzoic acid M.P. 213°.   Nitro deriv. M.P. 130°.

SULPHONIC ESTERS

LIQUID

B.P.

150°/15 mm. Methyl Benzenesulphonate $C_6H_5 \cdot SO_2 \cdot OCH_3$
On boiling with dil. NaOH yields methyl alc. B.P 65°
and Na benzenesulphonate (q.v.). On boiling with
conc. KI soln. yields methyl iodide B.P. 43°. On
warming with phenol + NaOH yields anisole B.P.
154°; with β-naphthol yields β-naphthyl methyl ether
M.P. 72°. Addition compd with dimethylaniline M.P.
180°.

156°/15 mm. Ethyl Benzenesulphonate $C_6H_5 \cdot SO_2 \cdot OC_2H_5$
On boiling with dil. NaOH yields ethyl alc. B.P. 78°
and Na benzenesulphonate (q.v.). On boiling with
conc. KI soln. yields ethyl iodide B.P. 72°. On
warming with phenol + NaOH yields phenetole B.P.
172°; with β-naphthol yields β-naphthyl ethyl ether
M.P. 37°.

174°/10 mm. n-Butyl p-Toluenesulphonate
$CH_3 \cdot C_6H_4 \cdot SO_2 \cdot OC_4H_9$ (1:4)
On boiling with dil. NaOH yields n-butyl alc. B.P. 116°
and Na p-toluenesulphonate (q.v.). On boiling with
conc. KI soln yields n-butyl iodide B.P. 130°. On
warming with phenol + NaOH yields phenyl n-butyl
ether B.P. 210°.

SOLID

B.P.

28° Methyl p-Toluenesulphonate $CH_3 \cdot C_6H_4 \cdot SO_2 \cdot OCH_3$ (1:4)
B.P. 161°/10 mm. Addition compd. with dimethyl-
aniline M.P. 160°. Cf. Methyl Benzenesulphonate
B.P. 150°/15 mm.

32° Ethyl p-Toluenesulphonate $CH_3 \cdot C_6H_4 \cdot SO_2 \cdot OC_2H_5$ (1:4)
B.P. 173°/15 mm. Addition compd. with dimethyl-
aniline M.P. 48°. Cf. Ethyl Benzenesulphonate B.P.
156°/15 mm.

35° Phenyl Benzenesulphonate $C_6H_5 \cdot SO_2 \cdot OC_6H_5$
On heating with very conc. NaOH to about 200° yields
phenol M.P. 42° and Na benzenesulphonate (q.v.) On
warming with C_2H_5ONa in alc. yields phenetole B.P.
172°. With conc. $HNO_3 + H_2SO_4$ yields dinitro
deriv. M.P. 132°, which on boiling with NaOH soln.
yields p-nitrophenol M.P. 114° and Na m-nitrobenzene-
sulphonate (q.v.).

B.P.
39°   *o*-Cresyl Benzenesulphonate $C_6H_5 \cdot SO_2 \cdot OC_6H_4 \cdot CH_3$ (1:2)
On heating with very conc. NaOH to about 200°
yields *o*-cresol M.P. 31° and Na benzenesulphonate
(*q.v.*). On warming with C_2H_5ONa in alc. yields
o-cresyl ethyl ether B.P. 180°.

43°   *p*-Cresyl Benzenesulphonate $C_6H_5 \cdot SO_2 \cdot OC_6H_4 \cdot CH_3$ (1:4)
On heating with very conc. NaOH to about 200°
yields *p*-cresol M.P. 35° and Na benzenesulphonate
(*q.v.*). On warming with C_2H_5ONa in alc. yields
p-cresyl ethyl ether B.P. 189°.

45°   *m*-Cresyl Benzenesulphonate $C_6H_5 \cdot SO_2 \cdot OC_6H_4 \cdot CH_3$ (1:3)
On heating with very conc. NaOH to about 200°
yields *m*-cresol B.P. 202° and Na benzenesulphonate
(*q.v.*). On warming with C_2H_5ONa in alc. yields
m-cresyl ethyl ether B.P. 192°.

51°   *m*-Cresyl *p*-Toluenesulphonate
$$CH_3 \cdot C_6H_4 \cdot SO_2 \cdot OC_6H_4 \cdot CH_3 \ (4:3')$$
Cf. *m*-Cresyl Benzenesulphonate M.P. 45°.

53°   *o*-Cresyl *p*-Toluenesulphonate
$$CH_3 \cdot C_6H_4 \cdot SO_2 \cdot OC_6H_4 \cdot CH_3 \ (4:2')$$
Cf. *o*-Cresyl Benzenesulphonate M.P. 39°.

69°   *p*-Cresyl *p*-Toluenesulphonate
$$CH_3 \cdot C_6H_4 \cdot SO_2 \cdot OC_6H_4 \cdot CH_3 \ (4:4')$$
Cf. *p*-Cresyl Benzenesulphonate M.P. 43°.

95°   Phenyl *p*-Toluenesulphonate $CH_3 \cdot C_6H_4 \cdot SO_2 \cdot OC_6H_5$
Cf. Phenyl Benzenesulphonate M.P. 35°. With conc.
$H_2SO_4 + HNO_3$ yields a dinitro deriv. M.P. 115°, which
on boiling with NaOH yields *p*-nitrophenol M.P. 114°
and Na 2-nitro-4-toluenesulphonate (chloride M.P.
36°, amide M.P. 144°).

ALKYL SULPHATES

LIQUID

B.P.
188°   Methyl Sulphate $SO_2(OCH_3)_2$
D. 1·321 (25°). Insol. in cold water; hydrolysed on
boiling. Odourless (vapour very poisonous). On
boiling with dil. NaOH yields methyl alc. B.P. 65° and
Na methylsulphate; on boiling with conc. KI soln
yields methyl iodide B.P. 43°. With phenol + dil.
NaOH yields anisole B.P. 154°; with β-naphthol
yields β-naphthyl methyl ether M.P. 72°. With
aniline yields dimethylaniline B.P. 193°.

SULPHINIC ACIDS

272

B.P.
208°

Ethyl Sulphate $SO_2(OC_2H_5)_2$

D. 1·172 (25°). Insol. in cold water; slowly hydrolysed on boiling. On boiling with dil. NaOH yields
ethyl alc. B.P. 78° and Na ethylsulphate; on
boiling with conc. KI soln. yields ethyl iodide B.P. 72°.
With phenol + dil. NaOH in warm yields phenetole
B.P. 172°; β-naphthyl ethyl ether M.P. 37°. With
aniline yields ethylaniline B.P. 206° and diethylaniline
B.P. 216°.

ALKYLSULPHURIC ACIDS

LIQUID

Methylsulphuric $CH_3O·SO_2OH$

Free acid is a hygroscopic liquid. Na and K salts are
sol. in alc. NH_4 salt M.P. 135°. Ca salt is extremely
sol. in water. Gives no pptè with $BaCl_2$ in dil. HCl in
cold; $BaSO_4$ pptes. on boiling. On warming soln. of
salt with Na_2S yields methyl sulphide B.P. 37°.

Ethylsulphuric $C_2H_5O·SO_2OH$

Free acid is a hygroscopic liquid. Na and K salts are
sol. in alc. NH_4 salt M.P. 99°. Ca and Ba salts are
extremely sol. in water. Gives no pptè with $BaCl_2$
in dil. HCl in cold; $BaSO_4$ is ppted slowly on boiling. On warming soln of salt with Na_2S yields ethyl
sulphide B.P. 92°.

SULPHINIC ACIDS

SOLID

M.P.
83°

Benzenesulphinic $C_6H_5·SO_2H$

Slightly sol. in cold water, readily in ether. With
$KMnO_4$ soln. yields benzenesulphonic acid (q.v.).
With Zn dust + HCl yields thiophenol B.P. 169°.
With H_2S in very dil. alc. soln. yields phenyl disulphide
M.P. 60°. With PCl_5 yields benzenesulphochloride
M.P. 14°, B.P. 246°d. On fusion with KOH yields
benzene B.P. 80°.

86°

p-Toluenesulphinic $CH_3·C_6H_4·SO_2H$ (1:4)

Slightly sol. in cold water, readily in ether. With
$KMnO_4$ soln. yields p-toluenesulphonic acid M.P. 92°.
With Zn dust + HCl yields p-thiocresol M.P. 43°.
With H_2S in very dil. alc. soln. yields p-tolyl disulphide
M.P. 48°. With PCl_5 yields p-toluenesulphochloride
M.P. 69°. On fusion with KOH yields toluene B.P.
110°.

THIOCARBOXYLIC ACIDS

LIQUID

B.P.
93° Thioacetic   CH$_3$·COSH
     Pale yellow. Unpleasant odour. D. 1·074 (10°).
     Sol. in 20 vols. of cold water ; soln. on boiling yields
     H$_2$S and acetic acid. With CuSO$_4$ gives red-brown
     ppte of Cu salt which blackens on boiling. With
     aniline yields H$_2$S and acetanilide M.P. 114°.

SOLID

M.P.
24° Thiobenzoic   C$_6$H$_5$·COSH
     • Oxidised in ether soln. by air to benzoyl disulphide
     M.P. 130°. On long boiling with water, or with dil.
     NaOH, yields benzoic acid M.P. 121° and H$_2$S. With
     aniline yields H$_2$S and benzanilide M.P. 161°.

SULPHOCHLORIDES

SOLID

M.P
10° o-Toluenesulphochloride   CH$_3$·C$_6$H$_4$·SO$_2$Cl (1:2)
     B.P. 126°/10 mm. D. 1·339 (20°). Insol. in and very
     slowly decomposed by cold water ; on boiling yields
     o-toluenesulphonic acid M.P. 57° and HCl. With Zn
     dust + dil. HCl yields o-thiocresol M.P. 15°, B.P.
     194°. Amide M.P. 153°. Anilide M.P. 136°. Phenyl
     ester M.P. 52°.

14° Benzenesulphochloride   C$_6$H$_5$·SO$_2$Cl
     B.P. 246°d. (116°/10 mm.). D. 1·274 (20°). Insol.
     in and very slowly decomposed by cold water ; on
     boiling yields benzenesulphonic acid M.P. 65° and
     HCl. With Zn dust + dil. HCl yields thiophenol
     B.P. 169°. Amide M.P. 153°. Anilide M.P. 105°.
     Phenyl ester M.P. 35°.

68° α-Naphthalenesulphochloride   C$_{10}$H$_7$·SO$_2$Cl (1)
     B.P. 194°/13 mm. On boiling with water yields
     α-naphthalenesulphonic acid M.P. 85–90° and HCl.
     With Zn dust + dil. HCl yields α-thionaphthol B.P.
     285°d. (145°/10 mm.). Amide M.P. 150°. Anilide
     M.P. 112°. Phenyl ester M.P. 75°.

69° p-Toluenesulphochloride   CH$_3$·C$_6$H$_4$·SO$_2$Cl (1:4)
     B.P. 145°/15 mm. On boiling with water yields
     p-toluenesulphonic acid M.P. 92° and HCl. With Zn
     dust + dil. HCl yields p-thiocresol M.P. 43°. Amide
     M.P. 137°. Anilide M.P. 103°. Phenyl ester M.P. 95°.

M.P.
76°   β-Naphthalenesulphochloride $C_{10}H_7 \cdot SO_2Cl$ (2)
      B.P. 201°/13 mm. On boiling with water yields
      β-naphthalenesulphonic acid M.P. 124° and HCl.
      With Zn dust + dil. HCl yields β-thionaphthol M.P.
      81°. Amide M.P. 217°. Anilide M.P. 132°. Phenyl
      ester M.P. 98°.

SULPHONAMIDES

SOLID

M.P.
137°   p-Toluenesulphonamide $CH_3 \cdot C_6H_4 \cdot SO_2NH_2$ (1:4)
       Sparingly sol. in cold water; sol. in dil. NaOH, alc.,
       and ether. On boiling with 20% HCl yields NH_4
       p-toluenesulphonate; with 75% H_2SO_4 yields toluene
       B.P. 110°. With methyl sulphate + dil. NaOH yields
       dimethyl deriv. M.P. 79°. With (1 mol.) benzyl
       chloride + NaOH in dil. alc. yields benzyl deriv. M.P.
       116°. With $KMnO_4$ soln. yields p-sulphonamido
       benzoic acid d. 280°.

150°   α-Naphthalenesulphonamide $C_{10}H_7 \cdot SO_2NH_2$ (1)
       Almost insol. in cold water; sol. in dil. NaOH, alc.,
       and ether. On boiling with 20% HCl yields NH_4
       α-naphthalenesulphonate. With (1 mol.) benzyl chlor-
       ide + NaOH in alc. yields benzyl deriv. M.P. 137°.

153°   Benzenesulphonamide $C_6H_5 \cdot SO_2NH_2$
       Sparingly sol. in cold water; sol. in dil. NaOH, alc.,
       and ether. On boiling with 20% HCl yields NH_4
       benzenesulphonate; with 80% H_2SO_4 yields benzene
       B.P. 80°. With methyl sulphate + dil. NaOH
       yields dimethyl deriv. M.P. 47°. With (1 mol.)
       benzyl chloride + NaOH in dil. alc. yields benzyl
       deriv. M.P. 88°.

153°   o-Toluenesulphonamide $CH_3 \cdot C_6H_4 \cdot SO_2NH_2$ (1:2)
       Sparingly sol. in cold water; sol. in dil. NaOH, alc.,
       and ether. On boiling with 20% HCl yields NH_4
       o-toluenesulphonate; with 75% H_2SO_4 yields toluene
       B.P. 110°. With $K_3Fe(CN)_6$ soln. yields o-sulphon-
       amidobenzoic acid M.P. 154°, which on heating
       yields o-sulphobenzoic imide M.P. 220°.

217°   β-Naphthalenesulphonamide $C_{10}H_7 \cdot SO_2NH_2$ (2)
       Almost insol. in cold water; sol. in dil. NaOH,
       slightly sol. in ether. On boiling with 20% HCl
       yields NH_4 β-naphthalenesulphonate. With methyl
       sulphate + dil. NaOH yields dimethyl deriv. M.P. 96°.

With (1 mol.) benzyl chloride + NaOH in alc. yields
benzyl deriv. M.P. 124°.

220° o-Sulphobenzoic Imide

$$C_6H_4 \underset{SO_2}{\overset{CO}{\diagup \diagdown}} NH \quad (1{:}2)$$

Almost insol. in water, readily sol. in dil. NaOH or
Na_2CO_3. Na deriv. (' saccharin ') has intensely sweet
taste. On boiling with 20% HCl yields NH_4 o-sulpho-
benzoate M.P. about 175°, which on warming with
$SOCl_2$ yields o-sulphobenzoic anhydride M.P. 128°.
On warming at 120° with resorcinol + conc. H_2SO_4
yields sulphonfluorescein (forms red soln. in dil. NaOH
with green fluorescence). With methyl sulphate +
dil. NaOH yields methyl deriv. M.P. 131°. With
benzyl chloride + NaOH in alc. yields benzyl. deriv.
M.P. 118°. p-Nitrobenzyl deriv. M.P. 174°.

SUBSTITUTED SULPHONAMIDES

SOLID

M.P.
103° p-Toluenesulphonanilide $CH_3 \cdot C_6H_4 \cdot SO_2 \cdot NH \cdot C_6H_5$ (1:4)
Insol. in water ; sol. in very dil. NaOH and in most
organic liquids. Na deriv. is slightly sol. in conc.
NaOH. On boiling with 20% HCl yields p-toluenesulphonic acid (q.v.) and aniline B.P. 183°. With
methyl sulphate + dil. NaOH yields methyl deriv.
M.P. 94°, which on boiling with HCl yields methylaniline B.P. 193°.

112° Benzenesulphonanilide $C_6H_5 \cdot SO_2$ NH$\cdot C_6H_5$
Resembles p-Toluenesulphonanilide (above). Methyl
deriv. M.P. 79°. With benzyl chloride + NaOH in
alc. yields benzyl deriv. M.P. 119°.

THIOAMIDES
Simple and Substituted

SOLID

M.P.
74° Allylthiourea $CH_2{:}CH \cdot CH_2 \cdot NH \cdot CS \cdot NH_2$
Readily sol. in hot water and in alc. ; insol. in benzene.
On boiling with conc. NaOH yields Na_2S, NH_3, and
allylamine B.P. 53°. Yields Ag_2S with ammon.
$AgNO_3$. With ethyl iodide in alc. forms addition
product M.P. 72°. With acetyl chloride in acetone
yields S-acetyl deriv. M.P. 103°d., which with NaOH
yields N-acetyl deriv. M.P. 95°. With bromine in
alc. yields bromopropylene-iso-thiourea HBr M.P. 140°.

M.P.

153° Thiocarbanilide $C_6H_5\cdot NH\cdot CS\cdot NH\cdot C_6H_5$

Insol. in water; sol. in dil. NaOH and in alc. On boiling with conc. NaOH yields aniline B.P. 183° and Na_2S. On boiling with 20% HCl yields phenyl isothiocyanate B.P. 221° (sharp odour) and aniline HCl. With methyl sulphate + 15% NaOH yields S-methyl deriv. M.P. 109°. On boiling with HgO in alc. yields HgS and carbanilide M.P. 238°.

154° Phenylthiourea $C_6H_5\cdot NH\cdot CS\cdot NH_2$

Sol. in hot water, in alc., and in dil. NaOH. On boiling with conc. NaOH yields NH_3, Na_2S, and aniline B.P. 183°. On boiling with 20% HCl yields phenyl isothiocyanate B.P. 221° (sharp odour) and NH_4Cl. On heating with aniline yields thiocarbanilide M.P. 153° and NH_3.

180° Thiourea $NH_2\cdot CS\cdot NH_2$

Sol. in 11 parts of cold water; sparingly sol. in ether and in cold abs. alc. After melting gives test for NH_4SCN. On boiling with conc. NaOH yields NH_3, Na_2S, and NaSCN. With $K_4Fe(CN)_6$ + dil. acetic acid gives green colour, soon changing to blue. Forms addition compd with NH_4SCN M.P. 144°. On heating with benzyl chloride in dil. alc. yields benzyl-iso-thiourea HCl M.P. 174°. On heating with methyl sulphate + water yields methyl-iso-thiourea sulphate M.P. 241°, which with NH_4OH yields methyl mercaptan B.P. 6° and guanidine sulphate (q.v.). On standing with methyl iodide yields methyl-iso-thiourea HI M.P. 117°. On warming with ethyl sodiomalonate in abs. alc. yields thiobarbituric acid M.P. 235°.

182° Thiosemicarbazide $NH_2\cdot CS\cdot NH\cdot NH_2$

Sol. in water. Hydrochloride M.P. 188°. On boiling with conc. NaOH yields NH_3, Na_2S, and hydrazine. On warming with acetic anhydride yields acetyl deriv. M.P. 165°. With acetone yields isopropylidene deriv. M.P. 179°. Benzal deriv. M.P. 159°. With 2:4-dinitrochlorobenzene yields dinitrophenyl deriv. M.P. 210°d. On warming with methyl iodide in abs. alc. yields addition product M.P. 140°.

SULPHUR-CONTAINING AMINO ACID

d.260° l-Cystine $COOH\cdot CH(NH_2)\cdot CH_2\cdot S\cdot S\cdot CH_2\cdot CH(NH_2)\cdot COOH$

Almost insol. in water and in dil. acetic acid; sol. in dil. HCl and in NH_4OH. Sol. with decomp. in dil. NaOH or Na_2CO_3 (yielding Na_2S). Optically

active ; $[a]_{\text{D}}$ in dil. HCl $= -224°$. Forms a blue insol.
Cu salt. With Sn + HCl yields cysteine (sol. in
water; gives blue colour with $FeCl_3$). With $NaHCO_3$
soln + benzoyl chloride yields benzoyl deriv. M.P.
180°. β-Naphthalenesulphonyl deriv. M.P. 214°.

AMINOSULPHONIC ACIDS

SOLID

d.   Metanilic $NH_2 \cdot C_6H_4 \cdot SO_3H$ (1:3)
Decomposes on heating above 300°. Sol. in about
60 parts of cold water. Yields no quinone on boiling
with MnO_2 + dil. H_2SO_4. With bromine water
yields sol. di- and tribromo derivs. On heating Na
salt with NaOH at 280–290° yields m-aminophenol
M.P. 122°.

d.   Sulphanilic $NH_2 \cdot C_6H_4 \cdot SO_3H$ (1:4)
Decomposes on heating above 300°. Sol. in about
170 parts of cold water. On heating Na salt with
NaOH yields aniline B.P. 183°. With bromine water
yields 2:4:6-tribromoaniline M.P. 119°. On boiling
with MnO_2 + dil. H_2SO_4 yields benzoquinone M.P.
115°. Diazo deriv. is colourless, almost insol. in
water, explosive when dry. Azo-β-naphthol deriv.
is an orange dye. On heating with PCl_5 yields
p-chlorosulphonanilide of dichlorophosphoric acid
$(POCl_2 \cdot NH \cdot C_6H_4 \cdot SO_2Cl)$ M.P. 158°.

d.   Naphthionic $NH_2 \cdot C_{10}H_7 \cdot SO_3H$ (1:4)
Chars without melting. Almost insol. in cold water
and dil. acids, sol. in dil. NaOH. Salts have blue
fluorescence in soln. On heating with NaOH or on
boiling with 75% H_2SO_4 yields α-naphthylamine
M.P. 50°. Diazo deriv. is sol. in water. Azo-β-
naphthol deriv. is a red dye.

NITROSULPHONIC ACIDS

SOLID

M.P.
48° m-Nitrobenzenesulphonic $NO_2 \cdot C_6H_4 \cdot SO_3H$ (1:3)
Readily sol. in cold water, less so in conc. HCl. On
reduction with Sn + HCl yields metanilic acid (q.v.).
With PCl_5 yields chloride M.P. 60° (yields sulphinic
acid M.P. 98° with cold $NaHSO_3$ soln.). Amide M.P.
161°. Anilide M.P. 131°.

M.P.
86°   2-Nitrotoluene-4-sulphonic $CH_3 \cdot C_6H_3(NO_2) \cdot SO_3H$ (1:2:4)
Resembles *m*-Nitrobenzenesulphonic acid (above).
Chloride M.P. 36°. Amide M.P. 144°. Anilide M.P.
109°.

133°   4-Nitrotoluene-2-sulphonic $CH_3 \cdot C_6H_3(NO_2) \cdot SO_3H$ (1:4:2)
Resembles *m*-Nitrotoluenesulphonic acid (above), but
is less sol. Chloride M.P. 44°. Amide M.P. 186°.
Anilide M.P. 148°.

THIOCYANATES

LIQUID

B.P.
130°   Methyl $CH_3 \cdot SCN$
D. 1·078 (16°). Almost insol. in water. On boiling
with alc. KOH yields NH_3, KCN, K_2CO_3 and methyl
disulphide B.P. 110°. With Zn + HCl yields methyl
mercaptan B.P. 6° and HCN.

145°   Ethyl $C_2H_5 \cdot SCN$
D. 1·015 (15°). Insol. in water. On boiling with
alc. KOH yields NH_3, KCN, K_2CO_3 and ethyl disulphide B.P. 153°. With Zn + HCl yields ethyl mercaptan B.P. 36° and HCN.

182°   *n*-Butyl $CH_3 \cdot CH_2 \cdot CH_2 \cdot CH_2 \cdot SCN$
D. 0·967 (17°). Insol. in water. On boiling with alc.
KOH yields NH_3, KCN, K_2CO_3 and butyl disulphide
B.P. 234°. With Zn + HCl yields butyl mercaptan
B.P. 97° and HCN.

SOLID

M.P.
41°   Benzyl $C_6H_5 \cdot CH_2 \cdot SCN$
B.P. 256°. Insol. in water. With HNO_3 yields
benzoic acid M.P. 121° and some benzaldehyde B.P.
179°. On boiling with alc. KOH yields NH_3, KCN,
K_2CO_3 and benzyl disulphide M.P. 71°. With Zn +
HCl yields benzyl mercaptan B.P. 194° and HCN.

*ISO*THIOCYANATES

LIQUID

B.P.
150°   Allyl $CH_2 : CH \cdot CH_2 \cdot N : CS$
Very sharp odour. D. 1·016 (15°). Slightly sol. in
water, readily in alc. On long boiling with 20%
HCl yields COS and allylamine B.P. 53°. On warming with NH_4OH yields allylthiourea M.P. 74°. On

B.P.

      gently warming with aniline yields allyl phenyl-thiourea M.P. 98°.

221°   Phenyl $C_6H_5 \cdot N:CS$

      Sharp odour. D. 1·129 (23°). Insol. in water. On warming with NH_4OH yields phenylthiourea M.P. 154°; with aniline yields thiocarbanilide M.P. 153°.

ARYL PHOSPHATES

LIQUID

B.P.

264°   Tri-o-cresyl $PO(OC_6H_4 \cdot CH_3)_3$ (1:2)
/20 mm.   Heavy oil, insol. in water. D. 1·192 (19°). With HNO_3 in acetic acid yields 6-nitro-o-cresol M.P. 69°. On heating with KCN yields o-tolunitrile B.P. 204° and o-cresol M.P. 31°.

SOLID

M.P.

48°   Triphenyl $PO(OC_6H_5)_3$

      B.P. 245°/11 mm. On heating with C_2H_5ONa in abs. alc. yields phenetole B.P. 172°; with $Ba(OH)_2$ in alc. yields phenol M.P. 42° and Ba diphenyl-phosphate (free acid M.P. 61°). With conc. H_2SO_4 + HNO_3 yields tri-p-nitro deriv. M.P. 155°. On heating with KCN yields benzonitrile B.P. 190° and phenol.

78°   Tri-p-cresyl $PO(OC_6H_4 \cdot CH_3)_3$ (1:4)

      Resembles Triphenyl Phosphate (above). On heating with KCN yields p-tolunitrile M.P. 29° and p-cresol M.P. 35°.

ALKALOIDS

Alkaloids, in common with many other basic nitrogenous substances, yield in general precipitates when aqueous solutions of their salts are treated with the following general reagents :

Sodium carbonate :   white or yellowish ppte. of free alkaloid.
Phosphomolybdic acid :   white or yellowish ppte.
Phosphotungstic acid :   white or yellowish ppte.
Platinic chloride :   light yellow or yellow ppte.
Auric chloride :   yellow ppte.
Iodine in KI :   brown ppte.
Mercuric iodide in KI :   white or yellowish ppte.
Bismuth iodide in KI :   white or yellowish ppte.
Tannic acid :   white or yellowish ppte.
Picric acid :   yellow ppte, often crystalline.

Colours are produced with many alkaloids by the special reagents indicated below :
  (I) Concentrated sulphuric acid.
 (II) Concentrated sulphuric acid and subsequent addition of a small quantity of finely powdered $K_2Cr_2O_7$.
(III) Erdmann's reagent ; concentrated sulphuric acid containing 0.5% or less of HNO_3.
(IV) Fröhde's reagent : a solution of about 1 gram of sodium or ammonium molybdate in 100 c.c. of conc. H_2SO_4.
 (V) Mandelin's reagent : a solution of about 1 gram of sodium metavanadate in 100 c.c. of conc. H_2SO_4. Any other convenient vanadate, vanadic oxide, or a vanadic salt may be employed for this reagent.
(VI) The alkaloid is intimately mixed with five times its weight of powdered cane sugar and the mass moistened with conc. H_2SO_4.

The colour reactions of a few of the most common alkaloids with the above reagents are set forth in tabular form on the opposite page.

LIQUID

B.P.
170°   *d*-Coniine

      Dextrorotatory, $[a]_D^{19°} = +16°$.   D. 0.862   (0°) Fairly sol. in water or CS_2, miscible with organic liquids. After standing for five minutes with alcoholic CS_2 the mixture gives a brown ppte with $CuSO_4$. Colours phenolphthalein pink in 50% alcohol. Gives a white ppte with $HgCl_2$. With HCl gas gives red colour changing to blue. Hydrochloride M.P. 208°. Acetyl deriv. B.P. 125°/14 mm. Benzoyl deriv. is an oil.

250°   Nicotine

      Levorotatory, $[a]_D = -161°$. Miscible with water or organic liquids. On warming with conc. HCl gives light violet or brown colour, changed to orange with conc. HNO_3. On warming one drop with 2 c.c. of epichlorohydrin gives red colour. Colours phenolphthalein pink only in presence of water or very dil. alcohol.

SOLID

M.P.
57°   Quinine (Hydrated). See Quinine M.P. 175°.
98°   Cocaine

      Levorotatory, $[a]_D^{20°} = -15°$ (in $CHCl_3$). Sparingly sol. in water, readily in organic liquids. With $KMnO_4$

Brucine.	Pink.	Red-brown.	Yellow, then red.	Red, then red-brown.	Pink, then orange.	—
Cevadine.	Yellow; red on warming.	Dull green.	Yellow, then red.	Yellow, then red, then slowly green.	Dull yellow, then red.	Yellow, then green, then blue.
Cinchonine.	Colourless; brown on warming.	Clear green.	—	—	Colourless; violet with one drop of conc. HNO_3	—
Cocaine.	Colourless.	Dull brown.	Yellow.		—	—
Codeine.	Colourless; blue on warming.	Dull brown.	Red.	Green, then blue.	Dull blue-green.	Pink; then purple, then slowly blue.
Coniine.	Colourless.	Clear green.	Colourless.	Pink-yellow.	Colourless.	Colourless.
Morphine.	Pink; violet, then brown on warming.	Greenish brown.	Pink.	Purple, then green.	Purple, then gray.	Red.
Narcotine.	Greenish yellow; brown, then red, then violet on warming.	Brown.	Orange-yellow.	Green.	Orange, then pink.	Brown.
Nicotine.	Colourless; brown on warming.	Dull green.	Colourless.	Colourless.	Colourless.	Colourless.
Quinine.	Colourless with blue fluorescence.	Clear green.	—	Green.	Colourless; violet with one drop of conc. HNO_3.	—
Strychnine.	Colourless.	Blue-violet.	—	—	Blue, then violet; red on warming. Pink with NH_4OH.	—

salts give purple ppte. of the permanganate. **With**
K_2CrO_4 in presence of HCl gives yellow ppte. On
warming with conc. H_2SO_4 and C_2H_5OH yields
characteristic odour of ethyl benzoate. On hydrolysis yields CH_3OH, benzoic acid M.P. 121°, and
ecgonine M.P. 198°d. Hydrochloride M.P. 186°.
Mercuridhloride M.P. 123°. With aqueous iodine on
solns. of salts yields periodide M.P. 161°. Methiodide
M.P. 164°.

105° Brucine (Hydrated). See Brucine M.P. 178°.

108° Hyoscyamine (*l*.Atropine)
Levorotatory, $[a]_D = -21°$ (in abs. alc.). Sparingly sol. in water, readily in organic liquids. On
heating yields atropine M.P. 115° partially; completely on warming with alcoholic KOH. Gives
purple colour with conc. HNO_3. On warming to 85°
with acetic anhydride yields apoatropine M.P. 60°.
Platinichloride M.P. 200°d. Aurichloride M.P. 165°
(does not melt under hot water). Picrate M.P. 165°.

115° Atropine (*dl*. Hyoscyamine)
Optically inactive. Almost insol. in water, fairly sol.
in ether or benzene, readily in alc. and $CHCl_3$. On
evaporating to dryness on water-bath with fuming
HNO_3, and adding KOH to residue, gives violet
colour changing to red. On adding aqueous $HgCl_2$
to alcoholic soln. gives yellow ppte. On warming
to 85° with acetic anhydride yields apoatropine
M.P. 60°. Hydrochloride M.P. 165°. Hydrobromide
M.P. 162°. Platinichloride M.P. 207°d. Aurichloride
M.P. 137° (melts under hot water). Picrate M.P. 175°.

128° Piperine
Optically inactive. Insol. in water, sol. in organic
liquids. On hydrolysis yields piperic acid M.P. 216°
and piperidine B.P. 105°. Soln. in conc. H_2SO_4
yellow changing to greenish brown. See Substituted
Amides.

146° Cevadine (Hydrated). See Cevadine M.P. 205°.

147° Papaverine
Optically inactive. Insol. in water or ether, sparingly
sol. in benzene or cold alc., sol. in $CHCl_3$. Soln.
in conc. H_2SO_4 colourless, changing to violet on
warming. On adding $K_2Cr_2O_7$ to soln. in dil. acid,
yields orange or yellow ppte. of bichromate. With
bromine water yields bromo deriv. M.P. 144°. Hydro-

M.P

chloride M.P. 220°d.   Hydrobromide M.P. 213°d.
Platinichloride M.P. 198°.   Picrate M.P. 179°d.

155°   Codeine
Levorotatory, $a = -13°$ (in alcohol).   Fairly sol.
in water, readily in alc. or $CHCl_3$, insol. in ligroin.
Gives no colour with $FeCl_3$.   With H_2SO_4 and then
adding a crystal of $FeSO_4$ gives blue colour.   Hydrochloride M.P. 264°.

171°   Quinidine
Dextrorotatory, $[a]_D = +274°$ (in 1 vol alc. + 2
vols $CHCl_3$).   Almost insol. in water, $CHCl_3$, CS_2, or
ligroin, readily sol. in alc. or ether.   Gives dull ppte.
with Kl.   With small quantity bromine water and
then adding a few drops H_4OH gives green colour.
Hydrochloride on heating alone gives violet colour
and violet vapours.   Soln. in dil. H_2SO_4 fluoresces
blue.   With Mandelin's reagent same as Quinine.

175°   Quinine
Levorotatory, $[a]_D^{15°} = -142°$ (5% in alc.).   Sparingly
sol. in water, sol. in organic liquids.   Somewhat sol.
in NH_4OH.   Soln. of sulphate gives white ppte. with
NH_4, oxalate.   Soln. in mixture of acetic acid and
alc. gives black ppte on warming with alc. iodine.
With small quantity of bromine water and then
adding a few drops of NH_4OH gives green coloration,
changed to red on addition of $K_3Fe(CN)_6$.   Hydrochloride on heating alone assumes violet colour and
gives off violet vapours.

176°   Narcotine
Levorotatory in neutral soln., dextrorotatory in acid
soln.   Almost insol. in water, sol. in organic liquids.
Salts react acid in soln.   With conc. H_2SO_4 gives
green coloration changing to red-brown, dull violet
on warming.   On adding $K_2Cr_2O_7$ to soln. in conc.
H_2SO_4 gives brown colour.   On warming with conc.
H_2SO_4 and adding a drop of $FeCl_3$ gives red-brown
colour changing to crimson.   Green coloration with
Fröhde's reagent.   With Erdmann's reagent gives
orange yellow colour.   With Mandelin's reagent gives
orange colour changing to pink.   With sugar and conc.
H_2SO_4 gives brown colour.

178°   Brucine
Levorotatory, $[a]_D =$ about $-120°$ (in $CHCl_3$).   Soln.
in conc. H_2SO_4 pink, slowly changing to yellow.

M.P.

Red colour with conc. HNO_3, changing to yellow-brown on evaporating at 100° : residue gives violet colour with $SnCl_2$. Gives red colour on warming with soln. of $HgNO_3$.

205° Cevadine (Veratrine)

Optically inactive. Insol. in water, sol. in organic liquids. Soln. in conc. H_2SO_4 yellow, changing to red on warming. Soln. in conc. HCl violet, changing to red on boiling. On distillation alone yields β-picoline B.P. 143°. Mercurichloride M.P. 172°d. Benzoyl deriv. M.P. 170–180°.

207° Cinchonidine

Levorotatory, $[a]_D = -108°$ (in 1 vol. alc. + 2 vols. $CHCl_3$). Almost insol. in water or ether, sol. in alc. or $CHCl_3$. Solns. not fluorescent. Gives no colour with bromine water and NH_4OH. With PCl_5 in $CHCl_3$ yields chloride M.P. 108°, which with Fe filings in dil. H_2SO_4 yields desoxycinchonidine M.P. 61°. Acetyl deriv. M.P. 42°.

230° Morphine

Levorotatory, $[a]_D$ in NaOH = about −70°. Almost insol. in water, cold alc., ether, benzene, or $CHCl_3$. Somewhat sol. in hot ethyl or amyl alcs. Sol. in excess of NaOH, not in NH_4OH. Soln. in conc. H_2SO_4 pink, changing to orange ; violet, then brown on warming. Red colour with conc. HNO_3, changing to yellow on warming. On heating to 100° with conc. H_2SO_4 and adding a small crystal of $FeSO_4$ gives red colour, changing to violet. Solns. of salts liberate iodine from HIO_3. In presence of dil. acetic acid gives blue colour with $FeCl_3$, changing to red on warming. Reduces $FeCl_3$ to $FeCl_2$, resulting soln. giving blue ppte with $K_3Fe(CN)_6$. With a soln. of 1 drop of formalin in 1 c.c. conc. H_2SO_4 gives purple colour, changing to blue.

264° Cinchonine

Dextrorotatory, $[a]_D = +229°$ (0·2% in alc.). Almost insol. in cold water or ether, fairly sol. in alc. or $CHCl_3$ without fluorescence. With a small quantity of chlorine water and then a few drops of NH_4OH gives light yellow ppte. On adding $K_4Fe(CN)_6$ to soln. of salts gives yellow ppte. (sol. in hot water, crystallising on cooling). Hydrochloride on heating assumes violet colour and evolves violet vapours.

M.P.
268°   Strychnine

Levorotatory in alc. Almost insol. in cold water,
ether, or benzene; sol. in hot alc. or $CHCl_3$. More
sol. in aqueous alc. than in either water or absolute
alc. Dissolves in conc. H_2SO_4 to colourless soln,
unchanged on warming; soln. gives blue colour,
changing to red, and finally yellow, on addition of
1 drop of HNO_3 and a crystal of $K_2Cr_2O_7$.

EXAMINATION OF DYES

The qualitative investigation of dyes and colouring matters,
while not differing essentially from the examination of other
organic compounds, has nevertheless been systematised to such
an extent that it may be stated to resemble in a considerable
degree the systematic qualitative investigation of inorganic
substances.

Before proceeding upon the lines of the scheme developed
by Rota,[1] indicated below, it is advisable to ascertain what
elements and ionisable metals or acids are present in the pure
dye. This will then limit the deductions which may be drawn
from the systematic investigation.

In the scheme of Rota, dyes are first divided into two categories by the addition of 4 or 5 drops of concentrated hydrochloric acid and a similar amount of a 10% solution of stannous
chloride upon 5 c.c. of a 0.1% solution of the dye in water
or aqueous alcohol. Should this solution appear to be decolorised
owing to reduction, but only incompletely, the solution may be
warmed nearly to boiling, with further addition, if necessary, of
stannous chloride. The first category includes all dyes whose
solutions are decolorised by this reducing agent; the second includes those whose colour in presence of hydrochloric acid per-
sists after addition of the stannous chloride.

I. Includes nitro, nitroso, azo, and quinoneimide dyes.

II. Includes hydroxyquinone and triphenylmethane dyes.

These two categories are each subdivided into two classes:

I. To the colourless reduced solution add a few drops of $FeCl_3$
solution, or shake with air after neutralising with dilute
alkali.

Class Ia. Includes dyes whose reduction products are not
reoxidised to the original dyes, owing to the
formation of amines:
Nitro, Nitroso, and *Azo* dyes.

[1] *Chem. Zeit.* (1898), 437.

Ib. Includes dyes which form leuco bases by the action
of stannous chloride and are therefore regenerated on oxidation :
Quinoneimide dyes.

II. To the warm aqueous solution add a few drops of strong
potash.

Class IIa. The solution is decolorised, or a turbidity is
produced : dyes containing basic radicles, such
as *Di-* and *Triphenylmethane amino* dyes,
Auramines, *Acridines*, &c.

Class IIb. The solution is unaltered in appearance : dyes
containing acid groups, such as : *Diphenylmethane*
and *Hydroxyketonic* dyes containing no basic
radicles.

These classes may be considered independently, information
as to their nature being obtained from their behaviour towards
ether in presence of dilute alkali and acid, towards a solution of
ferric chloride, and towards cotton, silk, and wool fibres.

Class Ia.

(1) **Nitro** dyes. Yellow or orange in colour ; soluble in water ;
dye silk and wool direct, but not cotton. On partial
reduction may yield red nitroamino derivatives.

(a) *Nitroamino* dyes. Soluble in ether in presence of
alkali, insoluble in presence of acid.

(b) *Simple nitrophenolic* dyes. Soluble in ether in
presence of acid, insoluble in presence of alkali.

(c) *Sulphonated nitro* dyes. Insoluble in ether under
all circumstances.

(2) **Nitroso** dyes. Brown or green in colour ; many insoluble in
water ; give Liebermann's reaction.

(a) *Simple nitroso* dyes. Insoluble in water, soluble in
alcohol. Soluble in ether in presence of acetic acid.

(b) *Sulphonated nitroso* dyes. Soluble in water, insoluble
in ether under all circumstances.

(3) **Azo** dyes. Treat aqueous solution with dilute alkali and
ether, wash ethereal extract with water, and treat it with
dilute acetic acid.

(a) *Simple basic aminoazo* dyes. Pass into the ether, and
are removed from it by the acid.

(b) *Simple neutral hydroxyazo* dyes. Pass into the ether,
and are not removed from it by the acid.

(c) *Simple acidic azo* dyes (containing carboxyl groups).
Do not pass into the ether from alkaline solution,

but are extracted from solution rendered acid by dilute acetic acid.

(d) *Sulphonated azo* dyes. Insoluble in ether under all circumstances ; may be differentiated by their behaviour towards nitrous acid.

Class Ib.

Render the aqueous solution alkaline, extract with ether, and wash the ethereal extract with water.

(1) The ethereal extract,—coloured or colourless,—imparts the original colour to 5% acetic acid : **Basic** dyes ; dye wool in alkaline solution.

    (a) Solution readily reduced by addition of HCl and SnCl$_2$:

        Oxazines, Thionines (Thiazines).

    (b) Solution reduced with difficulty,—only on warming with considerable excess of stannous chloride :

        Indulines (colour-bases precipitated by NH$_4$OH ; give blue colour with conc. H$_2$SO$_4$, blue colour on dilution).

        Safranines (colour-bases precipitated by KOH, not by NH$_4$OH ; give green colour with conc. H$_2$SO$_4$, blue then violet on dilution).

(2) The ethereal extract is coloured, but does not give up its colour to 5% acetic acid : **Neutral** dyes, insoluble in water, soluble in alcohol.

    Indophenols (blue ; changed in colour on warming with dil. HCl.)

    Indogenides (red or blue ; unchanged by HCl ; yield isatin with HNO$_3$.)

(3) The ethereal extract is colourless, and imparts no colour to 5% acetic acid ; **Acidic** dyes ; soluble in water ; dye wool in acid solution.

    (a) *Oxazones* (pass into ether from solution rendered acid with acetic acid).

    (b) *Sulphonated indogenides* and *sulphonated thionines* (readily reduced by HCl and SnCl$_2$; insoluble in ether).

    (c) *Sulphonated indulines* (reduced by HCl and SnCl$_2$ with difficulty ; insoluble in ether).

Class IIa.

Render aqueous solution alkaline, extract with ether, and wash ethereal extract with water.

(1) The ethereal solution,—coloured or colourless,—imparts the

original colour to 5% acetic acid : **Basic** dyes ; dye wool in solution rendered alkaline with NH_4OH.

(a) *Auramines* (colourless ethereal solution without fluorescence ; imparts non-fluorescent yellow colour to acetic acid. Aqueous solution is decolorised by KOH ; decomposed by HCl).

(b) *Acridines* (colourless ethereal solution with green fluorescence. Aqueous solution gives a ppte. with KOH ; not greatly altered by HCl ; coloured red by HNO_3).

(c) *Fuchsines* (coloured or colourless ethereal solution without fluorescence ; purple, blue, or green colour imparted to acetic acid. Aqueous solution decolorised on warming with KOH ; generally coloured yellow by HCl).

(d) *Pyronines* (colourless ethereal solution without fluorescence ; imparts pink colour with fluorescence to acetic acid. Aqueous solution decolorised by KOH ; gives yellow colour with HCl ; dyes cotton direct).

(e) *Rhodamines* (behave like Pyronines, but unchanged by HCl).

(2) The ethereal solution is coloured, but imparts no colour to acetic acid : **Neutral** dyes ; insoluble in water, soluble in alcohol.

Quinophthalones (ethereal solution yellow without fluorescence. Alcoholic solution the same ; unchanged by aqueous acid or alkali).

(3) The ethereal solution is colourless, and imparts no colour to acetic acid : **Acidic** dyes ; mostly soluble in water, dye wool in acid solution.

(a) *Sulphonated fuchsines* (purple, blue or green in colour ; decolorised by KOH ; barely changed by HCl ; do not dye cotton direct).

(b) *Sulphonated rhodamines* (red or violet in colour ; aqueous solutions fluorescent ; unchanged by KOH ; precipitated by HCl ; do not dye cotton direct).

(c) *Sulphonated quinophthalones* (yellow colour without fluorescence ; unchanged by acid or alkali ; do not dye cotton direct).

(d) *Thiazoles* (brown-yellow or orange in colour ; somewhat fluorescent in aqueous solution ; dye cotton direct).

Class IIb.

Treat a solution of the dye in alcohol with a few drops of a 0·1% solution of ferric chloride.

(1) The solution remains unchanged : **Triphenylmethane** dyes containing no amino radicles.

    (*a*) *Aurines* (mostly insoluble in water ; soluble in alcohol without fluorescence ; solution or suspension in water does not dye wool direct).

    (*b*) *Phthaleins* (mostly soluble in water or alcohol, often with fluorescence ; boiling aqueous solution dyes wool direct).

(2) The solution is coloured greenish : **Hydroxyketonic** dyes ; mostly insoluble in water ; do not dye direct.

    (*a*) Dissolve in 1% KOH to yellow or orange solution ; *Monoketone* dyes :

        Benzophenones (tend to be decolorised with decomposition on acidification with HCl).

        Flavones (give intense yellow colour without decomposition with HCl).

    (*b*) Dissolve in 1% KOH with either red, purple, violet, blue or green colour : *Hydroxydiketone* dyes (hydroxyquinones) :

        Simple anthraquinones (free dye precipitated from alkaline solution by acetic acid ; mostly soluble in ether ; do not dye direct).

        Sulphonated anthraquinones (no precipitate on acidification of alkaline solution ; insoluble in ether ; dye wool direct).

CHAPTER V

QUANTITATIVE DETERMINATION OF CONSTITUENT ELEMENTS

Estimation of Carbon and Hydrogen

THERE is only one satisfactory method for the estimation of carbon and hydrogen, namely the somewhat tedious process of 'combustion.' The principle involved is that of complete oxidation of the organic substance, with formation of carbon dioxide and water, which are collected separately and weighed.

The apparatus is arranged thus:

A is a gas-holder filled with pure oxygen.[1] B is a spiral wash-bottle containing concentrated sulphuric acid, C is a furnace with a combustion-tube, D is a sulphuric acid absorption-tube for collecting the moisture, and E is a potash absorption-tube for collecting the carbon dioxide.

The gas-holder consists of two large stoppered vessels, connected as shown in Fig. 6. The bottle containing the water should be placed in a position two to four feet above the level of the water in the bottle containing the gas. By this means sufficient pressure is obtained to overcome the considerable resistance of the complete apparatus. The gas-holder is filled with oxygen by first filling completely with

[1] For the combustion of very volatile organic liquids, pure air should be employed in place of oxygen. The air for this purpose is purified before entering the gas-holder by passing it through a plug of cotton wool, to remove dust, and through concentrated potash, to remove carbon dioxide and acid vapours. Liquids should be weighed out into a very small hard glass stoppered bottle, which is placed in the boat in an inclined position so that the liquid cannot escape except by volatilisation, the stopper being removed from the bottle and placed in the boat only on the insertion of the boat into the combustion-tube.

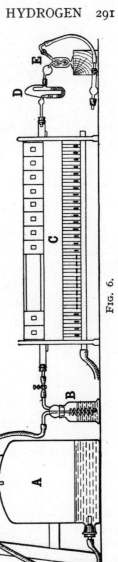

Fig. 6.

water, attaching a closed tube containing dry potassium permanganate to the upper tap, opening the lower tap so as to allow the excess of water to escape, and heating the permanganate tube (the contents of which should be held in position by a plug of glass wool) with a Bunsen burner passed to and fro so that the water escapes in a gentle stream. Pure oxygen from a cylinder, should this be available, may however be employed with considerable saving of time. When the

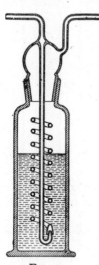

FIG. 7.

gas-holder is full of oxygen, the permanganate tube is removed, and the apparatus again fitted up as shown in Fig. 7, after shaking the gas with aqueous soda in order to remove any carbon dioxide which may be present.

The form of wash-bottle shown in Fig. 7 is the most suitable, since it affords a large surface for drying a rapid stream of gas-bubbles. Richardson's bubbler may also be employed, but the oxygen is not dried so efficiently by this as by the above apparatus.

The drying-bottle is attached to the combustion-tube by a glass tube fitted with an indiarubber stopper and an india-rubber tube on which is fixed a screw clamp to regulate the rate of the stream of oxygen.

The combustion-tube is charged with copper oxide, as indicated in Fig. 8. When organic halogen compounds are to be analysed, it is necessary to place a spiral of silver gauze at the further end, in order to decompose any halogen compound or to absorb any free halogen which may be present. The copper oxide spiral behind the boat serves two purposes : firstly to minimise the back-diffusion of vapours, and secondly to decompose any vapours which may have thus diffused. When organic sulphur compounds are to be analysed, the copper oxide must be mixed with granular, fused lead chromate. This has the effect of oxidising any sulphur dioxide to sulphuric acid, which is then converted into lead sulphate. The copper oxide, prepared by heating small pieces of copper wire in air or in oxygen, may be purchased ready for use. The copper oxide spirals can readily be prepared by rolling a suitable strip of copper gauze around a stout copper wire and oxidising the complete spiral in a Bunsen or blowpipe flame.

The furnace consists essentially of a series of Bunsen flames impinging upon the iron trough lined with asbestos which serves as the bed for the combustion-tube. Each burner is so constructed that its air and gas supply can be independently regulated. Above the tube a row of fireclay

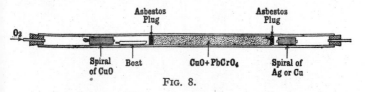

FIG. 8.

tiles, to serve as muffles, are arranged so as to regulate the temperature of the various parts of the tube.

The combustion-tube should be of a particular kind of hard glass of resistant nature, the internal diameter being approximately 10 mm. The sharp ends of the tube should be rounded by gently heating in the blowpipe flame, avoiding any deformation in this operation. The corks at the ends should be of indiarubber, and should fit accurately into the tube, so that no moisture can find its way between the cork and the glass.

The absorption apparatus is depicted in Fig. 9. The best form of water-absorbing apparatus is a Travers tube charged with pumice moistened with concentrated sulphuric acid. The water condensed in the first part of the tube is retained in the bulb so that it does not enter the acid. The trap, charged with sulphuric acid, indicates the rate at which the gases are passing through the absorption apparatus. The apparatus for the absorption of carbon dioxide is to be charged with a 50 per cent. solution of pure potassium hydroxide, drawing this up by suction by means of an indiarubber tube of sufficient length attached to the joint to which the soda-lime tube is afterwards affixed. The inner surfaces of the tubes of both portions of the absorption apparatus should, after filling,

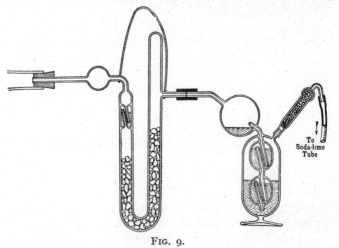

To
Soda-lime
Tube

FIG. 9.

be dried with small rolls of filter paper. The potash should be renewed after at most two grams of carbon dioxide has been absorbed, and the sulphuric acid after every twenty combustions. It is well to attach a soda-lime tube to the apparatus when in use, in order to prevent the absorption of any acid vapours from the atmosphere. The connection between the sulphuric acid and potash bulbs should be made with pressure-tubing, since the common thin indiarubber tubing permits the leakage of carbon dioxide.

After charging the combustion tube, it should be thoroughly burnt out in a slow stream of oxygen by raising the temperature gradually· to a dull red heat and allowing it to remain thus for an hour with all tiles in position. Any impurities are in this way oxidised and removed. After this operation a calcium chloride tube should be placed in the further end of the combustion-tube to keep out moisture, and the first half of the tube allowed to cool by extinguishing the appropriate burners and removing the tiles above the portion to be cooled. In the meantime a stream of pure dry oxygen should be passed through the absorption apparatus until a glowing splinter rekindles freely when placed in the issuing stream of gas. Since oxygen is dissolved in appreciable quantities by strong potash solution, it is necessary, not only to replace the air by oxygen, but also to saturate the potash therewith in advance.

The tubes are then removed, closed by means of pieces of glass rod inserted in pressure-tubing, carefully wiped free from dust and moisture by means of a silk cloth, and allowed to stand beside the balance for twenty minutes before weighing. This is necessary, since glass surfaces always acquire, on standing, a film of moisture of constant weight, and it is therefore important always to weigh the bulbs under comparable conditions. The sulphuric acid tube is weighed, after removing the caps of pressure-tubing and glass rod, by suspending the wire upon the hook of the balance. The potash bulb may be weighed, also without the caps, directly upon the pan. If the weighings are carried out expeditiously, no appreciable loss of weight will occur through escape of oxygen by diffusion. The substance—0·08 gram to 0·15 gram— is weighed out into the boat, which should rest directly on the balance-pan.

The absorption apparatus is then connected with the combustion-tube as shown in Fig. 9, care being taken that the inner face of the cork should be flush with the end of the sulphuric acid tube, and that the tubes of the two members of the absorption apparatus should meet inside the connecting pressure-tubing. The silver and copper oxide spirals are thereupon withdrawn by means of a long hooked wire, the oxygen supply tube and cork being momentarily removed, and the boat containing the weighed amount of substance inserted as far as possible into the combustion-tube. The spirals and the oxygen supply tube are then replaced and the stream of oxygen regulated so that it passes through the trap on the sulphuric acid tube at a rate of about one bubble per second.

The burners directly below the spirals are then lighted, and the tiles placed in position above them. The remaining burners may be successively turned on at intervals, proceeding from those already burning under the copper oxide, until the boat is sufficiently hot to have given up all the substance as vapour; or until the substance has completely carbonised. The intervals at which these burners are lighted should be carefully judged. Until experience in this portion of the operation has been acquired, it is advisable to proceed slowly, as any sudden rush of vapour, which might lead to imperfect combustion, is to be avoided.

When the volatilisation or carbonisation of the contents of the boat is complete, the entire tube should be heated nearly to dull redness, and the operation continued for at least twenty minutes after the last trace of substance has disappeared from the boat. The period at which carbon dioxide ceases to be present in the gases passing through the potash bulb can be detected by observing when the potash is no longer drawn up the tubes in the bulb during the intervals between the emission of bubbles of oxygen. Any water present in the unheated end of the tube is to be driven over by gentle warming with a small luminous flame or by applying a warm tile to the affected portion.

When all the carbon dioxide and water have been collected in the absorption apparatus, and the system contains only pure oxygen, the sulphuric acid tube and potash bulb are carefully removed, stoppered as before, and weighed again after standing for twenty minutes at the temperature of the balance-case. On removing the absorption apparatus, a calcium chloride tube is fitted at the further end of the combustion-tube by means of an indiarubber tube, and the stream of oxygen interrupted. Further combustions may be carried out after allowing the first part of the tube, containing the spirals and the boat, to cool completely.

The percentages of carbon and hydrogen in the substance may be calculated from the formulae :

$$\text{Percentage of C} = \frac{\text{Weight of } CO_2}{\text{Weight of substance}} \times \frac{300}{11}$$

$$\text{Percentage of H} = \frac{\text{Weight of } H_2O}{\text{Weight of substance}} \times \frac{100}{9}$$

Estimation of Nitrogen

The two chief methods for the estimation of nitrogen are those due to Dumas and to Kjeldahl. The Dumas method, while being the more complicated, is applicable to every type of organic nitrogen compound ; the Kjeldahl method, on the other hand, can be employed with certainty only for those types of compound in which the nitrogen exists in a non-oxidised form : that is to say, the analysis by this method of nitro and nitroso compounds, as well as of most hydrazo, azo, and azoxy compounds, is not to be recommended. Furthermore, cyclic nitrogen compounds, such as pyridine, cannot be analysed by the Kjeldahl method. The Kjeldahl method is chiefly applicable to the estimation of nitrogen in natural and industrial products, although the content of nitrogen in pure organic compounds may thus be estimated with a fair degree of accuracy.

(1) *The Dumas Method.*—The principle of this process is based upon the fact that nitrogenous compounds when heated with copper oxide in presence of carbon dioxide yield nitrogen in the elementary form, in some cases together with traces of oxides of nitrogen.

The apparatus consists of a combustion-tube of about 90 cm. in length, closed at one end, which is heated in a combustion furnace, and of a graduated tube filled with a concentrated potash solution for the collection of the nitrogen.

The tube is filled as shown in Fig. 10. A column of pure dry magnesite, 15 cm. in length, is first introduced into the tube, then a short plug of clean asbestos. Upon this is poured a 10 cm. column of coarse copper oxide, then 3 cm. of pure fine copper oxide, followed by 15 cm. of the fine copper oxide with which a weighed amount (0·1 gram to 0·5 gram, according to the anticipated percentage of nitrogen) of the substance has been intimately mixed upon a glazed paper. Upon this 5 cm. of fine copper oxide, and subsequently 25 cm. of coarse copper oxide are placed. Care must be taken that these layers are not so closely packed as to prevent the passage of gas. Finally, a second asbestos plug, and a copper spiral, 10 to 15 mm. in length, are inserted. The spiral must be

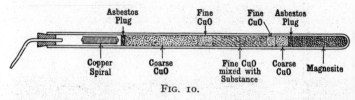

FIG. 10.

carefully reduced, previous to introduction, by plunging it, while still hot from a Bunsen flame, into a test-tube containing a wad of cotton-wool well soaked in methyl alcohol. The purpose of this copper spiral is to reduce any oxides of nitrogen which may be produced, nitrogen and copper oxide being formed.

An alternative arrangement is to employ a combustion-tube open at both ends, pure carbon dioxide being passed into the combustion-tube in the same way as the oxygen in the apparatus for determination of carbon and hydrogen. The carbon dioxide is prepared by heating a hard glass tube containing magnesite or sodium bicarbonate, or by the action of hydrochloric acid on calcite in a Kipp's apparatus.

It is advisable to insert some form of trap to prevent any drops of moisture arising from the decomposition of the carbonate from passing into the heated tube. The disposal of the remaining materials within the combustion-tube is identical in the two cases.

The apparatus is then fitted up as shown in Fig. 11, the furnace being inclined slightly so as to allow any moisture to run towards the end of the tube from which the gases are emitted. The other end of the tube should project about 7 cm. beyond the furnace.

The form of azotometer commonly employed is that devised by Schiff. This apparatus is charged with sufficient concentrated potassium hydroxide solution to cause the column to be completely filled on raising the reservoir. It should not be so full as to allow the liquid to

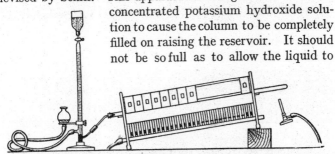

FIG. 11.

escape on lowering the reservoir to the level of the base of the azotometer. It is, however, necessary at first to place in the bottom of the azotometer sufficient mercury to form a trap which prevents the potash from coming into direct contact with the carbon dioxide. Pressure-tubing should be employed for all india-rubber connections.

The first operation is to heat the extreme projecting end of the tube, which contains the carbonate, gently with a Bunsen burner passed to and fro, in order to cause a rapid stream of carbon dioxide to drive out all air from the tube. When an external generator is employed, the bulk of the air may be swept out with carbon dioxide from a Kipp apparatus before employing the pure gas from the generator. During the first part of this procedure it is advisable to open the stop-cock of the azotometer, and to lower the reservoir so that

the smallest possible column of potash solution is affected
by the stream of carbon dioxide. When all the bubbles of
gas appear to be completely absorbed during their passage
through the potash, the reservoir is raised, and the stop-cock
closed upon the surface of the liquid. As soon as practically no
more unabsorbed gas is found to rise to the top of the azotometer,[1] the potash solution is driven, by raising the reservoir
and opening the stop-cock, into the narrow delivery tube so
as to expel all gas from it. The stop-cock is then closed,
and the reservoir lowered to its fullest extent.

The burners in the furnace under the copper spiral and the
coarse copper oxide, as well as those under the coarse copper
oxide nearest to the carbonate, are now to be lighted, and the
tiles placed above them. It will at this stage be unnecessary
to heat the magnesite with the Bunsen burner unless the
stream of bubbles entering the azotometer should become too
slow. It is advisable to regulate the stream of carbon dioxide
so that either two or three bubbles should be present in the
column of potash simultaneously.

After the coarse copper oxide and the spiral have attained a
dull red heat, the burners may gradually be lighted, proceeding
from those under the coarse copper oxide towards those under
the magnesite, placing the tiles in position above the burners
as they are lighted.

When all the burners are alight, it is to be observed whether
the volume of nitrogen still increases, and when but few
bubbles pass through the potash unabsorbed, a rapid stream
of carbon dioxide is again passed through the apparatus by
heating the projecting end of the tube. By this means all
the nitrogen is driven into the azotometer.

[1] In practice it is found that absolutely complete absorption is
never reached, a fine froth of unabsorbed gas always collecting slowly
at the head of the column. The volume of this gas obtained during
a combustion is usually equivalent to about 0.3 % of nitrogen on a
0.2 gram sample, leading to a correspondingly high analytical result.
The gas has been shown experimentally to consist of carbon monoxide,
formed by the action of the hot copper spiral upon the carbon dioxide,

When the combustion is thus completed, the indiarubber connecting tube is closed by means of a screw-clamp, the tube and cork expeditiously removed from the combustion-tube, and the furnace extinguished. The reservoir is then raised as high as possible, and the apparatus allowed to stand for five minutes in order that the last traces of carbon dioxide may be absorbed. After disconnecting the azotometer and extinguishing the furnace, a slow stream of the gas is passed through the combustion-tube until it is cold, in order to prevent the copper spiral from becoming oxidised by air.

The gas in the azotometer may then be transferred to a graduated tube by opening the stop-cock and driving it over by raising the reservoir. This is performed by filling the cup at the top of the azotometer with water so that the surface of the water is above the level of the end of the capillary delivery tube, which should contain no bubbles of air. The graduated tube, completely full of water, is closed by the finger and placed in the water in the cup in such a position that the end of the capillary tube enters the mouth of the graduated tube. The nitrogen expelled from the azotometer by raising the reservoir and opening the stop-cock is thus collected in a graduated tube. This is then transferred, after closing the open end with the finger, to a long glass cylinder containing cold water, clamped in position, and allowed to stand for twenty minutes in order to acquire the room temperature.

The volume of the gas is read off after adjusting the position of the graduated tube so that the level of the water within the tube is identical with that of the water outside it. It is necessary to observe the barometric pressure at the time of reading, as well as the temperature of the water in the cylinder, the temperature of the gas being taken as that of the water with which it is in contact.

The percentage of nitrogen may be calculated from the formula :

$$\frac{100}{S} \cdot V(B - p) \cdot \frac{0 \cdot 0012507}{760(1 + 0 \cdot 003665 \cdot t)}$$

where S is the weight in grams of the substance taken, V the observed volume of nitrogen, B the barometric pressure in mm. of mercury, and p the vapour-pressure of water at the temperature t.

The following table gives the mantissae of the logarithms of the expression

$$\frac{0 \cdot 0012507}{760(1 + 0 \cdot 003665.t)}$$

for temperatures between 10° and 25°:

t		t		t		t	
10°	0·200707	14°	0·194606	18°	0·188595	22°	0·182662
11°	0·199172	15°	0·193097	19°	0·187107	23°	0·181195
12°	0·197647	16°	0·191594	20°	0·185618	24°	0·179723
13°	0·196128	17°	0·190087	21°	0·185040	25°	0·178266

The characteristic of these logarithms is − 6.

The following table gives in mm. of mercury the vapour-pressure of water at temperatures between 10° and 25°:

t		t		t		t	
10°	9·165	14°	11·908	18°	15·357	22°	19·659
11°	9·792	15°	12·699	19°	16·346	23°	20·888
12°	10·457	16°	13·536	20°	17·391	24°	22·184
13°	11·162	17°	14·421	21°	18·495	25°	23·550

Should it be desired to read the volume of the gas directly upon the azotometer scale, 50 per cent. potash should be employed, in which case the vapour-pressure of the liquid is negligibly small. The levels of the liquid in the reservoir and in the column should of course coincide, and a full hour should be allowed for the gas to attain the room-temperature. This method of reading is, however, not to be recommended for accurate work, as it is impossible to avoid the formation of froth upon the surface of the potash.

The analysis of certain compounds,—notably those in which an alicyclic group is directly attached to a nitrogen atom,— sometimes leads to incorrect results, these being due to an excessive volume of gas collected in the azotometer. In such cases the error is ascribable to the formation of methane, which, in the absence of oxygen, is but incompletely destroyed by the hot copper oxide. In order to obviate this difficulty, the granular copper oxide should be replaced by fused lead chromate, and the substance, before mixing with the fine copper oxide, mixed with three to four times its bulk of coarsely-powdered lead chromate or freshly-precipitated cuprous chloride. Under these circumstances no methane passes with the nitrogen into the azotometer.

A serious source of error is introduced by the incomplete reduction of nitric oxide to nitrogen when the column of hot reduced copper is too short. On the other hand, if this be made sufficiently long to effect this reduction, the carbon dioxide is partially reduced to carbon monoxide. Further errors may be caused by the evolution of gases occluded in the copper oxide and copper if the preliminary heating has not been carried out for a sufficient length of time. On account of these defects the Dumas method is inapplicable where results of high accuracy are desired. With practice, however, conditions may be chosen such that the total errors balance one another sufficiently well to yield fairly reliable analytical figures.

(2) *The Kjeldahl Method.*—This process depends upon the fact that the majority of organic nitrogen compounds in which the nitrogen exists in a non-oxidised form, when heated with concentrated sulphuric acid, are completely destroyed, with formation of ammonium sulphate.

Exceptions to this rule have been cited above, but it is to be noticed that compounds containing methyl groups directly attached to nitrogen are seldom completely decomposed, appreciable quantities of methylamines being present with the ammonia. This gives rise, however, to no inaccuracy in the determination, since the methylamines are strong bases, and may be distilled over entirely from a boiling alkaline solution.

A weighed quantity—0·2 gram to 1·0 gram, according to the anticipated percentage of nitrogen—of the finely-powdered pure substance is placed with about 0·2 gram of crystallised

copper sulphate and about 5 grams of pure acid potassium
sulphate in a long-necked, round-bottomed Jena flask of
300 c.c. capacity, and 25 c.c. of pure concentrated sulphuric
acid is added from a pipette. The flask, loosely stoppered
by a glass bulb, as shown in Fig. 12 is then heated nearly
to boiling in an inclined position upon a sand-bath—or upon
a tripod over a small free flame which does not come into
actual contact with the flask itself—until all initial decomposition is complete. This may be re-
garded as having taken place when
active evolution of sulphur dioxide has
ceased and the liquid has acquired a
uniform brown colour, no unattacked
lumps of substance remaining in the
liquid. Some fifteen minutes' heating
will be required. This must be carried
out under a good hood, or other pro-
vision made to lead off the large volume
of sulphur dioxide which is evolved.

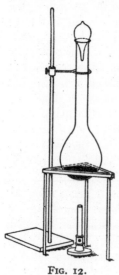

The flame is now raised and the
acid heated to gentle boiling until the
colour has entirely disappeared; this
requires 1–3 hours. The presence of
the acid potassium sulphate permits a
higher temperature to be attained than
would be the case were sulphuric acid
employed alone. The oxidation may

FIG. 12.

also be effected with the addition of a globule of mercury as
an oxygen-carrier.

When the oxidation is complete, the flask is allowed to
cool, the contents diluted with about 100 c.c. of distilled
water, and the solution, after cooling, carefully washed into
a round-bottomed flask of at least one litre capacity, diluting
with pure water to about 300 c.c. Some pieces of porous
earthenware, or a small quantity of finest pure zinc filings
(zinc dust cannot be employed for this purpose as it is liable

to contain nitrogenous impurities), are added in order to
induce regular ebullition.

A distinct excess—100 c.c. for every 25 c.c. of sulphuric
acid originally employed—of a 40 per cent. solution of pure
sodium hydroxide is then carefully poured down the side of
the flask, so that it forms a separate layer below the dilute
acid solution. By this manner of adding the alkali no
ammonia can escape until the contents of the flask are
mixed by agitation.

The flask is then fitted to a vertical condenser, the lower end of which
just dips below the surface of a decinormal solution of sulphuric acid of
known volume, sufficient to neutralise
rather more than the anticipated
amount of ammonia. A Kjeldahl trap
should be interposed between the flask
and the condenser, in order to prevent
any alkaline solution which may be
splashed up from the boiling liquid from
reaching the contents of the receiver.

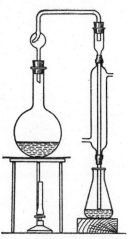

FIG. 13.

The liquid in the round-bottomed
flask is then mixed by gentle shaking
and heated ; cautiously at first, to
avoid too rapid an evolution of am-
monia, and vigorously after a few minutes. Heating should
be continued until the volume of liquid is reduced by at least
one-third. It is well to add a few drops of methyl-orange
solution to the standard acid before beginning the distillation, so that more acid can be at once added should at any
time the contents of the receiver become alkaline.

At the completion of the distillation the receiver is lowered
from the end of the condenser and the heating discontinued.
The excess of standard acid remaining is determined by
running in standard alkali from a burette until the methyl-
orange indicates an alkaline reaction, finally determining

the end-point accurately by titration with standard acid.

It is essential to carry out a blank experiment, using exactly the same quantities of the different reagents under precisely the same conditions, as any of the materials enumerated above may be contaminated with ammonia. The volume of standard acid neutralised in the blank experiment is deducted from the volume of acid neutralised in the actual determination.

The percentage of nitrogen in the substance may be calculated from the formula :

$$\frac{\text{Number of gram-equivalents of ammonia}}{\text{Weight of substance}} \times 1400$$

Estimation of Halogens

The chief methods for the estimation of the halogens are that of fusion with potash,—that due to Piria and Schiff, —and, of widest scope, that devised by Carius.

The Carius method is applicable to practically all types of organic halogen compounds, and gives excellent results. It requires however considerable time, and involves the use of a sealed tube.

The Piria and Schiff method can be employed only when the substance is not highly volatile. This restriction applies likewise to the method by fusion with potash.

For the estimation of iodine, the method of Seeker and Mathewson is especially recommended.

(1) *The Carius Method.*—The only chlorine and bromine compounds which fail to give good results by this method are the highly halogenated aromatic derivatives, such as hexachlorobenzene. Iodine compounds often give unreliable results, since silver iodide is appreciably soluble in a nitric acid solution of silver nitrate. Free iodine is moreover formed in some instances.

About 0·1 gram to 0·3 gram of the substance is weighed out into a small glass tube sealed at one end, this being allowed to slide to the bottom of a bomb-tube of about 50 cm. length which contains from 3 to 4 grams of fuming nitric acid and a slight excess of finely-powdered pure silver nitrate over that necessary for the anticipated result.

Without allowing the nitric acid to come into contact with the substance in the small tube, the bomb-tube is sealed, carefully annealed in the luminous flame, and when cold wrapped in paper and placed in an inclined position in the bomb-furnace. Care must be taken when sealing the tube that the walls at the constriction are of sufficient thickness to withstand the high pressure subsequently developed.

The temperature is raised gradually to 300°, or higher if possible, and the tube heated for at least six hours.

When cold, the tube is opened, while still in the furnace, by heating the capillary end of the constriction with a Bunsen flame. This softens the glass so that the pressure in the tube blows open a small hole through which the gases escape. The tube is then removed from the furnace and the end cut off by scratching around the top of the tube with a sharp file or glass-knife and applying a small piece of red-hot glass to the mark, care being taken that no broken glass falls into the tube. The silver halide is completely washed out with distilled water, boiled with water to remove any silver nitrate enclosed within the precipitate, collected on a weighed Gooch crucible, gently ignited, and weighed after being allowed to cool in a desiccator. It is advisable, when estimating chlorine, to dissolve the silver chloride in strong ammonia, filter, and reprecipitate by the addition of nitric acid before finally collecting on a Gooch crucible. Silver bromide, though less soluble in ammonia than the chloride, should, whenever possible, be purified in this way before collection on the Gooch crucible. This precaution serves the double purpose of removing any minute glass splinters and freeing the precipitate from enclosed particles of silver nitrate.

(2) *Fusion with Potash.*—This method is chiefly employed for the analysis of fairly stable and non-volatile solids in which it is desired to estimate both halogen and sulphur simul-

taneously. It is however applicable to compounds containing either halogen or sulphur alone, and gives good results.

A weighed amount of the substance (0·1 to 0·5 gram) is mixed in a nickel or silver crucible with about 10 grams of pure powdered potassium hydroxide and 5 grams of sodium peroxide, and the crucible heated in an air-bath at 80° for an hour. It is then gently heated over a small flame until the mass has melted to a thin liquid, whereupon the heating is discontinued, and the cooled melt dissolved in water.

After acidifying the solution with nitric acid in the cold, the halogen should first be precipitated by adding an excess of aqueous silver nitrate and filtering off the precipitate on a Gooch crucible. An excess of hydrochloric acid is added to the filtrate and the liquid filtered free of silver chloride. The filtrate is then boiled in order to drive off the bulk of the nitric acid, and to the boiling solution, which should be rendered distinctly acid with hydrochloric acid, an excess of hot barium chloride solution is added, and the barium sulphate filtered off when cool on a Gooch crucible, ignited and weighed.

(3) *The Method of Piria and Schiff.*—This method is applicable to all organic substances except those which

are highly volatile. In the case of liquids it is advisable to analyse in this way only those which combine directly with lime or sodium carbonate.

About 0·1 gram to 0·3 gram of the substance is weighed out into a small platinum crucible, and the remainder of the vessel completely filled with an

FIG. 14.

intimate mixture of one part of pure dry sodium carbonate and four parts of calcium oxide. The crucible is placed in an inverted position in a larger crucible, which is then filled with the same mixture, so that the smaller crucible is completely covered.

The crucible is heated in a large Bunsen or blow-pipe

flame, so that the outer portions attain a high temperature before the substance in the inner crucible begins to decompose. The whole is finally heated to redness, and the mixture treated with water when cold. The solution is thereupon rendered acid with nitric acid, care being taken that the temperature does not rise to any great extent. After filtering the cold solution, a slight excess of aqueous silver nitrate is added, the mixture warmed, and the silver halide collected on a weighed Gooch crucible, washed, gently ignited, and weighed as before.

When the substance contains iodine, sodium carbonate alone should be employed, as calcium iodate, which would be formed were lime present, is extremely soluble in water. After acidifying, any iodine which has separated is converted to iodide by adding the minimum quantity of sulphurous acid, and the hydriodic acid precipitated and weighed as silver iodide.

(4) *The Method of Stepanow.*—This method is applicable to all types of organic halogen compound, including those of the aromatic series, though failures have been reported with compounds containing nitro groups. It depends on the reducing action of sodium in absolute alcohol and upon the action of sodium ethoxide upon organically combined halogens.

A weighed sample of the substance (about 0·5 gram) is dissolved in 20–40 c.c. of absolute alcohol in a flask fitted with a reflux condenser. To the boiling solution is gradually added metallic sodium (cut into clean strips) amounting to 25–50 times the quantity calculated from the equation :

$$R.Cl \text{ (Br or I)} + C_2H_5OH + 2Na = RH + NaCl + C_2H_5ONa$$

and based upon the anticipated halogen-content of the substance. When all has been added, the mixture is heated with a free flame until all the sodium has reacted. The mixture is then allowed to cool, is diluted with water, filtered if necessary, acidified with dilute nitric acid, and titrated by the Volhard method.

(5) *The Method of Robertson* (*J. C. S.* 1915, 902).—The

halogen compound is heated with sulphuric and chromic acids and a slow current of dry air bubbled through the solution. The halogen and halogen acid evolved are absorbed in alkaline hydrogen peroxide. After the reaction is complete, the alkaline solution is heated to boiling, cooled, acidified with nitric acid and halogen estimated by Volhard's method.

(6) *Estimation of Iodine.*—This method, devised by Seeker and Mathewson, is applicable to the estimation of iodine in organic compounds in which chlorine or bromine may also be present. The principle is based on the formation of iodic acid on boiling with potassium permanganate and nitric acid, chlorine and bromine being volatilised and thus removed.

For substances of an acidic nature the procedure is as follows : to a weighed quantity (0·3 gram to 0·5 gram) of the substance is added 5 c.c. of a 10 per cent. solution of caustic soda and 35 c.c. of a 7 per cent. solution of potassium permanganate. The porcelain beaker containing this mixture is then covered with a watch-glass, and 10 c.c. of concentrated nitric acid added from a pipette, the point of which is inserted below the covering glass. The resulting mixture is agitated and warmed on the water-bath until spattering ceases, after which the watch-glass is removed, and the solution evaporated to dryness, care being taken to prevent the access of any reducing gases to the mixture. The residue is again treated with 5 c.c. of concentrated nitric acid and 5 c.c. of the 7 per cent. permanganate solution, and the mixture evaporated to dryness.

The residue is then treated with about 50 c.c. of distilled water and 5 c.c. of concentrated nitric acid, followed by 40 c.c. of a saturated aqueous solution of sulphurous acid—solution being assisted by breaking up any lumps with a glass rod. An excess of silver nitrate is added to the clear solution, the mixture boiled in order to expel excess of sulphurous acid, and the precipitate of silver iodide filtered off, ignited, and weighed.

When the substance is not of an acidic nature, and contains no halogen other than iodine, it may be decomposed by prolonged treatment with alcoholic potash, and the silver iodide precipitated after distilling off the bulk of the alcohol and acidifying with dilute nitric acid. This method is of course applicable only to organic derivatives of iodine which are not highly volatile and in which this element is readily removed by alkali. Should chlorine or bromine be present, the residue after complete evaporation of the alcohol may be treated with permanganate and nitric acid as above.

When the substance contains iodine which cannot be removed by alkali, as in the case of aryl iodides, it may be boiled under reflux with the mixture of potassium permanganate and nitric acid, this treatment being continued for at least two hours after decomposition is apparently complete. The mixture is finally evaporated to dryness, the residue dissolved in a mixture of dilute nitric acid and sulphurous acid, and the silver iodide precipitated in the manner described.

The results obtained by this, as by other methods for the estimation of iodine in organic compounds, may be somewhat low—as much as 1 per cent. in some instances.

Estimation of Sulphur

The two important methods for the estimation of sulphur are that devised by Carius, and that of fusion with potash. The fusion method has already been described in connection with the estimation of halogens. The method of Piria and Schiff may also be employed, by adding to the sodium carbonate a mixture of one part of potassium chlorate and eight parts of sodium nitrate. This last method is however liable to lead to explosions, and is therefore not recommended.

The Carius Method.—The principle is essentially the same as that for the estimation of halogen.

In many cases a considerable amount of gas is evolved, and explosions are liable to occur. In view of this fact, it is occasionally advisable to heat the tube only to 200°, allow it to cool, open it to allow the gases to escape, and then to seal it up again and heat to 300°. In opening, the end must first be gently heated so as to drive any liquid there collected back into the main body of the bomb-tube, and the tip finally strongly heated so as to allow the pressure of gas to force open a small hole in the capillary. After cutting off the end of the tube, the contents are washed out, filtered, and the sulphuric acid precipitated as barium sulphate.

Many sulphur compounds, notably aliphatic sulphides, cannot thus be analysed, as the sulphones formed by the action of the nitric acid are often so stable as to resist all further attempts at decomposition in this way. It is therefore advisable to employ the fusion method whenever possible, but when the substance is too volatile for this, or stable sulphones are produced, the contents of the tube, after treatment by the Carius method, may be washed out into a nickel basin, rendered strongly alkaline with an excess of highly concentrated aqueous potash, evaporated to dryness on the water-bath or in the air-bath, and then submitted to fusion. The cooled melt is dissolved in water, and the sulphuric acid precipitated and weighed as barium sulphate.

Estimation of Phosphorus

The principal method for estimating phosphorus in organic compounds is that due to Neumann, which has been rendered extremely simple by the modifications suggested by Plimmer and Bayliss.

About 0·2 gram to 0·3 gram of the substance (rather larger quantities may be necessary when determining the phosphorus-contents of proteins, etc.) is weighed out into a round-bottomed Jena flask and treated with 20 c.c. of a mixture of equal volumes of concentrated nitric and sulphuric acids. The flask is then heated as in the Kjeldahl process, with occasional additions of nitric acid, until the liquid is entirely colourless.

The liquid is diluted when cold with 150 c.c. of water, and 100 c.c. of a 50 per cent. solution of ammonium nitrate are added. The solution is then warmed to 70–80°, and a slight excess (40 c.c. for every 60 mgr. of phosphoric anhydride) of a 10 per cent. solution of ammonium molybdate is added.

The contents of the flask are thereupon thoroughly shaken for about one minute, and set aside for a quarter of an hour, after which the precipitate is collected on a small Gooch crucible provided with an ashless filter-paper in place of the usual asbestos filter, and washed with a small quantity of cold water. The precipitate is then washed back, together with the filter-paper, into a clean round-bottomed flask, and sufficient seminormal sodium hydroxide to dissolve it, with about 5 c.c. in excess, is added from a burette. After boiling the solution vigorously for fifteen minutes until no more ammonia is evolved, the flask is cooled in a stream of water, the contents diluted to about 150 c.c., and a few drops of phenolphthalein added. Should no pink colour be produced, more alkali is run in from the burette, and the solution again boiled.

Seminormal sulphuric acid is now added from a burette with about 1 c.c. in excess, the solution boiled to expel all carbonic acid, and seminormal alkali run in from the burette until a pink colour is just perceptible.

The percentage of phosphorus may be calculated from the formula :

$$\frac{\text{Number of equivalents of NaOH}}{\text{Weight of substance}} \times 110 \cdot 81$$

Phosphorus may also be estimated, in non-volatile substances and in those that combine with alkalies, by fusion with potash, with the addition of potassium nitrate or sodium peroxide to the fused mass to serve as an oxidising agent. The cooled melt is dissolved in water, the solution rendered acid with nitric acid, and the ammonium phosphomolybdate precipitated by warming to 70–80° with ammonium nitrate and ammonium molybdate treated in the manner above described.

CHAPTER VI

QUANTITATIVE DETERMINATION OF RADICLES

WHEN examining a compound in which certain, groups have been detected, but which has not been definitely identified, much assistance may be obtained by a quantitative estimation of the groups.

Thus, should a base be under examination, an attempt should be made to prepare a pure crystalline salt, such as the hydrochloride or sulphate, and the ionised acid estimated volumetrically or gravimetrically. The salts of weak bases may conveniently be analysed by titration of a weighed quantity with standard alkali in presence of phenolphthalein, while salts of all classes of bases with halogen hydracids may be titrated with standard silver nitrate, employing the Volhard method to determine the end-point. The neutralisation equivalent of acids may be determined by titrating a weighed quantity (0·1 gram to 0·2 gram) of the acid dissolved or suspended in water or aqueous alcohol with decinormal soda or baryta solution, employing phenolphthalein as an indicator.

These simple and expeditious estimations should be carried out upon every base or acid under qualitative examination. In the following pages some of the more complicated operations necessary for the quantitative determination of radicles are described.

Decomposition of Metallic Derivatives

In order to determine with great accuracy the equivalent of an acid, salts of silver, calcium, barium, sodium, or potassium may be prepared and analysed.

The silver salt should, when insoluble in water, be selected for this purpose, since its isolation, purification, and decomposition can be simply and rapidly effected. A small quantity of the acid is either exactly neutralised with perfectly pure soda (best prepared from metallic sodium and absolute alcohol, with subsequent addition of water), the neutralisation point being detected by litmus paper,—or, when practicable, the simpler method may be adopted of adding a slight excess of pure aqueous ammonia and then boiling off this excess. After adding a sufficient quantity of silver nitrate to the solution of the salt, the precipitate is filtered off, recrystallised when possible from hot water, well washed with water, dried on a porous plate in the steam oven or toluene bath for an hour, and allowed to cool in a desiccator. About 0·2 gram to 0·3 gram is weighed out into a porcelain crucible, and ignited, gently at first, until all decomposition is complete, and finally strongly, so as to remove any free carbon. Ignition must be repeated until the crucible with the residue of metallic silver has attained constant weight.

The equivalent of the acid may be calculated from the formula :

$$107 \cdot 88 \left(\frac{\text{Weight of Ag salt}}{\text{Weight of Ag}} - 1 \right)$$

When the acid contains halogen, the residue after decomposition should, when cold, be cautiously treated with a small quantity of concentrated nitric acid, ammonium halide being added when the reaction is complete. The crucible is then heated and the residue weighed as silver halide.

The calcium or barium salts, if insoluble, may be employed when the silver salt is soluble. These may be prepared either by treating a soluble metallic or ammonium salt with calcium chloride or by adding freshly filtered baryta or lime water to the acid itself until a faintly alkaline reaction is produced.

Care must be observed in drying the preparation, as calcium or barium salts may contain water of crystallisation.

A weighed quantity is gently ignited in a crucible over a Bunsen flame until a pure white residue is obtained. This is again ignited after adding a few small chips of pure ammonium carbonate until constant weight is reached. The residue then consists of calcium carbonate or barium carbonate.

The equivalent of the acid may be calculated from the formulae :

For calcium salts : $50 \cdot 05 \times \dfrac{\text{Weight of Ca salt}}{\text{Weight of CaCO}_3} - 20 \cdot 05$

For barium salts : $98 \cdot 69 \times \dfrac{\text{Weight of Ba salt}}{\text{Weight of BaCO}_3} - 68 \cdot 69$

The calcium carbonate resulting from the decomposition of calcium salts may with advantage be strongly ignited over a blowpipe flame until no loss of weight occurs on further ignition. The residue after this treatment consists of calcium oxide.

The equivalent of the acid may be calculated from the formula :

$$28 \cdot 05 \times \frac{\text{Weight of Ca salt}}{\text{Weight of CaO}} - 20 \cdot 05$$

Barium carbonate cannot be quantitatively converted into barium oxide in this way.

When the sodium or potassium salt can be obtained in a pure state, the equivalent of the acid may be determined in the following manner. A weighed quantity is gently heated in a platinum crucible over a minute flame until all initial decomposition is complete. The residue is then allowed to cool, treated with a few drops of concentrated sulphuric acid, and again heated over a small flame until all the sulphuric acid is volatilised, care being taken to avoid spurting. If any carbon now remains, this process must be repeated. The residue, after strong ignition, is weighed as sodium or potassium sulphate, and the equivalent calculated from the formulae :

For sodium salts : $71 \cdot 04 \times \dfrac{\text{Weight of Na salt}}{\text{Weight of Na}_2\text{SO}_4} - 23 \cdot 00$

For potassium salts : $87 \cdot 14 \times \dfrac{\text{Weight of K salt}}{\text{Weight of K}_2\text{SO}_4} - 39 \cdot 10$

When the substance under examination is a base which does form well-defined salts with mineral acids, the platinichloride may be employed for the determination of the equivalent. This is prepared by dissolving the free base in hydrochloric acid and adding platinic chloride :

$$2\text{B} \cdot \text{HCl} + \text{PtCl}_4 = (\text{B} \cdot \text{H})_2 \text{PtCl}_6$$

The double compound separating out is filtered off and recrystallised, from alcohol if possible. Should it be insoluble in alcohol, epichlorohydrin may often be employed as a solvent, and alcohol added until a turbidity appears, when the salt will crystallise on standing.

A weighed quantity (0·2 gram to 0·3 gram) of the platinichloride is gently warmed in a platinum crucible over a small flame until initial decomposition is complete, then ignited to dull redness, and the residue weighed as pure platinum.

The equivalent of the base may be calculated from the formula :

$$97 \cdot 5 \times \dfrac{\text{Weight of platinichloride}}{\text{Weight of Pt}} - 203 \cdot 88$$

Cuprichlorides and aurichlorides may be prepared and analysed in a similar manner, the residues consisting respectively of cupric oxide and metallic gold. Porcelain crucibles should, of course, be employed in these cases.

Hydrolysis of Esters and Amides

This process may be applied when the original substance is either an ester or a simple or substituted amide, but also when an acyl derivative of an alcohol, phenol, or amine has been prepared by the methods indicated in Chapter II. It thus constitutes an indirect method for the estimation of hydroxyl and primary or secondary amino groups.

About 1 gram to 2 grams of the substance is weighed out into a flask containing 25 c.c. of normal alcoholic potash and about 50 c.c. of absolute alcohol, and the mixture boiled on the water-bath for two to three hours under reflux. Should the substance be soluble in hot water, aqueous alkali may be employed. About 50 c.c. of the alcohol is then distilled off, the remainder diluted with the same quantity of water, filtered if necessary, and a few drops of indicator added. Should the original substance be precipitated on the addition of water, the hydrolysis must be continued for a further period of time before proceeding.

When simple amides and acyl derivatives of strong bases which are volatile with steam are thus treated, it is necessary to boil the solution until the distillate shows no alkaline reaction, before titrating with standard acid. No quantitative results can, of course, be obtained by this process with acyl derivatives of strong bases which are not volatile with steam.

The excess of alkali, after removal of strong bases, is then titrated with normal sulphuric acid. It is advantageous in many cases to employ phenolphthalein as an indicator, adding a slight excess of standard acid, warming to expel carbonic acid, cooling, and running in normal alkali from a burette until a pink coloration appears. As a general rule, methyl-orange should be selected as the indicator after the hydrolysis of phenolic esters, while phenolphthalein should exclusively be employed after the hydrolysis of derivatives of weak acids.

When for any reason this process cannot be employed, as for example for the hydrolysis of acyl derivatives of strong bases which are not volatile or of polyhydroxylic phenols (solutions of which in alkali acquire dark colours on exposure to air), the substance should—provided that the acid produced by the hydrolysis be volatile with steam—be boiled for three hours with a large excess of a strong solution of phosphoric acid or benzenesulphonic acid under reflux. The liquid is then distilled, the contents of the flask being taken down nearly

to dryness.   Water is then added, and the operation repeated
until the liquid passing over is neutral to litmus.   The distillate is titrated with standard alkali in presence of phenolphthalein or methyl-orange.

This process can be applied to the hydrolysis of substituted amides which are so stable as to resist the action of
alcoholic potash.   As an example of this type of compound
phenacetin may be cited.

The latter method is generally applicable to the hydrolysis
of nitriles.   When nitriles and simple amides have been
hydrolysed by phosphoric acid, the residue in the distilling
flask after removal of the free volatile organic acids by distillation may be rendered alkaline with soda and distilled
into standard acid, as in the Kjeldahl process.   The ammonia
value thus obtained serves as a check on the acid value
obtained by the hydrolysis of the amide or nitrile.

Estimation of Primary or Secondary Amines

This process, based on the acetylation by means of acetic
anhydride of primary and secondary amines, can generally be
employed for the estimation of weak secondary amines in
presence of weak tertiary amines.   When, for instance, it
is desired to estimate the amount of the imino group present
in a commercial sample of methylaniline, the procedure is
as follows : about 1 gram of a substance is accurately weighed
out into a small flask, and a weighed quantity (about 2 grams)
of acetic anhydride added as rapidly as possible.   A reflux air
condenser (a long glass tube) is fitted to the flask and the
mixture allowed to stand at the room temperature for thirty
minutes to one hour.   When the reaction is complete, the
contents of the flask are diluted with about 50 c.c. of water,
and heated on the water-bath for an hour, in order to convert
the excess of acetic anhydride into acetic acid.   After cooling,
the amount of acetic acid present in the free state and as the
salt of the tertiary base is titrated with normal sodium
hydroxide solution in presence of phenolphthalein.   This

method is, of course, not practicable when the tertiary amine is a base sufficiently strong to impart a pink colour to phenol-phthalein.

Since it is difficult to obtain acetic anhydride in a perfectly pure state, a blank experiment must be carried out simultaneously, in order to ascertain the relative proportion of acetic acid and acetic anhydride in the reagent employed.

This process serves as a rough method for the determination of the equivalent of a primary or a secondary amine, being the converse of the method based on the hydrolysis of substituted amides.

Estimation of Methoxyl or Ethoxyl Groups

The following method, due to Zeisel, is based upon the fact that methyl or ethyl ethers or esters, on treatment with hot aqueous hydriodic acid, are quantitatively decomposed with formation of methyl or ethyl iodide. It is applicable to the analysis of all methoxyl or ethoxyl compounds which are not highly volatile.

In the original procedure of Zeisel the substance is heated with hydriodic acid in a flask immersed in a glycerol or oil bath, and a slow stream of pure carbon dioxide passed through the flask. The vapours of hydriodic acid, water, and alkyl iodide, together with the carbon dioxide, are passed through a reflux condenser jacketed with water at a temperature between 40° and 50°, then through a wash-bottle immersed in a bath of water at 40–50° containing red phosphorus and water, in order to remove any free iodine and traces of uncondensed hydriodic acid, and finally through alcoholic silver nitrate.

The apparatus and procedure of Zeisel's original method have been much simplified by the suggestions of Hewitt and collaborators. Since the separation of the alkyl iodide vapour from that of aqueous hydriodic acid consists essentially of a fractional distillation, the reflux condenser jacketed with warm water may be replaced by a suitable distilling column or its equivalent ; it has also been shown that pyridine can be employed for the absorption of the alkyl iodide instead of the alcoholic silver nitrate. This latter replacement is of two-fold advantage : on the one hand it enables the iodide to be estimated by the more rapid volumetric method of Volhard, and on the other hand it disposes of the practically insurmountable difficulties encountered when mercaptans [1] are simultaneously evolved on boiling with hydriodic acid.

The apparatus is constructed as shown in Fig. 15. The decomposition vessel consists of a flask of 80–100 c.c. capacity to which is attached a neck about 40 cm. long, bearing near the top a side tube of the type employed in the Claisen distillation flask (page 3). In the upper end of the tube is stoppered a water-cooled tube which may be inserted to any desired distance ; 2–3 cm. above the bulb is a side-tube for the entrance of carbon dioxide, provided with a trap to prevent back-diffusion and to observe the rate of flow of the gas. The vapours pass from the decomposition vessel through a wash-flask surrounded by a water-bath at a suitable temperature into the absorption vessel (modified from a design by Cumming) consisting of four traps integrally connected in series.

An accurately weighed sample (0·2–0·3 gram) of the substance is placed in the decomposition flask, together with a few chips of unglazed porcelain, and upon it is poured a cooled mixture [2] of 25 c.c. of 50–57 per cent. aqueous hydriodic acid and 15 c.c. of pure acetic anhydride. A small quantity

---

[1] Many sulphur-containing substances give off hydrogen sulphide during decomposition ; this can be removed by passing the vapours through a bath of cadmium sulphate solution, which withholds it in the form of cadmium sulphide. When, however, mercaptans are given off as is the case with many compounds containing sulphur attached to alkyl), these are not retained by the cadmium sulphate and yield insoluble silver mercaptides which are only incompletely removed from the silver iodide even on long boiling with excess of nitric acid.

[2] Much heat is developed on mixing the hydriodic acid and acetic anhydride ; the latter should be slowly added to the former, cooling with ice-water and agitating during the addition.

of a similar solution is placed in the trap of the carbon dioxide inlet tube. The wash-flask is provided with a 1–2 cm. deep layer of water in which a small quantity of red phosphorus is suspended, and in the absorption vessel 10 c.c. of pure pyridine is distributed between the four traps.

A slow stream (1–2 bubbles per second) of carbon dioxide is passed through the apparatus, and the reaction mixture is gently boiled over a small flame. When methoxyl is being estimated, the flame and exposed length of water-cooled tube are so adjusted that the temperature of the issuing vapours remains at 20–25°; the bath surrounding the wash-flask is held at 45–50°. For ethoxyl, the vapours must leave the decomposition vessel at 29–30° and the water-bath be maintained at 75–80°. The water-cooled tube prevents the escape of the bulk of the vapours of iodine, acetic acid, water, and hydriodic acid which are not condensed in the long neck of the decomposition flask; the wash-flask containing water and phosphorus retains any traces that may escape. The absorption of the alkyl iodide by the pyridine can be observed by the formation of a yellow colour; if the rate of carbon dioxide be not too fast, very little colour will be developed in the third trap and none in the fourth. When no further increase of colour is noted, the decomposition may be regarded as substantially complete, but the process is carried on for 30 minutes longer. The reaction requires from one to three hours in all.

The pyridine is washed out into a 500 c.c. beaker or conical flask, rinsing the absorption vessel with several changes of distilled water. After diluting to 200–250 c.c. the solution is boiled vigorously for a few minutes in order to expel any hydrogen sulphide or volatile mercaptans, and cooled. A known excess of decinormal silver nitrate solution is added, and the solution acidified with dilute nitric acid.[1] A few

---

[1] The silver nitrate must be added first, as there is a danger of iodide being partially oxidised to iodine on acidification if it be not first converted into silver iodide.

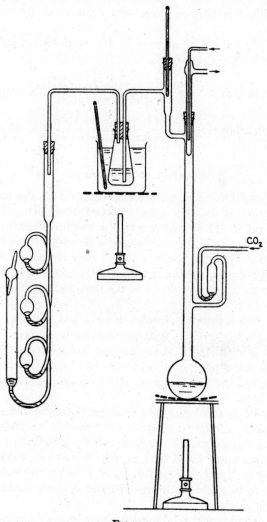

FIG. 15.

drops of ferric alum solution are then added, and the
excess silver is titrated back with decinormal thiocyanate
solution.

The percentage of alkoxyl in the original substance is
calculated from the formulae :

For Methoxyl : $\dfrac{\text{No. of c.c. of N/10 AgNO}_3}{\text{Weight of subtance}} \times \text{·0031}$

For Ethoxyl : $\dfrac{\text{No. of c.c. of N/10 AgNO}_3}{\text{Weight of substance}} \times \text{·0045}$

Estimation of Unsaturation

(1) *Ethylenic.*—The most general method for the estimation of ethenoid linkages is that of bromine addition. This is
carried out in the following way : a weighed quantity (0·3
gram to 1·0 gram) of the substance is dissolved in 10 c.c. of
pure carbon tetrachloride in a 500 c.c. stoppered flask, 20 c.c.
of a N/3 bromine solution in carbon tetrachloride added, and
the mixture allowed to stand in the dark for about eighteen
hours.

The flask is thereupon cooled in ice, about 25 c.c. of water
rapidly added, and the mixture thoroughly shaken. After
addition of about 25 c.c. of a 10 per cent. solution of potassium
iodide in water and 75 c.c. of water, the iodine liberated by
the excess of the bromine is titrated with decinormal sodium
thiosulphate.

In order to avoid escape of bromine, the water and potassium iodide solution may most conveniently be added by
removing the stopper of the flask, rapidly substituting for it
a dropping-funnel fitted with a cork, completely immersing
the flask in a freezing mixture, and allowing the water or
solution to be drawn in by the reduced pressure consequent
upon the cooling.

The extent to which bromination may have simultaneously
taken place is determined by adding, after the completion of

the titration, about 5 c.c. of a 2 per cent. solution of potassium iodate, and again titrating the resultant iodine. By this procedure the hydrobromic acid formed during the bromination liberates hydriodic acid on the addition of potassium iodide ; this hydriodic acid reacts with the iodate so as to form free iodine :—

$$KIO_3 + 6HI = KI + 6I + 3H_2O$$

Twice the amount of the bromine thus estimated as hydrobromic acid is to be deducted from the bromine addition value before calculation.

For determining the amount of unsaturated compounds present in a mixture of fatty acids or in fats the method of Hübl is generally employed. This process is based on the fact that an alcoholic solution of iodine in presence of mercuric chloride yields what may be regarded as a solution of iodine chloride, which reacts with ethylenic compounds with formation of chloroiodo addition products. In the modification of this process due to Wijs, iodine chloride itself,—prepared by passing chlorine into a solution of iodine,—is employed.

The iodine solution is made up in two parts : the first consisting of 25 grams of pure iodine dissolved in pure 95 per cent. alcohol and diluted with this solvent to 500 c.c. ; the second consisting of 30 grams of pure mercuric chloride dissolved in the same solvent and diluted to 500 c.c. Equal volumes of the two solutions are mixed, allowed to stand for twenty-four hours, then standardised against decinormal thiosulphate solution, and employed forthwith.

A weighed quantity (0·5 gram to 1·0 gram) of the substance is introduced into a stoppered flask of 500 c.c. capacity and dissolved in 10 c.c. of pure chloroform, whereupon 25 c.c. of the standardised iodine solution are added from a pipette. Should the liquid not remain entirely clear on mixing, more chloroform is added. The flask is then stoppered and set aside in the dark at the room temperature for twelve hours.

If, after so standing for two hours, the dark brown colour of the iodine has vanished, a further quantity of the iodine solution is added.

When the twelve hours have elapsed, the liquid is treated with 25 c.c. of a 10 per cent. solution of potassium iodide and diluted with 300 c.c. of water. In the event of a red precipitate of mercuric iodide separating on dilution, further potassium iodide is added. Decinormal thiosulphate is then run in from a burette until the colour of the iodine has almost disappeared, the end-point being determined after the addition of a small quantity of starch solution.

It is necessary to carry out a blank experiment simultaneously and under identical conditions, as not only is the chloroform employed for dissolving the substance liable to absorb the iodine chloride, but the titre of the iodine solution may undergo a slight alteration during the period of time occupied by the experiment.

The 'iodine number' of a fat or other substance, as obtained by this method, is the number of grams of iodine which would be absorbed by 100 grams of the unsaturated compound or mixture.

This process is applicable only to those unsaturated compounds in which the ethenoid linkages are not situated in conjunction with groups rich in residual affinity. Mere aggregation of substituents around such a linkage also may tend to prevent the quantitative formation of addition products. Thus crotonic acid and cinnamic acid absorb but little iodine, maleic acid and fumaric acid none whatever, while even allyl alcohol is not completely saturated under the above conditions. Satisfactory results are however obtained with the unsaturated acids and glycerides occurring in natural fats.

(2) *Acetylenic.*—Acetylenic compounds containing a hydrogen atom attached to a triply-bound carbon atom may be quantitatively examined either by treating with a solution of silver nitrate in water or in alcohol, and titrating the free acid

after filtering off the product and precipitating the excess of silver with sodium chloride solution :

$$R \cdot C \vdots CH + AgNO_3 = R \cdot C \vdots C \cdot Ag + HNO_3,$$

or by preparing the silver derivative of the compound by treatment with ammoniacal silver nitrate, filtering off the precipitate, and drying it on a porous plate in a vacuous desiccator. A weighed quantity of this derivative is treated in a porcelain crucible with aqua regia, and finally gently ignited, the residue being weighed as silver chloride.

Fehling's Solution

Fehling's solution, being a mild oxidising agent, may be employed for the estimation of aldehyde, hydrazine, and other easily oxidisable groups ; but its chief application is to the estimation of sugars.

Standard Fehling's solution is made up in two parts : the first consisting of 69·28 grams of pure crystallised copper sulphate dissolved in water and diluted to one litre, the second consisting of 350 grams of Rochelle salt (sodium potassium tartrate) and 120 grams of pure sodium hydroxide (sticks) dissolved in water and diluted to 1 litre.

To estimate the amount of sugar in a solution,—which should be diluted so that 10 c.c. are approximately equivalent to 10 c.c. of the mixed Fehling's solution,—5 c.c. of each constituent of Fehling's solution are measured out into a basin, diluted with about 40 c.c. of dilute sodium hydroxide solution, and gently boiled. The sugar solution is thereupon run into the boiling mixture from a burette in successive portions of 1 c.c., pausing after each addition to allow the reduction to complete itself, until the last portion causes the complete disappearance of the blue colour. The operation is then repeated, adding 2 c.c. less of the sugar solution rapidly, and finally determining the end-point accurately by adding the sugar solution in drops until the blue colour just vanishes. This operation must be carried out expeditiously, as the cuprous oxide thus precipitated tends to be reoxidised by air to the cupric salt, the blue colour returning after a short lapse of time.

It may be taken that every 5 c.c. of the copper sulphate solution are equivalent to 0·050 gram of a hexose.

The chief disadvantage of this method of employing Fehling's solution is the difficulty with which the end-point is determined. This may be evaded by the use of a solution of ferrous thiocyanate in dilute hydrochloric acid as an external indicator. When results of extreme accuracy are required an excess of Fehling's solution may be employed with a known volume of the sugar solution, and the cuprous oxide precipitated after boiling for three or four minutes, collected on a weighed Gooch crucible, washed successively with water, alcohol, and ether, dried for an hour in a steam oven, and weighed.

The most satisfactory method, however, for the estimation of sugars by means of Fehling's solution is that recommended by Bertrand. The principle is based on the fact that cuprous oxide is dissolved by an acid solution of ferric sulphate with formation of cupric sulphate and ferrous sulphate :

$$Cu_2O + Fe_2(SO_4)_3 + H_2SO_4 = 2CuSO_4 + 2FeSO_4 + H_2O$$

The resulting ferrous salt is estimated by titration with permanganate solution.

The solutions required for the method as modified by Bertrand are prepared as follows :

A. 40 grams of pure crystallised copper sulphate (freed from ferrous sulphate by recrystallising from very dilute nitric acid) dissolved in water and diluted to 1 litre.

B. 200 grams of Rochelle salt, 150 grams of pure sodium hydroxide (sticks), made up with water to 1 litre.

C. 50 grams of ferric sulphate, 200 grams of pure sulphuric acid, made up with water to 1 litre.

D. 5 grams of pure potassium permanganate dissolved in water and diluted to 1 litre.

The ferric sulphate solution ought not to reduce permanganate; should it do so, permanganate is added to it until further addition imparts a pink colour to the solution. The potassium permanganate is to be carefully standardised against ammonium oxalate or oxalic acid.

The sugar solution under examination should contain not less than 0·5 gram nor more than 4·5 grams of the sugar to the litre.

The procedure is as follows: 20 c.c. of each constituent of the Fehling's solution (A and B) are measured out into a conical flask and heated to gentle boiling, whereupon 20 c.c. of the sugar solution is added from a pipette, and the mixture boiled for exactly three minutes. The precipitated cuprous oxide is then allowed to settle for an instant, and the supernatant liquor filtered by decanting as completely as possible on to a Gooch crucible packed with asbestos, as little cuprous oxide as possible being allowed to settle upon the filter. The residue in the flask is then washed with tepid water and the liquor again decanted upon the filter.

To the residue is now added just sufficient of the ferric solution (C) to cause it to dissolve completely with formation of a green solution. This solution is at once filtered into a clean filtering flask through the Gooch crucible so as to dissolve the cuprous oxide retained on the asbestos, and the flask and filter washed out with water. The filtrate is immediately titrated as rapidly as possible with the standard permanganate solution (D) until a pink colour just appears.

The amount of copper precipitated as cuprous oxide may be calculated from the equations:

$$Cu_2O + Fe_2(SO_4)_3 + H_2SO_4 = 2CuSO_4 + 2FeSO_4 + H_2O$$
$$2KMnO_4 + 10FeSO_4 + 9H_2SO_4 =$$
$$5Fe_2(SO_4)_3 + 2KHSO_4 + 2MnSO_4 + 8H_2O$$

Whence $\qquad KMnO_4 \equiv 5Cu$
i.e. $\qquad\quad 158\cdot0 : 317\cdot8.$

The following figures, obtained experimentally by Bertrand,

indicate the number of milligrams of copper precipitated as cuprous oxide on treating sugar solutions containing 10 to 100 milligrams of the sugar in each 20 c.c. of solution. It will be observed that the results, although reproducible, are not strictly quantitative.

Number of Milligrams of sugar estimated	Dextrose.	'Invert [1] Sugar.'	Number of Milligrams of Copper precipitated.				
			Galactose.	Mannose.	Arabinose.	Maltose.	Lactose.
10	20·4	20·6	19·3	20·7	21·2	11·2	14·4
20	40·1	40·4	37·9	40·5	41·9	22·2	28·4
30	59·1	59·3	56·2	59·5	62·0	33·3	42·1
40	77·5	77·7	73·9	78·0	81·5	44·1	55·4
50	95·4	95·4	91·2	95·9	100·6	55·0	68·5
60	112·8	112·6	108·3	113·3	119·3	65·7	81·4
70	129·8	129·2	125·0	130·2	137·5	76·5	94·1
80	146·1	145·3	141·3	146·9	155·3	87·2	106·7
90	162·0	161·1	157·6	163·3	172·7	98·0	119·1
100	177·8	176·5	173·6	179·4	189·8	108·4	131·4

The figures for levulose may be estimated from those given for dextrose and 'invert sugar.'

Pavy's Solution

In this, which may be regarded as a modification of Fehling's solution, the sodium hydroxide is partially replaced by ammonia. Cuprous oxide is soluble in ammonia with formation of a colourless solution ; the point at which the blue colour of the cupric ammonium salt disappears may thus be determined with greater accuracy than when the solution is rendered turbid by the precipitated cuprous oxide, as in the estimation of sugars by Fehling's solution.

Pavy's solution is prepared, like Fehling's solution, in two portions : the first consisting of 8·316 grams of pure crystallised copper sulphate dissolved in water and diluted to 1 litre ; the second consisting of a mixture of 40·8 grams of Rochelle salt, 40·8 grams of pure potassium hydroxide, 600 c.c. of strong aqueous ammonia (sp. gr. 0·880), diluted to 1 litre. It may

---

[1] A 0·5 per cent. solution obtained by heating 4·750 grams of sucrose in 50 c.c. of 2 per cent. HCl to 100° for 10 to 15 minutes, cooling, neutralising, and diluting to 1 litre.

also be prepared from Fehling's solution (p. 327) by diluting
120 c.c. of the copper sulphate solution with water to 1 litre,
and diluting 120 c.c. of the alkaline solution of Rochelle salt
with 600 c.c. of concentrated ammonia (sp. gr. 0·880) and
sufficient 10 per cent. caustic soda solution (sp. gr. approximately 1·12) to make up to 1 litre. The Pavy's solution thus
prepared is, as compared with Fehling's
solution, capable of oxidising one-tenth the
amount of glucose. Thus a mixture of 25
c.c. of each of the two constituents of
Pavy's solution corresponds to 0·025 gram
of glucose. The sugar solution should be
so diluted with weak ammonia that 10 c.c.
corresponds approximately to 25 c.c. of the
copper sulphate solution.

To carry out an estimation, 25 c.c. of
each constituent are measured out into a
conical flask of 500 c.c. capacity and diluted
with 50 c.c. of water or dilute ammonia.
A small piece of porous earthenware is
added, and the flask closed by a doubly
bored indiarubber stopper through which
pass the point of the burette and a long
glass tube bent in the form shown in Fig.
16. This tube serves partly as a reflux condenser and partly to discharge the evolved
ammonia above the level of the head of the
operator.

FIG. 16.

The solution in the flask is heated so as
to boil gently, and the sugar solution then run in from the
burette in successive portions of about 1 c.c. until the colour
is discharged, and the operation repeated, as in the case of
Fehling's solution, by rapidly adding a slight deficiency of
the sugar solution to a fresh quantity of the Pavy's solution,
and accurately determining the end-point by adding the
remaining portion of the sugar solution in separate drops.

Care must be taken that the solution boils evenly through-out the operation, as, in the event of an interruption, any air drawn into the flask would at once reoxidise the cuprous ammonium salt.

Sucrose, which does not reduce Fehling's solution or Pavy's solution, may be estimated by hydrolysing to 'invert sugar,' which, after neutralisation and dilution to standard volume, is titrated against Fehling's solution or Pavy's solution. Hydrolysis or 'inversion' of sucrose is performed by warming a 1 per cent. solution of sucrose in water with one-tenth its volume of concentrated hydrochloric acid for fifteen minutes on the water-bath, cooling, exactly neutralising with sodium carbonate, diluting to a suitable concentration (about 0·4 per cent.), and adding from a burette to a definite volume of the boiling cupric reagent, or treating according to the method recommended by Bertrand.

The result, as expressed in milligrams of 'invert sugar,' is to be multiplied by the factor 0·94822 in order to deduce the amount of sucrose present, since 332·18 grams of sucrose on hydrolysis yield 350·19 grams of an equal mixture of dextrose and levulose.

Sucrose in presence of dextrose or some other reducible sugar may thus be estimated by dividing the solution into two portions, and determining the extent to which Fehling's solution is reduced before and after hydrolysis. The amount of dextrose is given by the value before hydrolysis, while the amount of sucrose may be calculated from the difference between the values found before and after hydrolysis.

CHAPTER VII

DETERMINATION OF SOME PHYSICAL PROPERTIES

THE examination of physical properties of organic compounds is of the greatest value for identification or determination of constitution. Thus the molecular weight of the compound under examination may be estimated with a fair degree of accuracy by cryoscopic or ebullioscopic determinations, and with great accuracy, in the case of volatile substances, by determination of the vapour-density. The density of organic liquids under qualitative examination should in all cases be determined, reference being made to the tables in Chapter IV. The rotatory power should likewise be determined in all substances in which optical activity is suspected. The refractive power of substances of which the empirical formula and molecular weight have been ascertained is frequently of great service in establishing the constitution. The procedure for the determination of this last physical property is of so simple a nature when a Pulfrich or an Abbe refractometer is available that it is not here described; the conclusions which may be deduced from the experimental data so obtained are described in the text-books [1] of physical chemistry.

Determination of Molecular Weight

(1) *The Cryoscopic Method.*—This method, based on the phenomenon of the depression of the freezing-point of a liquid on the introduction of a solute, is the most generally

---

[1] This subject is fully treated in Smiles's *Relations between Chemical Constitution and Physical Properties* (Longmans), 1910.

applicable, and its simplicity is such that it may well be the first to be employed for the determination of molecular weight. It is important, however, that a solvent be selected which will dissolve the substance under examination to the extent of at least 10 per cent. in the cold.

The apparatus is constructed as shown in Fig. 17. The Beckmann thermometer A is inserted in the inner tube B, and secured by means of the doubly bored indiarubber stopper C. A stirring-rod of glass, D, at the lower end of which is fused a stout platinum ring which passes round the bulb of the thermometer, is fitted so as to slide without friction through a piece of glass tube inserted in the second hole of the stopper. In cases when the solvent employed—for example acetic acid—is of a hygroscopic nature, it is advisable to replace this tube by a glass bulb, as shown (E) in Fig. 18, through which dry air is slowly aspirated. The tube B is provided with a side tube, F, of sufficient diameter to permit of the introduction of the substance when required. The portion of the tube B below the side tube is fixed by means of a short wide cork in a larger tube, G, which is jacketed with a bath maintained at a temperature about 2° below the melting point of the solvent.

To carry out the determination, the Beckmann thermometer is set so that, at the temperature at which the pure solvent freezes, the head of the column of mercury stands in the upper portion of the stem. This is effected by warming the bulb of the thermometer until the column has risen to the reservoir R, inverting the thermometer, and gently tapping the metal head until the contents of the reservoir are united to the main body in the stem. The bulb is then placed in a bath the temperature of which lies about 2° above the freezing-point of the solvent, and the metallic head of the thermometer again tapped so that the mercury in the reservoir is detached from the stem.

A weighed quantity (about 15 grams) of the pure solvent is placed in the inner tube B, and the apparatus fitted together.

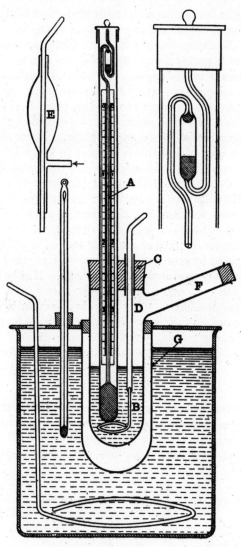

FIG. 17.

The charging of the tube with the liquid is most easily effected by weighing it before and after addition of the solvent.

When the thermometer indicates a slight supercooling, the stirring-rod is gently moved up and down at a rate of about twenty strokes to the minute. As soon as crystals begin to form, the temperature rises to a definite point, at which it remains constant for some time. This point is read on the scale by means of a small microscope of special design attached to the thermometer by means of a clip. Accuracy to the thousandth part of a degree is possible in this way.

After a repetition and confirmation of the freezing-point of the pure solvent, a weighed quantity (about 0·2 gram to 0·5 gram) of the substance is added through the side-tube F, and, after complete solution, the new freezing-point determined. When the substance is a solid, it may be introduced either in a small boat constructed of platinum foil, or in the form of a pellet prepared by pressing the finely-powdered substance in a small percussion-mortar of suitable design. If it be a liquid, the best plan is to add it from a pyknometer, weighing this before and after addition. For the sake of certainty of results, it is advantageous to add the substance in two or more stages, determining the freezing-point after each addition.

The molecular weight is calculated from the formula :

$$M = \frac{c \cdot p}{t}$$

where M is the molecular weight, c the constant for the liquid, p the number of grams of substance per 100 grams of solvent, and t the depression of the freezing-point.

The following substances are commonly employed as solvents :—

	M.P.	c.		M.P.	c.
Water	0°	19	Diphenyl Ether	28°	80
Nitrobenzene	5°	71	Phenol	42°	72
Benzene	5°	50	p-Toluidine	43°	51
Bromoform	9°	143	Thymol	50°	92
Ethylene Bromide	9°	118	Diphenylamine	54°	88
Acetic Acid	16°	39	Naphthalene	80°	69

(2) *The Ebullioscopic Method.*—This method should be employed to the exclusion of the cryoscopic method only when the substance is not sufficiently soluble in any suitable solvent, owing to the difficulty of the manipulation and the uncertainty of the results. The principle rests upon the elevation of the boiling-point of a liquid by the presence of a dissolved substance.

The construction of the apparatus is somewhat similar to that employed for the cryoscopic method. The inner tube containing the solvent presents no essential difference in arrangement except that a stout platinum wire is fused through the bottom to serve as a conductor of heat, and that the stirring-rod is replaced by a collection of glass or garnet beads, to facilitate gentle ebullition. Before adding the solvent, it is necessary to determine the weight of the inner tube when charged with the beads. The air-bath surrounding the inner tube is jacketed with the vapour of the boiling solvent, with which the outer jacket is charged for this purpose. Reflux condensers are attached to both the inner tube and the outer jacket. The whole apparatus is heated by two small Bunsen flames, placed under opposite corners, so that the liquid in the jacket boils vigorously and the solvent in the tube receives sufficient heat to maintain it in steady ebullition. The temperature is read, when constant, upon the previously adjusted Beckmann thermometer.

A weighed pellet of the substance is then added, either by removing the reflux condenser attached to the inner tube for an instant, or, if possible, by allowing it to fall through the condenser tube. The solvent must be kept boiling throughout the entire operation, otherwise inaccurate results may be obtained. The boiling-point, which is observed to rise during solution of the substance, is recorded when constant. Subsequent additions of the substance may be made, and the new boiling-points again noted.

When the last reading has been recorded, the apparatus is allowed to cool, and the thermometer and condenser

removed from the inner tube, which is then weighed, in order
to ascertain the quantity of solvent actually employed. An
allowance of 0·2 gram for easily condensed liquids and of
0·4 gram for highly volatile liquids should be deducted from
the total amount, in order to correct for condensed liquid
retained in the condenser. Correction should be made for
any barometric change occurring during the operation.

The molecular weight is calculated from the formula :

$$M = \frac{100 \, c \cdot w}{W \cdot t}$$

where M is the molecular weight of the solute, c the molecular
elevation of boiling-point for 100 grams of the solvent, w the
weight of substance taken, W the weight of solvent taken, and
t the observed elevation of boiling-point.

The following solvents are commonly employed for this
purpose :

	B.P.	c.		B.P.	c.
Ethyl Ether . .	35°	21·1	Carbon Tetrachloride	78°	48·0
Carbon Disulphide .	46°	23·7	Benzene . . .	80°	26·7
Acetone. . .	56°	16·7	Water . . .	100°	5·2
Chloroform . .	61°	36·6	Acetic Acid . .	119°	25·3
Methyl Alcohol .	66°	9·2	Ethylene Bromide .	129°	63·2
Ethyl Acetate .	77°	26·1	Phenol . . .	181°	30·4
Ethyl Alcohol .	78°	11·5	Aniline . . .	183°	32·2

It is to be remarked that in both the cryoscopic and the
ebullioscopic methods, solutions of hydroxylic substances in
non-hydroxylic solvents, such as benzene or chloroform, may
give rise to abnormally high results, owing to association. It
is therefore advisable in all cases to carry out the determination in at least two different solvents, of which one should
possess a constitution chemically comparable to that of the
substance under examination.

Determination of Vapour-Density

When the substance can be examined in the form of
vapour, the molecular weight may be estimated with great
accuracy by determining the vapour-density. The two most

important methods are those due to Victor Meyer and to Hofmann.

(1) *The Victor Meyer Method.*—This method is applicable to substances which can be heated at least thirty degrees above their boiling-points under atmospheric pressure without decomposition. The operation is extremely simple, and the process possesses the additional advantage that no mercury is employed.

In the apparatus, a small loosely-stoppered bottle containing a weighed quantity (about 0·1 gram) of the substance is allowed to fall from the cool upper part of the tube into the heated bulb A, where the substance volatilises, and thereby displaces air from the upper part of the tube, this air being collected over water in the graduated vessel in the water-trough B. When all the air is driven over, the volume is read.

The simplest device for allowing the bottle containing the weighed quantity of substance to fall when required consists of an indiarubber

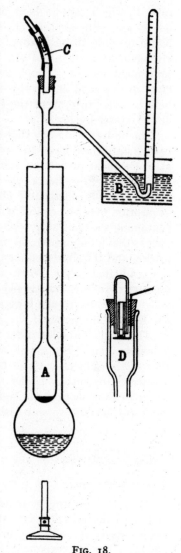

Fig. 18.

tube, C, which can be bent aside after the insertion of the
bottle and subsequently straightened so as to allow the
bottle to slide through and fall into the heated bulb. The
arrangement as depicted (D) in Fig. 18 is, however, more
convenient for use, though less simple in construction. A
layer of dry sand or asbestos is placed in the bottom of the
bulb in order to prevent the bottle from breaking the walls
of the vessel by its fall.

The bulb is heated by the vapour of a liquid boiling in the
bath B until the temperature of the bulb and tube is constant,
at which point no further bubbles of air are driven through
the delivery-tube under the surface of the water. The
graduated tube, completely filled with water, is then placed
in position over the end of the delivery-tube, and the bottle
containing the substance released from the upper part of the
tube so that it falls into the heated bulb. Instant volatilisation
occurs, and the displaced air is driven over and collected in
the graduated tube. When no further air passes over, the
graduated tube is transferred to a long cylinder filled with
water, the water-trough lowered from the delivery-tube, and
the heating interrupted.

The compound selected for the vapour-bath should possess
a boiling-point lying about twenty or thirty degrees above
that of the substance under examination, so that the latter
volatilises instantly. Under these circumstances inaccuracy
owing to diffusion need not be feared. Compounds commonly
employed for the vapour-bath are :

	B.P.			B.P.
Water	100°	Ethyl Benzoate	.	213°
Chlorobenzene	132°	Quinoline	.	239°
Bromobenzene	157°	IsoAmyl Benzoate	.	262°
Aniline	183°	a-Bromonaphthalene	.	279°
Dimethylaniline	193°	Diphenylamine	.	310°

It is to be borne in mind that the exact temperatures
employed do not enter into the calculation. It is therefore
not necessary to make certain of the purity of the substances
employed for the vapour-bath.

The volume of the air is determined in precisely the same manner as is the nitrogen produced in the analysis of nitrogen compounds by the Dumas method (p. 301).

The vapour-density is calculated from the formula :

$$D = \frac{31070 \cdot W(273 + t)}{V(B - p)}$$

where D represents the density of the vapour reduced to N.T.P., W the weight of substance taken, t the temperature of the air and surrounding water, B the barometric pressure reduced to 0°, p the vapour-pressure of water at the observed temperature, and V the observed volume of the air.

A list setting forth the vapour-pressure of water, expressed in mm. of mercury, at temperatures between 10° and 25°, will be found on p. 302.

(2) *The Hofmann Method.*—This method is particularly adapted to the determination of the vapour-density of substances which are not stable at their boiling-points under atmospheric pressure, but which may be volatilised without decomposition under reduced pressure.   The procedure is more complicated than in the Victor Meyer method, which, however, it does not surpass in point of accuracy.

A glass tube, sealed at one end, 90 cm. in length and 12 mm. to 15 mm. in diameter, graduated in mm. and calibrated so that the volume corresponding to the graduations is accurately known, is filled with pure dry mercury and inverted into a mercury-trough, care being taken that the interior of the tube is perfectly clean and dry.   Three small Anschütz thermometers are affixed to the tube at equal distances by means of cotton thread or fine copper wire, and the vapour-jacket attached as shown in Fig. 19.   It is advisable to cover the indiarubber stopper through which the barometer-tube passes with a layer of mercury, in order to prevent the hot liquid condensed in the jacket from coming into contact with it.

The column of mercury is then heated to constant tem-

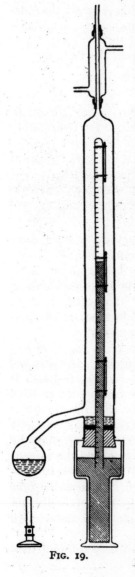

FIG. 19.

perature in the vapour of the liquid which is boiled in the bulb of the jacket, the temperatures registered by the three Anschütz thermometers being carefully noted. It is necessary that the liquid employed should be absolutely pure, thus boiling at constant temperature. When the surface of the mercury has become steady, as should be the case after the column has been surrounded by the vapour for three to five minutes, the height of the top of the column above the level of the mercury in the trough is accurately measured.

A small loosely-stoppered bottle, such as is employed in the method of Victor Meyer, containing a weighed quantity (0·05 gram to 0·1 gram) of the substance, is then inserted into the open end of the tube under the mercury in the trough. The bottle rapidly rises to the top of the column, and as the contents volatilise (in so doing expelling the stopper), the surface of the column of mercury sinks. When the level has become stationary, the height of the column is again measured, and the heating of the liquid in the bulb discontinued.

From the data observed as above indicated can be calculated the volume occupied by the vapour at the known temperature of the vapour in the jacket. It is however necessary to ascertain the barometric pressure corrected to 0° at the time of the experiment and the volume occupied by the glass bottle and its stopper. This last figure, which is to be deducted from the observed volume of vapour, can be found by dividing the weight in grams of the empty stoppered bottle by the density of glass (approximately 2·5). It is also necessary to measure the lengths of the portions of the mercury column which are heated and unaffected by the vapour in the jacket, as well as the temperature of the mercury in the trough. The depression of the column due to the weight of the bottle is negligible.

The density of the vapour reduced to N.T.P. is calculated from the formulae :

$$D = \frac{760(1 + 0 \cdot 003665 \cdot t)W}{0 \cdot 0012934 \cdot B \cdot V}$$

$$B = \frac{b}{1 + 0 \cdot 00018 \cdot t} - \left(\frac{b'}{1 + 0 \cdot 00018 \cdot t'} + \frac{b''}{1 + 0 \cdot 00018 \cdot t''} + s \right)$$

where D represents the required density, V the volume of the vapour at t', t the room temperature, t' the temperature of the vapour in the jacket, t'' the temperature of the part of the column not heated by the vapour in the jacket, W the weight of substance volatilised, b the height of the barometer at the room temperature, b' the length of the part of the column heated by the vapour in the jacket, b'' the length of the part of the column not heated by the vapour, s the vapour-pressure of mercury at the temperature t', and B the pressure reduced to 0° under which the volume of the vapour was measured. The factor 0·00018 is introduced in order to correct for the decrease in density of mercury at the temperature t.

The following table gives the vapour-pressure, expressed in mm. of mercury, of mercury at temperatures between 100° and 320° :

100°	0·75	180°	11·00	260°	96·73
120°	1·53	200°	19·90	280°	155·17
140°	3·06	220°	34·70	300°	242·15
160°	5·00	240°	58·82	320°	368·73

The following compounds are commonly employed for the vapour-jacket :

	B.P.		B.P.
Water	100°	Acetophenone	200°
Acetic Acid	119°	Ethyl Benzoate	213°
Chlorobenzene	132°	Diethylaniline	213°
m-Xylene	139°	Quinoline	239°
IsoAmyl Acetate	142°	IsoAmyl Benzoate	262°
Bromobenzene	157°	α-Bromonaphthalene	279°
Aniline	183°	Methyldiphenylamine	296°
Dimethylaniline	193°	Diphenylamine (M.P. 54°)	310°

For temperatures near 300° diphenylamine is frequently employed, but methyldiphenylamine possesses the advantage of being a liquid at ordinary temperatures. When employing diphenylamine it is advisable to replace the Liebig water-jacketed condenser by an air-condenser of sufficient length.

Density of Liquids

The density of a liquid can be determined with a high degree of accuracy by means of a very small pyknometer, the volume of which need not exceed 0·8 c.c. This can readily be constructed in the blowpipe flame from a piece of thick-walled capillary tubing. The mark may be etched on the stem by coating with a thin layer of paraffin wax, cutting the wax at the required point with the edge of a sharp knife, and then moistening the incision with a solution

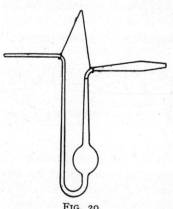

FIG. 20.

of hydrofluoric acid, removing this and the wax after a few seconds. The wire for suspending the pyknometer on the balance should be of platinum, so that the weight of the empty apparatus may remain constant.

Pure water is drawn in by dipping the point of the pyknometer in the water and sucking the further end of a long
indiarubber tube attached to the shorter limb. When the
water is just past the mark, the tube is detached, and the
pyknometer placed as completely as possible in a small beaker
of water at a known temperature and allowed to remain in this
bath for about two minutes, after which the excess of liquid
is removed by inclining forwards the pyknometer, still in the
beaker, until a piece of filter-paper applied to the fine end has
absorbed a quantity of the liquid sufficient to bring the level
in the other limb exactly to the mark. The pyknometer is
then removed from the bath, inclined so that the liquid in the
fine end flows back into the body of the pyknometer, carefully
wiped completely dry with a silk cloth, and weighed without
delay, suspending by means of the wire on the hook of the
balance.

The volume of liquid contained in the pyknometer at the
observed temperature can be calculated from the observed
weight of water. The following table gives the volume in c.c.
of 1 gram of water at temperatures between 0° and 31°.

0°	1·000129	8°	1·000114	16°	1·000999	24°	1·002641
1°	1·000072	9°	1·000176	17°	1·001160	25°	1·002888
2°	1·000031	10°	1·000253	18°	1·001348	26°	1·003144
3°	1·000009	11°	1·000345	19°	1·001542	27°	1·003408
4°	1·000000	12°	1·000451	20°	1·001744	28°	1·003682
5°	1·000010	13°	1·000570	21°	1·001957	29°	1·003965
6°	1·000030	14°	1·000701	22°	1·002177	30°	1·004250
7°	1·000067	15°	1·000841	23°	1·002405	31°	1·004550

Corrections for the change in volume of the pyknometer with
temperature can be calculated from the coefficient of cubical
expansion of glass, 0·00002584.

The density of the substance under examination is determined in exactly the same manner, by filling the pyknometer,
removing the excess of liquid while in a bath of known temperature, drying, and weighing. It is, of course, necessary
to know the weight of the pyknometer when empty and
thoroughly dry.

Pyknometers can be obtained in which the density of a much greater volume of liquid can be determined, but the form of pyknometer above described yields results sufficiently accurate for practically all requirements in the course of work on organic compounds. These large pyknometers are usually provided with glass caps for the ends, in order to minimise loss of substance by evaporation. The operations involved in their use are the same as those indicated above, with the exception that a longer time must be allowed for the acquisition of the temperature of the bath.

In another form of pyknometer a flask of known capacity is filled with the liquid, placed in a bath at known temperature, and a stopper with a capillary boring inserted, the excess of liquid expelled through this boring being removed. The

FIG. 21.

flask, which has previously been tared, is then weighed after thoroughly drying the surface.

When it is desired to determine the density of a liquid with an accuracy of only about one part in a thousand, as is the case with liquids submitted to qualitative examination, extremely rapid determinations can be effected by the use of the pyknometer devised by Cripps. A slight excess of the liquid is drawn up at the known room temperature into the capillary-pointed pipette, by pressing and then releasing the indiarubber bulb. This pipette is then removed from the ground socket by means of a silk cloth held between the fingers, and wiped completely dry, care being taken that the temperature of the pyknometer is not raised by contact with the fingers, and weighed upon the pan of the balance. The pyknometer, the weight of which when empty and completely dry must be accurately determined, may be standardised by filling with distilled water at known temperature and weighing.

Determination of Optical Rotation

The polarimeter may be employed not only for determining the specific rotation of optically active compounds, but also for estimating the concentration of solutions of active substances of known rotatory power.

The instrument consists essentially of two Nicol prisms, A and B, one of which (A) is capable of free rotation about the common axis. This Nicol is termed the Analyser. The other Nicol (B) remains fixed in position, and is termed the Polariser. Between the two Nicols, nearer to the polariser, a quartz plate, C, is interposed so as to obscure half the field. This plate causes the transmitted light to vibrate in a plane inclined at a definite angle from that of the entering light.

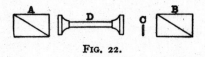

FIG. 22.

Between this plate C and the analyser is placed a tube, D, containing a column of the liquid under examination, the length of which is accurately known. Polarimeter-tubes containing columns of ether 10 cm. or 20 cm. length are generally employed. Monochromatic light must be employed, the source of which is usually a sodium flame, which emits fairly pure sodium D light. This light may, however, be rendered more pure by interposing a bichromate cell. Lenses are inserted for the purpose of condensing the light on the polariser, and also to serve as a telescope by which the split disc can be viewed. The angle through which the analyser is turned is read off on a circular scale graduated in fractions of degrees and provided with a vernier and a movable microscope.

In order to find the zero-point of the instrument, the polarimeter-tube is removed, the sodium flame adjusted so as to throw a maximum amount of light upon the lens behind the polariser, and the illuminated split disc brought into focus by adjusting the eyepiece of the telescope. The zero-point, which should be the mean of several determinations, is that point indicated on the scale at which the illumination on both sides of the split disc is equal. In a well-adjusted instrument this point should be within a few minutes of the

zero on the scale; it may however vary with different observers, so that the zero-point should be determined afresh before every experiment or series of experiments.

To determine the specific rotation of a substance, a polarimeter-tube, perfectly clean and dry, of which the internal length is known, is completely filled with the substance itself if a liquid, or with a solution, of known concentration and density,[1] of the substance in some pure solvent.

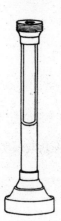

This is performed by unscrewing the cap A at one end of the polarimeter-tube, removing the glass plate B, filling the tube so that the surface of the liquid forms a projecting meniscus, sliding the plate back into position so as to leave no bubbles of air, and replacing the cap after removing any adhering drops of liquid; care being taken to screw the cap on with sufficient force to close the tube completely, but not so strongly as to break the cemented juncture between the glass and the metal.

FIG. 23.

This tube is then placed in position in the polarimeter so as to acquire the room temperature. Any convection currents within the liquid obscure the transmitted light, so that the tube must at no time be touched with the fingers at the glass

---

[1] It is generally sufficient, when examining solutions, to know merely the concentration in terms of grams per 100 c.c. of solution, in which case the density need not be determined.

portion. In some forms of polarimeter-tube the column is jacketed with water at a known constant temperature, the water being either motionless, or in the form of a stream such as in the jacket of the Liebig condenser.

When temperature equilibrium is attained, the analyser is set so that equal intensity of light on each half of the illuminated disc is reached, and the angle again accurately read. This figure, referred to the zero-point initially obtained in the absence of the polarimeter-tube, gives the observed angle of rotation.

The specific rotation $[a]_D^t$ of a pure liquid, observed by sodium D light at the temperature t, is calculated from the formula :

$$[a]_D^t = \frac{a}{l.d}$$

where a represents the observed angle of rotation, l the length in decimeters of the column of liquid in the polarimeter-tube, and d the density of the liquid at the temperature at which the rotation is observed.

The specific rotation of an active compound dissolved in a pure liquid or in a liquid of known composition, observed by sodium D light [1] at the temperature t, may be calculated from either of the formulae :

$$[a]_D^t = \frac{100.a}{l.c} \text{ or } \frac{100.a}{l.d.p}$$

where c represents the number of grams of active substance present in 100 c.c. of solution, and p the percentage of solute by weight ; the other symbols representing the same factors as in the formula above.

It is to be noted that both the concentration of the solution and the nature of the solvent may occasion appreciable

---

[1] There is an increasing tendency to employ the mercury green line (546·1 $\mu\mu$.) as the standard wave-length, since a much more convenient and intense source of light can be obtained by the use of a mercury vapour lamp and a suitable light-filter than with a sodium flame.

variations in the specific rotation of an active compound. It is therefore advisable to carry out the experiment under standard conditions.

The concentration of a solution of an optically active substance may, as stated above, be estimated by the use of the polarimeter. This procedure involves the assumption that changes in dilution have no effect upon the specific rotation, an assumption which is justifiable, however, in the case of the sugars, for the estimation of which the polarimeter is largely employed in technical analysis.

The number of grams of active substance present in a litre of solution may be calculated from the formula :

$$\frac{1000.a}{l.[a]}$$

where a represents the observed angle of rotation, l the length in dcm. of the column of liquid, and $[a]$ the known specific rotation of the substance.

It may here be remarked that certain compounds, such as dextrose, the chemical constitution of which changes at a measurable rate in a freshly prepared solution, may yield variable results, according to the length of time during which the solution has been allowed to stand. Thus the rotation of a freshly prepared solution of dextrose falls to about one-half the initial value after standing for some hours, owing to an isomeric change. Such a change in rotatory power is termed Mutarotation. The change is instantly effected in the case of dextrose by the addition of a trace of alkali or ammonia.

Cane sugar and glucose can be independently estimated in the same solution by utilising the effect of hydrolysis. The solution containing both sucrose and dextrose is divided into two equal portions, one of these 'inverted,'—by warming to 100° for fifteen minutes with dilute hydrochloric acid—and then neutralised, and both made up to the same volume. The number of grams of each constituent per litre of the solution thus obtained may be calculated, after determining the rotation of each, by solving the simultaneous equation :

$$l(52 \cdot 8x + 66 \cdot 5y) = 1000.a$$
$$l(52 \cdot 8x - 21 \cdot 2y) = 1000.a'$$

where x and y are respectively the number of grams of glucose and cane sugar present in a litre of solution, a and a' the rotations of the non-inverted and inverted solutions respectively, and l the length in cm. of the columns in the tubes. The numbers 52·8 and 66·5 are the respective specific rotations of dextrose and sucrose ; 21·2 is the value for invert sugar, with reference to sucrose, corrected for the molecular proportion of water taken up by the saccharose in its conversion into dextrose and levulose. Polarimetric observations should be made at a temperature as near as possible to 20°.

INDEX OF SUBSTANCES

To correspond with Chapter IV.

Acenaphthene, 109
Acetal, 127
Acetaldehyde, 126
  Ammonia, 209
  Cyanohydrin, 233
Acetaldol, 128
Acetaldoxime, 229
Acetamide, 211
Acetanilide, 218
Acetic Acid, 136
  Anhydride, 150
Acetnaphthylamide, 218, 220
Acetoacetanilide, 217
Acetone, 130
  Cyanohydrin, 232
Acetonitrile, 231
Acetophenetidide, 219
Acetophenone, 131
  oxime, 230
Acetotoluidide, 218, 219
Acetoxime, 229
Acetoxylidide, 218
Acetylacetone, 131
Acetyl Bromide, 185
  Chloride, 185
  Diphenylamine, 217
Acetylene Tetrachloride, 168
Acetyl Phenetidine, 219
Acetylphenylhydrazine, 218
Acetyl Piperidine, 216
Acetylsalicylic Acid, 149
Acetyl Toluidine, 218, 219
  Xylidine, 218

Aconitic Acid, 144
Acrolein, 136
Acrylic Acid, 142
Adipic Acid, 141
Alanine, 227
Aldol, 128
Alizarin, 135
Alloxan, 213
Allyl Acetate, 151
  Alcohol, 114
Allylamine, 192
Allyl Benzoate, 153
  Bromide, 170
  Chloride, 167
  Formate, 151
  Iodide, 172
  isoThiocyanate, 278
Allylthiourea, 275
Aminoacetanilide, 220
Aminoazobenzene, 252
Aminoazotoluene, 252
Aminobenzoic Acid, 224
Aminobutyric Acid, 226, 227
Aminocresol, 209
Aminodimethylaniline, 198
Aminophenol, 208, 209
Aminosalicylic Acid, 226
Amyl Acetate, 151
  Alcohol, 115
Amylamine, 193
Amylaniline, 202
Amyl Benzoate, 154
  Bromide, 170
  Butyrate, 152
  Carbamate, 222

Amyl Carbonate, 153
  Chloride, 168
  Chloroformate, 186
Amylene, 104
Amyl Ether, 110
  Formate, 151
  Iodide, 172
  Mercaptan, 263
  Nitrate, 257
  Nitrite, 257
  Oxalate, 154
  Phthalate, 155
  Propionate, 152
  Salicylate, 158
  Succinate, 154
  Sulphide, 264
  Valerate, 152
Amygdalin, 166
Anethole, 113
Aniline, 196
Anisaldehyde, 129
Anisic Acid, 149
Anisidine, 197, 198
Anisole, 111
Anisoyl Chloride, 185
Anthracene, 110
Anthranilic Acid, 224
Anthraquinone, 135
Antipyrine, 235
Apiole, 113
Arabinose, 163
Arbutin, 165
Asparagine, 225
Aspartic Acid, 226
Atropine, 282
Azelaic Acid, 139
Azobenzene, 251
Azotoluene, 251, 252

Azoxybenzene, 253
Azoxytoluene, 253

Barbituric Acid, 215
Benzalacetone, 132
Benzalaniline, 209
Benzal Chloride, 169
Benzaldehyde, 128
  Cyanohydrin, 233
Benzaldoxime, 229
Benzamide, 212
Benzanilide, 220
Benzene, 105
Benzeneazocresol, 252
Benzeneazonaphthol, 252
Benzenedisulphonic Acid, 266
Benzene Hexachloride, 169
Benzenesulphinic Acid, 272
Benzenesulphochloride 273
Benzenesulphonamide, 274
Benzenesulphonanilide 275
Benzenesulphonic Acid, 267
Benzidine, 200
Benzil, 132
Benzildioxime, 230
Benzilic Acid, 146
Benzoic Acid, 140
  Anhydride, 150
Benzoin, 133
Benzonitrile, 231
Benzophenone, 132
  Oxime, 230
Benzoquinone, 134
Benzotoluidide, 219, 220
Benzotrichloride, 169
Benzoyl Chloride, 185
  Phenylhydrazine, 220
  Piperidine, 217
  Toluidide, 219, 220
Benzyl Acetate, 153
  Alcohol, 117

Benzylamine, 193
Benzylaniline, 202
Benzyl Benzoate, 155
  Bromide, 171
  Butyrate, 154
  Chloride, 169
  Cinnamate, 155
  Cyanide, 232
  Disulphide, 265
  Ether, 111
  Ethyl Ether, 111
  Formate, 153
  Iodide, 173
Benzylmalonic Acid, 140
Benzyl Mercaptan, 263
  Methyl Ether, 110
  Oxalate, 155
  Phthalate, 155
  Salicylate, 158
  Succinate, 155
  Sulphide, 265
  Sulphone, 266
  Sulphoxide, 266
  Thiocyanate, 278
Benzylurea, 213
Biuret, 214
Borneol, 120
Bornyl Acetate, 155
Bromal, 183
  Alcoholate, 183
  Hydrate, 183
Bromoacetal, 183
Bromoacetanilide, 259
Bromoacetic Acid, 187
Bromoacetophenone, 184
Bromoacetyl Bromide, 185
Bromoaniline, 257, 258
Bromoanisole, 178, 179
Bromobenzene, 174
Bromobenzoic Acid, 188, 189
Bromocamphor, 185
Bromocyclohexane, 171
Bromocymene, 175
Bromoethyl Acetate, 191
  Ether, 178
Bromoform, 170

Bromohydroquinone, 182
Bromomethyl Acetate, 190
Bromonaphthalene, 175, 176
Bromophenetole, 179
Bromophenol, 181
Bromophenylhydrazine, 258
Bromopropionic Acid, 187
Bromopropionyl Bromide, 185
Bromostyrene, 171
Bromotoluene, 175
Brucine, 281, 283
Butyl Acetate, 151
  Alcohol, 114, 115, 118
Butylamine, 193
Butylaniline, 202
Butyl Benzoate, 154
  Bromide, 170
  Butyrate, 152
  Carbamate, 222
  Carbonate, 152, 153
  Chloride, 167
  Chloroacetate, 191
  Chloroformate, 186
  Citrate, 157
Butylene Bromide, 170, 171
Butyl Ether, 110
  Formate, 151
  Iodide, 172
  Mercaptan, 262
  Nitrate, 257
  Nitrite, 257
  Oxalate, 153, 154
  Phenylacetate, 154
  Phthalate, 155
  Propionate, 151, 152
  Salicylate, 158
  Succinate, 154
  Sulphide, 264
  Tartrate, 157
  Thiocyanate, 278
  Toluenesulphonate, 270
Butyraldehyde, 126, 127
Butyramide, 212

Butyranilide, 217
Butyric Acid, 136, 137
  Anhydride, 150
Butyronitrile, 231
Butyryl Chloride, 185

Caffeine, 228
Camphene, 108
Camphor, 133
Camphoric Acid, 141
  Anhydride, 150
Camphoroxime, 230
Camphorquinone, 135
Camphorsulphonic
  Acid, 269
Capric Acid, 138
Caproic Acid, 137
Caprylic Acid, 137
Carbanilide, 221
Carbazole, 202
Carbon Disulphide,264
  Tetrabromide, 171
  Tetrachloride, 168
Carbostyril, 209
Carvacrol, 121
Carvone, 132
Catechol, 124
Cetyl Alcohol, 119
Cevadine, 281, 284
Chloral, 182
  Alcoholate, 183
  Hydrate, 184
Chloroacetal, 183
Chloroacetamide, 259
Chloroacetanilide, 259
Chloroacetic Acid, 187
Chloroacetone, 184
Chloroacetophenone,
  185
Chloroacetyl Chloride,
  185
Chloroaniline, 257, 258
Chloroanisole, 178
Chlorobenzaldehyde,
  183
Chlorobenzene, 173
Chlorobenzoic Acid,
  188, 189
Chlorocyclohexane, 168
Chloroethyl Acetate,
  190
  Ether, 177, 178

Chloroform, 167
Chlorohydroquinone,
  182
Chloromethyl Acetate,
  189
Chloromethyl Ether,
  177
  Ethyl Ether, 177
Chloronaphthalene,174
Chlorophenetole, 178
Chlorophenol, 181
Chloropicrin, 259
Chloropropionic Acid,
  186, 187
Chlorotoluene, 173
Cinchonidine, 284
Cinchonine, 281, 284
Cineole, 110
Cinnamaldehyde, 129
Cinnamanilide, 219
Cinnamic Acid, 143
Cinnamyl Alcohol, 118
  Cinnamate, 155
Citraconic Acid, 143
  Anhydride, 150
Citral, 129
Citric Acid, 146
Citronellal, 129
Citronellol, 117
Codeine, 281, 283
Cocaine, 280, 281
Coniferin, 166
Coniine, 280, 281
Coumaric Acid, 147
Coumarin, 160
Creatine, 215
Creatinine, 215
Cresol, 120, 122
Cresyl Acetate, 155,
  156
  Benzenesulphonate,
  271
  Benzoate, 156
  Carbonate, 156
  Methyl Ether, 111
  Toluenesulphonate,
  271
Crotonaldehyde, 127
Crotonic Acid, 143
Cumene, 106
Cyanoacetic Acid, 233
cycloHexane, 105

cycloHexanol, 116, 118
cycloHexanone, 131
cycloHexene, 105
cycloHexyl Acetate,
  152
  Formate, 152
Cymene, 107
Cystine, 276

Decahydronaphthal-
  ene, 107
Dextrin, 165
Dextrose, 163
Diacetin, 154
Diacetone Alcohol, 131
Diacetyldioxime, 231
Diacetylphenylene-
  diamine, 220, 221
Diaminophenol, 207
Diamylamine, 195
Dianisidine, 201
Dibenzyl, 108
Dibenzylamine, 195
Dibenzylaniline, 205
Dibenzylurea, 220
Dibromoaniline, 258
Dibromobenzene, 175,
  176
Dibromomethyl Ether,
  177
Dibromophenol, 181
Dibromopropionic
  Acid, 188
Dibutylamine, 194
Dibutylaniline, 204
Dicyandiamidine, 211
Dichloroacetic Acid,
  187
Dichloroacetone, 184
Dichloroaniline, 258
Dichlorobenzene, 173,
  174
Dichloroethylene, 167
Dichloroethyl Ether,
  177, 178
Dichloromethyl Ether,
  177
Dichlorophenol, 181
Dichlorophthalic Acid,
  189
Dichloropropyl Ether,
  178

Diethylamine, 194
Diethylaniline, 204
Diethylcarbanilide, 217
Diethyl Ketone, 130
Diethyltoluidine, 203, 204
Digitalin, 166
Dimethylacetal, 126
Dimethylamine, 194
Dimethylaminoazo-benzene, 252
Dimethylaminobenz-aldehyde, 205
Dimethylaminophenol, 207
Dimethylaniline, 203
Dimethylcarbanilide, 218
Dimethylglyoxime, 231
Dimethylguanidine, 211
Dimethyltoluidine, 203, 204
Dimethylxanthine, 228
Dinitroanisole, 243
Dinitroaniline, 254, 255
Dinitrobenzene, 240, 241
Dinitrobenzoic Acid, 248
Dinitrobromobenzene, 261
Dinitrochlorobenzene, 260
Dinitronaphthalene, 241
Dinitronaphthol, 245
Dinitrophenol, 245
Dinitrophenylhydra-zine, 255
Dinitrosalicylic Acid, 247
Dinitrotoluene, 239
Dinitroxylene, 240
Dipentene, 107
Diphenyl, 108
Diphenylamine, 202
Diphenylguanidine, 213
Diphenylhydrazine, 235
Diphenylmethane, 108

Diphenylnitrosoamine, 249
Dipropylamine, 195
Dipropylaniline, 204
Ditolylamine, 202
Ditolylurea, 221

Elaidic Acid, 143
Epichlorohydrin, 178
Ethylacetanilide, 217
Ethyl Acetate, 151
Acetoacetate, 159
Acetonedicarboxy-late, 160
Ethylal, 127
Ethyl Alcohol, 114
Ethylamine, 192
Ethyl Aminobenzoate, 223
Ethylaniline, 201
Ethyl Anisate, 154
Anthranilate, 223
Ethylbenzene, 105
Ethyl Benzenesulphon-ate, 270
Benzoate, 153
Ethylbenzylaniline, 204
Ethyl Benzylmalon-ate, 154
Ethyl Bromide, 170
Bromoacetate, 190
Bromopropionate, 191
Butyrate, 151
Caprate, 154
Caproate, 152
Caprylate, 153
Carbamate, 222
Carbanilate, 222
Carbonate, 151
Chloroacetate, 190
Chloroformate, 186
Chloropropionate, 190
Cinnamate, 154
Citrate, 157
Cyanoacetate, 233
Dichloroacetate, 190
Disulphide, 264
Ethylene Bromide, 170
Bromohydrin, 179

Ethylene Chloride, 168
Chlorohydrin, 179
Ethylenediamin, 193
Ethylene Glycol, 117
GlycolDiacetate, 152
Glycol Dibenzoate, 155
Glycol Monoacetate, 152
Glycol Monoethyl Ether, 115
Iodide, 173
Ethyl Ether, 110
Ethylacetoacetate, 159
Formate, 151
Heptylate, 152
Hydroxybenzoate, 158
Ethylidene Chloride, 167
Ethyl Iodide, 171
Laurate, 154
Lactate, 156
Levulinate, 160
Malonate, 153
Ethylmalonic Acid, 140
Ethyl Mandelate, 157
Mercaptan, 262
Methylacetoacetate, 159
Methylmalonate, 152
Myristate, 154
Nitrate, 257
Nitrite, 257
Oxalate, 152
Oxamate, 223
Oxanilate, 222
Palmitate, 155
Pelargonate, 153
Phenylacetate, 153
Ethylphenylnitroso-amine, 249
Ethyl Phthalate, 154
Propionate, 151
Pyruvate, 159
Salicylate, 157
Sebacate, 155
Stearate, 155
Succinate, 153
Sulphate, 272
Sulphide, 264

Ethylsulphuric Acid, 272
Ethyl Tartrate, 157
Thiocyanate, 278
Toluenesulphonate, 270
Trichloroacetate, 191
Trichlorolactate, 191
Valerate, 151, 152
Eugenol, 121
Eugenol Methyl Ether, 112

Fluorene, 109
Formaldehyde, 127
Formamide, 210
Formanilide, 216
Formic Acid, 136
Formyl Diphenyl-amine, 217
Piperidine, 216
Fructose, 161
Fumaric Acid, 144
Furfural, 128
Furoic Acid, 140
Furyl Alcohol, 116

Galactose, 162, 163
Gallic Acid, 148
Geraniol, 118
Glucosamine, 194
Glucose, 163
Glutamic Acid, 225
Glutaric Acid, 139
Glycerol, 118
Diacetate, 154
Dibromohydrin, 180
Dichlorohydrin, 180
Monoacetate, 154
Monochlorohydrin, 180
Triacetate, 154
Tribromohydrin, 171
Tributyrate, 155
Trichlorohydrin, 168
Tripalmitate, 155
Tripropionate, 154
Tristearate, 155
Glycine, 225
Glycogen, 164
Glycollic Acid, 145

Guaiacol, 122
Guanidine, 210

Helicin, 165
Heptaldehyde, 128
Heptyl Alcohol, 116
Heptylic Acid, 137
Hexachlorobenzene, 174
Hexachloroethane, 169
Hexamethylenetetra-mine, 210
Hexane, 104
Hippuric Acid, 225
Hydrobenzamide, 210
Hydrocinnamic Acid, 138
Hydroquinone, 125
Diacetate, 156
Dimethyl Ether, 113
Monomethyl Ether, 123
Hydroxyazobenzene, 252
Hydroxybenzaldehyde 130
Hydroxybenzoic Acid, 147, 148
Hydroxynaphthoic Acid, 148
Hydroxyphenylgly-cine, 226
Hyoscyamine, 282

Indene, 107
Inositol, 120
Inulin, 164
Iodoacetic Acid, 188
Iodobenzene, 176
Iodoform, 173
Iodopropionic Acid, 188
Iodotoluene, 176
iso-Amyl. See Amyl
iso-Butyl. See Butyl
iso-Butyric. See Bu-tyric
iso-Eugenol. See Eu-genol, etc.
Itaconic Acid, 144

Lactic Acid, 145
Lactide, 161
Lactose, 164
Lauric Acid, 138
Leucine, 226
Levulinic Acid, 149
Levulose, 161
Limonene, 107
Linalool, 117

Maleic Acid, 144
Anhydride, 150
Malic Acid, 145
Malonamide, 213
Malonic Acid, 140
Maltose, 161
Mandelic Acid, 146
Mannitol, 119
Mannose, 162
Menthol, 119
Menthone, 132
Mesitol, 123
Mesitylene, 106
Mesityl Oxide, 131
Metanilic Acid, 277
Methylacetanilide, 217
Methyl Acetate, 151
Acetoacetate, 159
Methylal, 126
Methyl Alcohol, 113
Methylamine, 191
Methylaminophenol, 208
Methylaniline, 201
Methyl Anisate, 155
Anthranilate, 223
Benzenesulphonate, 270
Benzoate, 153
Bromoacetate, 190
Butyrate, 151
Methyl Caprate, 153
Caproate, 152
Caprylate, 152
Carbamate, 222
Carbonate, 151
Chloroacetate, 190
Chloroformate, 185
Cinnamate, 155
Citrate, 157
Methyldiphenylamine, 204

Methyl Disulphide, 264
Methylene Bromide, 170
  Chloride, 167
  Iodide, 172
Methylethylaniline, 203
Methyl Ethyl Ketone, 130
Methyl Formate, 150
Methylglucoside, 165
Methylguanidine, 211
Methyl Heptylate, 152
  Hydroxybenzoate, 158
  Iodide, 171
  Lactate, 156
  Laurate, 154
  Malonate, 152
Methylmalonic Acid, 141
Methyl Mandelate, 157
  Myristate, 154
Methylnaphthalene, 108
Methyl Nitrate, 257
  Oxalate, 155
  Palmitate, 155
  Pelargonate, 153
  Phenylacetate, 153
Methylphenylhydrazine, 234
Methylphenylnitrosoamine, 249
Methyl Phthalate, 154
  Propionate, 151
  Pyruvate, 159
  Salicylate, 157
Methylsalicylic Acid, 149
Methyl Sebacate, 155
  Stearate, 155
  Succinate, 152
  Sulphate, 271
  Sulphide, 264
Methylsulphuric Acid, 272
Methyl Tartrate, 157
  Thiocyanate, 278
  Toluenesulphonate, 270
  Valerate, 151

Michler's Hydride, 205
  Ketone, 205
Monoacetin, 154
Morphine, 281, 284
Mucic Acid, 147
Myristic Acid, 138

Naphthalene, 108
Naphthalenedisulphonic Acid, 267
Naphthalenesulphochloride, 273, 274
Naphthalenesulphonamide, 274
Naphthalenesulphonic Acid, 267, 268
Naphthalene Tetrachloride, 174
Naphthionic Acid, 277
Naphthoic Acid, 141
Naphthol, 124
Naphtholdisulphonic Acid, 268
Naphtholsulphonic Acid, 269
Naphthonitrile, 232
Naphthoquinone, 134
Naphthylamine, 199, 200
Naphthyl Benzoate, 156
  Ethyl Ether, 112, 113
  isoCyanate, 234
  Methyl Ether, 112, 113
  Salicylate, 158
Narcotine, 281, 283
Nicotine, 280, 281
Nitroacetaminotoluene, 256
Nitroacetanilide, 255, 256
Nitroaniline, 253, 254
Nitroanisole, 241, 242
Nitrobenzaldehyde, 245, 246
Nitrobenzamide, 255, 256
Nitrobenzanilide, 256
Nitrobenzene, 238
Nitrobenzenesulphonic Acid, 277

Nitrobenzoic Acid, 247, 248, 249
Nitrobenzyl Alcohol, 243
  Bromide, 252
  Chloride, 260, 261
Nitrobromobenzene, 260, 261, 262
Nitrochlorobenzene, 259, 260, 261
Nitrocinnamic Acid, 248, 249
Nitrocymene, 239
Nitrodichlorobenzene, 260
Nitromesitylene, 239
Nitronaphthalene, 239
Nitrophenetole, 242
Nitrophenol, 244
Nitrophenylhydrazine, 254
Nitrophthalic Acid, 248
Nitrosalicylic Acid, 247
Nitrosobenzene, 250
Nitrosodiethylaniline, 250
Nitrosodimethylaniline, 250
Nitrosodiphenylamine, 251
Nitrosomethylaniline, 251
Nitrosonaphthol, 250
Nitrosophenol, 251
Nitrotoluene, 238, 239
Nitrotoluenesulphonic Acid, 278
Nitrotoluidine, 253, 254
Nitroxylene, 238

Octyl Alcohol, 116
Oenanthic Acid, 137
Oleic Acid, 143
Orcinol, 123, 124
Oxalic Acid, 139, 142
Oxamide, 216
Oxanilic Acid, 224
Oxanilide, 221

Palmitic Acid, 138
Papaverine. 282

Paraldehyde, 127
Pelargonic Acid, 137
Pentachloroethane, 169
Pentaerythritol, 120
Pentane, 104
Phenacetine, 219
Phenanthrene, 109
Phenanthrenequinone, 135
Phenetidine, 198
Phenetole, 111
Phenetylurea, 214
Phenol, 122
Phenolphthalein, 125
Phenolsulphonic Acid, 268
Phenoxyacetic Acid, 148
Phenylacetamide, 213
Phenylacetanilide, 218
Phenyl Acetate, 155
Phenylacetic Acid, 139
Phenylacetonitrile, 232
Phenylacetyl Chloride, 185
Phenylalanine, 226
Phenyl Benzenesulphonate, 270
Benzoate, 156
Butyrate, 156
Carbonate, 156
Cinnamate, 156
Disulphide, 265
Phenylenediamine, 199, 200, 201
Phenyl Ether, 113
Phenylethyl Alcohol, 117
Phenylhydrazine, 234
Phenylglycine, 224
Phenyl isoCyanate, 234
isoThiocyanate, 279
Phenylmethylpyrazolone, 235
Phenylnitromethane, 236
Phenyl Phthalate, 156
Phenylpropiolic Acid, 144
Phenyl Propionate, 155, 156

Phenylpropyl Alcohol, 118
Phenyl Salicylate, 158
Sulphide, 265
Sulphone, 266
Sulphoxide, 265
Phenylthiourea, 276
Phenyl Toluenesulphonate, 271
Phenylurea, 213, 219
Phloroglucinol, 125
Phorone, 132
Phthalamide, 214
Phthalanil, 221
Phthalic Acid, 142
Phthalic Anhydride, 150
Phthalide, 161
Phthalyl Chloride, 185
Picoline, 206
Picramic Acid, 254
Picramide, 255
Picric Acid, 245
Picryl Chloride, 261
Pinacol, 118, 119
Pinacolone, 130
Pinene, 106
Piperazine, 207
Piperic Acid, 145
Piperidine, 206
Piperine, 218, 282
Piperonal, 129
Polyoxymethylene, 130
Populin, 166
Propiolic Acid, 142
Propionaldehyde, 126
Propionamide, 211
Propionanilide, 217
Propionic Acid, 136
Anhydride, 150
Propionitrile, 231
Propionyl Chloride, 185
Propyl Acetate, 151
Alcohol, 114
Propylamine, 192
Propylaniline, 202
Propylbenzene, 106
Propyl Benzoate, 153
Bromide, 170
Butyrate, 151
Carbamate, 222
Carbonate, 152

Propyl Chloride, 167
Chloroformate, 186
Propylene Bromide, 170
Chloride, 168
Glycol, 116
Propylethylene, 104
Propyl Formate, 151
Iodide, 172
Mercaptan, 262
Nitrate, 257
Nitrite, 257
Oxalate, 152, 153
Phthalate, 154
Propionate, 151
Salicylate, 158
Succinate, 154
Sulphide, 264
Protocatechuic Acid, 147
Pseudocumene, 106
Pseudocumenol, 123
Pyridine, 206
Pyrogallol, 125
Triacetate, 156
Pyromucic Acid, 140
Pyruvic Acid, 149

Quinidine, 283
Quinine, 280, 281, 283
Quinaldine, 207
Quinhydrone, 134
Quinoline, 206
Quinone, 134
Quinonemonoxime, 230

Raffinose, 162
Resorcinol, 124
Diacetate, 156
Dibenzoate, 156
Dimethyl Ether, 111
Monoacetate, 121
Monomethyl Ether, 121
Retene, 109

Safrole, 112
Salicin, 166
Salicylaldehyde, 128
Salicylamide, 212
Salicylic Acid, 147
Sarcosine, 225

Sebacic Acid, 140
Semicarbazide, 235
Starch, 165
Stearic Acid, 138
Stilbene, 109
Strychnine, 281, 285
Styrene, 106
Succinamide, 215
Succinanil, 219
Succinanilide, 221
Succinic Acid, 141
  Anhydride, 150
Succinimide, 212
Succinyl Chloride, 185
Sucrose, 163
Sulphanilic Acid, 277
Sulphobenzoic Acid, 268, 269
  Imide, 275
Sulphonal, 266
Sulphosalicylic Acid, 268
Sylvestrene, 107

Tannic Acid, 148
Tartaric Acid, 146
Terephthalic Acid, 142
Terpin Hydrate, 119
Terpineol, 119
Tetrabromoethane, 171
Tetrachloroethane, 168
Tetrachloroethylene, 158
Tetrachlorophthalic Acid, 189
Tetrahydronaphthalene, 108
Tetrahydroquinoline, 206
Tetramethyldiaminobenzophenone, 205
Tetramethyldiaminodiphenylmethane, 205
Theobromine, 228
Theophylline, 228
Thioacetic Acid, 273
Thiobenzoic Acid, 273
Thiocarbanilide, 276
Thiocresol, 263
Thiophenol, 263
Thiourea, 276

Thiosemicarbazide, 276
Thymol, 123
Thymol Methyl Ether, 112
Thymoquinone, 133
Thymyl Acetate, 156
Thymyl Benzoate, 156
Tolidine, 200
Toluene, 105
Toluenesulphinic Acid, 272
Toluenesulphochloride 273
Toluenesulphonamide, 274
Toluenesulphoanilide, 275
Toluenesulphonic Acid 267
Toluhydroquinone, 125
Toluic Acid, 139, 141
Toluidine, 197, 198
Tolunitrile, 232
Toluquinone, 133
Toluylenediamine, 199
Tolyl Disulphide, 265
Tolylhydrazine, 235
Tolyl Sulphide, 265
  Sulphone, 266
  Sulphoxide, 266
Tolylurea, 214
Triacetin, 154
Tribenzylamine, 196
Tribromoaniline, 258
Tribromoanisole, 179
Tribromophenetole, 179
Tribromophenol, 182
Tributyrin, 155
Trichloroacetic Acid, 187
Trichloroaniline, 258
Trichloroanisole, 179
Trichloroethane, 168
Trichloroethylene, 168
Trichlorolactic Acid, 188
Trichlorophenetole, 179
Trichlorophenol, 182
Tricresyl Phosphate, 279

Triethylamine, 196
Trimethylamine, 195
Trimethylene Bromide 171
  Bromohydrin, 180
  Chloride, 168
  Chlorohydrin, 180
  Glycol, 117
  Glycol Diacetate, 153
Trimethylethylene, 104
Trimethylxanthine, 228
Trinitroanisole, 243
Trinitrobenzene, 241
Trinitrobenzoic Acid, 248
Trinitrophenetole, 243
Trinitrotoluene, 240
Trional, 265
Trioxymethylene, 130
Tripalmitin, 155
Triphenylamine, 205
Triphenylcarbinol, 119
Triphenylguanidine, 219
Triphenylmethane, 109
Triphenyl Phosphate, 279
Tripropionin, 154
Tristearin, 155
Tyrosine, 227

Urea, 212
Uric Acid, 228
Urotropine, 210

Valeraldehyde, 127
Valeranilide, 218
Valeric Acid, 137
Valeronitrile, 231
Valeryl Chloride, 185
Valine, 227
Vanillic Acid, 148
Vanillin, 129
Veratrine, 284
Veratrole, 112

Xylene, 105, 106
Xylenol, 122, 123
Xylidine, 197, 198
Xylose, 162

GENERAL INDEX

Acetals, 91, 126–130
halogen-substituted, 183
Acetic anhydride, 42, 319
Acetylation, 42, 319
Acetyl chloride, 43
Acetylenic compounds, 15, 326
Acid anhydrides, 150
chlorides, 78
halides, 13, 63, 64, 185
Acids, amino. *See* Amino acids
carboxylic. *See* Carboxylic acids
halogen-substituted, 186–199
sulphinic. *See* Sulphinic acids
sulphonic. *See* Sulphonic acids
thiocarboxylic. *See* Thiocarboxylic acids
Acyloxy acids, 149
Adamkiewicz reaction, 53
Alcohols, 84–86, 113–120
halogen-substituted, 179, 180
primary, 84
secondary, 84
tertiary, 84
Aldehyde-ammonias, 28, 209, 210
Aldehydes, 86, 89, 90, 126–130
halogen-substituted, 184–186

Aldoses, 95
Aldoximes, 34, 229
Alkaloids, 53, 279–285
Alkoxy acids, 148, 149
Alkyl bromides, 63, 170, 171
carbamates. *See* Urethanes
chlorides, 63, 167–169
chloroformates, 64, 65, 185, 186
halides, 63, 66, 67
iodides, 62, 63, 68, 171–173
nitrates, 46, 47, 257
nitrites, 47, 257
sulphates, 57, 58, 271, 272
Alkyl sulphates, 54, 55, 272
Alkyl sulphites, 58
Alkylsulphuric acids, 272
Amides, hydrolysis, 317, 319
simple, 28, 64, 210–216
substituted, 32, 216–221
sulphonic. *See* Sulphonamides
Amines, 13, 35–44
aliphatic primary, 191–194
secondary, 194, 195
tertiary, 195, 196
aromatic primary 196–201
secondary, 201, 202
tertiary, 203–205

Amines, estimation, 319
halogen-substituted, 257–259
primary, 37, 38–41
secondary, 41
tertiary, 37, 44
Amino acids, 45, 223–227, 276
esters, 223
Aminophenols, 207–209
Amino sulphonic acids, 277
Ammonium salts, 28
Anhydrides, carboxylic. *See* Acid Anhydrides
Aryl halides, 67, 68, 173–176
bromides, 174–176
chlorides, 173–174
iodides, 68, 176
Azo compounds, 49, 251, 252, 286
Azoxy compounds, 49, 50, 253

Barium, estimation, 315, 316
Bases, heterocyclic, 37, 205–207
Beckmann rearrangement, 34
thermometer, 334, 337
Benzalamines, 41, 209, 210
Benzenesulphochloride 43, 83
Benzenesulphonylation, 43, 83

Benzidine transformation, 49
Benzoylation, 42, 82, 84
Benzoyl chloride, 42, 44, 82, 84
Benzyl*iso*thiourea, 56
Benzylphenylhydrazones, 94
Bertrand, 328
Bisulphite compounds, 54, 86, 87
Biuret reaction, 53
Boiling-point, 1–3
Bromides. *See* Alkyl bromides, etc.
Bromination, 75, 76, 83, 90, 91
Bromobenzenesulphochloride, 43
Bromo-hydrocarbons, 170, 171, 174–176

Calcium, estimation, 315, 316
Carbanilates, 83, 86
Carbohydrates, 91, 92, 161–165
Carbon, detection, 12
  estimation, 290–297
Carboxylic acids, 78–80, 136–149
  unsaturated, 142–145, 325
  halides, 185
Carius, 306, 307, 311
Cellulose, 97
Chlorides. *See* Alkyl chlorides, etc.
Chlorocarbonates. *See* Chloroformates
Chloro-hydrocarbons, 167–169, 173, 174
Combustion, 290–303
Cripps, 346
Cryoscopy, 333–336
Cumming, 321
Cyanohydrins, 32, 232, 233

Dealkylation, 77, 320–324

Density, liquid, 344–346
  vapour, 338–344
Diazotisation, 38, 39, 47
Dinitrobenzoic esters, 85, 86
Dinitrophenylhydrazones, 88
Disaccharides, 97
Distillation, 1–3, 7, 98, 102
  with steam, 102
Disulphides, 62, 264, 265
Dumas, 297–303
Dyes, 52, 285–289

Ebullioscopy, 337, 338
Ester-amides, 222, 223
Esterification, 78, 84
Esters, carboxylic, 81, 150–160
  halogen-substituted, 189–191
  hydrolysis, 81, 317, 319
  ketonic, 159, 160
  sulphonic, 58, 270, 271
Ethers, 77, 110–113
  halogen-substituted, 14, 65, 177–179
Ethoxyl, estimation, 320–324
Ethylenic compounds, estimation, 324–326

Fatty acids, 79, 136–138
Fehling's solution, 90–93, 97, 327–330
Fenton's test, 95
Furfural test, 95

Glucosides, 91, 92, 165, 166
Guanidines, 31, 33, 210, 211, 213, 215, 219

Halides, carboxylic.
  See Acid halides
Halogen, detection, 11
  estimation, 306–311
  -substituted acids, 186–189
  amides, 259
  amines, 257, 258
  ethers, 14, 65, 177–179
  nitro-hydrocarbons, 63, 259–262
Heterocyclic bases, 37, 205–207
Hewitt, 320
Hexoses, 95, 96, 161–164
Hofmann, 341–344
Hübl, 325
Hydantoic acids, 46
Hydrazines, 33, 34, 234–236
Hydrazo compounds, 48, 49, 236
Hydrazones, 33, 88, 94, 236, 237
Hydrocarbons, 72–77, 104–110
  unsaturated, 76, 77
Hydrogen, detection, 12
  estimation, 290–297
Hydrolysis, 317–319
Hydroxy acids, 79, 80, 145–148

Imides, 29, 210–216
Iodides. *See* Alkyl iodides, etc.
Iodine, estimation, 306, 310, 311
  number, 326
Iodoform test, 87
Iodo-hydrocarbons, 171–173, 176
*iso*Cyanates, 35, 234
*iso*Cyanides, 35, 41
*iso*Nitroso compounds, 47
*iso*Thiocyanates, 70, 278, 279

Johnston and Lynn, 5

Ketones, 86, 91, 130–
    133
    halogen-substituted,
        184, 185
Ketonic acids, 149
    esters, 159, 160
Ketoses, 95
Ketoximes, 34, 229–
    231
Kjeldahl, 297, 303–306

Lactones, 160, 161
Levulinic acid test, 96

Maquenne, 94
Melting-point, 3, 4, 6
    mixed, 102
Mercaptans, 61, 62,
    262, 263
Methoxyl, estimation,
    320–324
Methylphenylhydra-
    zine, 95
Meyer, 339–341
Millon's reagent, 53
Mixed   melting-point,
    102.
Mixtures, separation,
    98–102
Molecular weight, esti-
    mation, 333–344
Molisch's reaction, 91,
    92
Monosaccharides, 93,
    161–164
Mucic acid test, 96
Mustard oils. See *iso*-
    Thiocyanates

Naphthyl *iso*Cyanate,
    45
Nessler's solution, 89
Neumann, 312
Nitrates.   See Alkyl
    nitrites
Nitration, 76
Nitriles, 28, 31, 231–
    233
    substituted, 222,
        223

Nitrites.   See Alkyl
    nitrites
Nitro acids, 247
    alcohols, 243
    aldehydes, 245, 246
    amines, 253–255
Nitrobenzenesulpho-
    chloride, 43
Nitrobenzyl esters, 80,
    85
    ethers, 83
Nitro carboxylic acids,
    247–249
    amides, 255, 256
    compounds, 51, 52,
        237–249, 253–256,
        259–262, 277, 278,
        286
    ethers, 241–243
Nitrogen, detection, 9,
    10
    estimation, 297–306
Nitro-halogen com-
    pounds, 259–262
    hydrocarbons, 51,
        237–241
Nitrophenols, 52, 244
Nitroprusside test, 62,
    89
Nitrosoamines, 41, 249
Nitroso compounds, 41,
    44, 50, 249–251,
    286
Nitro sulphonic acids,
    277, 278
Nylander's solution, 93

Odour, 8
Orcinol test, 95
Osazones, 93, 94
Oxidation, 73, 74, 90,
    91
Oximes, 33, 87, 229–
    231
Oxygen, detection, 12,
    72

Paraldehydes, 91, 126–
    130
Pavy's solution, 330–
    332
Pentoses, 95, 162, 163

Picrates, 76
Piria and Schiff, 306,
    308, 311
Phenols, 82, 83, 120–
    125
    detection, 83
    halogen-substituted,
        181, 182
Phenylhydrazones, 88,
    236, 237
Phenyl *iso*cyanate, 44,
    83
Phloroglucinol test, 95
Phosphorus, detection,
    11
    estimation, 312, 313
Platinichlorides, 36,60,
    317
Platinum, estimation,
    317
Plimmer and Bayliss,
    312
Polarimetry, 347, 348
Polysaccharides, 97,
    164, 165
Potassium, estimation,
    316, 317
Proteins, 53
Prussian Blue test, 9,
    10, 69
Purines, 52, 228

Quaternary ammon-
    ium salts, 38
Quinones, 133–135

Recrystallization, 6, 7,
    102
Reducing agents, 48
Reid, 80, 83, 84
Robertson, 309
Rotation, optical, 347–
    351

Saccharic acid test, 96
Sandmeyer's reaction,
    39
Schiff's reagent, 89, 91
Schotten-Baumann re-
    action, 41, 82
Seeker and Mathew-
    son, 306, 310, 311

Semicarbazones, 89
Silver, estimation, 315
Smiles's test, 57, 61, 62
Sodium, estimation, 316, 317
Sodium fusion, 9
Solidifying point, 4, 6
Solubility, 7, 101, 102
Specific gravity, 344–346
Steam distillation, 101, 102
Stepanow, 309
Sugars, estimation, 327–332, 350, 351
Sulphates. *See* Alkyl sulphates
Sulphides, alkyl, 61, 264, 265
Sulphinic acids, 57, 272
Sulphochlorides, 56, 75, 273, 274
Sulphonamides, 43, 70, 274, 275

Sulphonation, 73, 75
Sulphones, 60, 265, 266
Sulphonic acids, 55, 56, 266–269
  simple, 266–268
  substituted, 268, 269, 277, 278
  esters, 58, 270, 271
Sulphonium salts, 59, 60
Sulphonyl chlorides. *See* Sulpho-chlorides
Sulphoxides, 60, 61, 265, 266
Sulphur, detection, 10, 11
  estimation, 311, 312

Thioamides, 71, 275, 276
Thiocarbamides. *See* Thioureas

Thiocarboxylic acids, 59, 273
Thiocyanates, 69, 278
Thioureas, 40, 71, 275, 276
Toluenesulphochloride 83
Trisaccharides, 97, 162

Unsaturation, 14, 15, 324–326
Ureas, 29, 33, 40, 212–215
Urethanes, 31, 33, 222

Vapour density, 338–344

Wijs, 325

Xanthydrol, 30

Zeisel, 320